GARGANTUA AND PANTAGRUEL

Turn to the end of this volume
for a complete list of titles
in the Modern Library

GARGANTUA AND PANTAGRUEL

BY

RABELAIS

EDITED, WITH AN INTRODUCTION BY
DONALD DOUGLAS

THE MODERN LIBRARY
PUBLISHERS : NEW YORK

CONTENTS

CONTENTS

INTRODUCTION

RABELAIS calls spirits from the vasty deep and at his bidding they rise in prodigious bulk from great ocean bottoms or break like monstrous djinns from a cloud-land of huge fancy. They cast toppling shadows on the heavens and sprawl drunken and gigantic over interminable plains. Their creator is a conjurer of the first magnitude, quite unlike the neat modern trickster who pulls jack-rabbits from plug hats or goldfish from a thimble, for the jack-rabbits are cows who jump over the moon and the goldfish are leviathans giving transport to the ultimate isles on the edge of the world. No doubt you have grown quite used to the hard bright realism of the modern world and an art wherein heroes are "true to life" because they never stand more than six feet in their stocking feet on a weighing machine recording pounds or inches to the sixteenth of a millimeter. No doubt you are inclined to feel at home and comfortable in a fiction where men exchange the small mean gossip of the common day and no giant ever darkens the length of Main Street with the shadow of his big toe. In our age we do have fantasy and satire; but it's inclined to measure man with a rule of thumb and not with a bean stalk growing into the gulfs between the stars. Rabelais builds the enormous façade of a Gothic cathedral scrolled with apes as big as mountains and angels whose wings bridge the long lanes of the seven seas.

Unless therefore you agree to abandon the charted measurements of most modern art and fiction you will find yourself lost in Rabelais like a man strayed into a labyrinth

radiating corridors like an horrendous nightmare. Judged by
the canons and vice-canons of our own age "Gargantua" and
"Pantagruel" appear like obscene characters scribbled by
a madman on a precipitous cliff. For our edification we have
novelists who make fun of lecherous and wine-bibbing cler-
gymen. We have no figure like the cloud-capping wantonness of Friar John. We have other novelists who shame us
into laughter at the tedious windbags got up as learned
judges and turning the majesty of the law into a dreary rig-
marole of pedantic verbiage. We have nothing like the various verdicts of Bridlegoose. We have still other novelists
who present graceless and delightful villains without conscience and remorse and decency and honor; but we have
nothing like that appalling practical joke which Panurge
played upon a lady in the streets of Paris. Indeed we like to
have our fantasy whimsical like the ingenuous adventures of
Peter Pan and our satire exact and painstaking like the es-
capades of the regrettable Elmer Gantry and our mythology
subtle in sly innuendo like the disquisitions of the pawn-
broker Jurgen. It is at least worthy of record that the elabo-
rate geographer of Poictesme has listed Rabelais as one of
the ten dullest authors in the world. It is also worthy of
record that one of the most popular operatic composers
of this century can put sheriffs and cowboys (instead of demigods and giants) into an opera without fear of public laughter; and that innumerable people object to the libretti of
Wagner's operas because the characters are not "real" persons in dress-suits.

None the less there's little danger of Rabelais ever dying
from neglect. Unfortunately for his real reputation he will
always be bought by men sneaking slyly into a bookstore
to get a book supposedly raucous with obscenity. He has a
reputation with the groundlings as a big-hearted "smutty"

author in whose pages we may gloat over certain famous chapters much as greatly daring young women read the last fifty pages of "Ulysses" and shocked professors call D. H. Lawrence a vulgar writer on the earthly strength of a few carefully marked passages. In actual life men have lost little of the joyous and whole-hearted ribaldry of the Middle Ages and the Renaissance; and yet stories held natural and appropriate to smoking rooms and modern dinner parties somehow become "indecent" once they get printed in a book. There's nothing either decent or indecent except the mind makes it so by its own health or corruption. Men of the most pure and scrupulous lives tell ribald histories with a sincere and altogether healthy-minded zest. The earth wears filth that she may bear flowers; and no man not a prig or a hypocrite can very well deny an invincible instinct which gathers men together for the purpose of stories told with wit and redeemed by gusty humor. In addition it is obviously ridiculous and unjust to estimate Rabelais' famous obscenity by the standards of our own time. He did not write for some future age any more than any artist writes for any age except his own age and people. Shakespeare never expected to be shorn for high-school editions and Aristophanes lost no sleep over the far-off event of the modern censor. Rabelais is no worse than the old *fabliaux*, the farces of the fifteenth century, the story-tellers of the sixteenth— and he is very little worse than great comic writers like Aristophanes and Swift except that he is fortunately free from the abusive orthodox intolerance of the Greek or the lowering ferocity of the mad dean. To cleanse Rabelais (as is done in the present edition) is not, as H. G. Wells would say, like cleaning rabbits for the table. It is like cleaning the immense Augean stables. It is like purifying the fertility of the earth or turning the curious and inventive mind into a glass house for fear of stones. By the laws of our own age it has become necessary and obligatory.

For a long time Rabelais was represented as a buffoon and a drunken priest with a nose like a red lantern and a mind like a village sot's. Nothing can be further from the truth. For all the whirling absurdities and the heaped grossness and the capricious fancies of his pages you see the light of his mind shine with the clear brilliance of a star. He achieved sense by the use of gigantic nonsense much as W. S. Gilbert in "The Mikado" satirised tories and statesmen by turning them into gentlemen of Japan. To achieve sense by nonsense is as good a way as ever has been found in this serious world, for too often sober satire works with the tedious industry of a plow decimating a few poor worms the while nonsense pours like a wind from the great sea. As yet no one has written a gigantic satire blowing down the dragging weariness and the spurious pretences of modern war; and until that time or until the appearance of a new "Don Quixote" or a new "Pantagruel" we may continue to suffer the actual penalties and the poisonous flatulence made by disingenuous politicians. Rabelais didn't include war in the scope of his laughter. War in the Middle Ages and the Renaissance was at least brilliant and picturesque; and Rabelais loved all things born from the lust and clamor of real life. Much of his satire must of necessity remain obscure and at times meaningless to anyone save the expert investigator of the Renaissance; but no one can miss the edged laughter and the joy of living and the hate of sterile asceticism and the contempt for pedantry and the praise of the healthy flesh which make the bone and blood of the man forever to stand in luminous and irresistible opposition to that dark distrust of life which for want of a better word we may call Calvinism.

Indeed Rabelais and Calvin stand in the Renaissance like

two huge angels with blades drawn for mortal combat as their spirits stand opposed in all ages and all times. Rabelais builds an ideal monastery with the motto and law "Do as you want" because he trusts the free play of the spirit and the flesh. Trust men and women even when they do wrong and injury and when they abuse the freest privileges. Lock the soul of man in a prison and constrain its power and desire with bolt and chain and you will see its heart blacken and its limbs rust and its mind grow to a green mold. Make women good with the fear of scandal and the power of swords and you have won a corrupt and corrosive victory. Elevate pedantry above learning and pruriency above honest vulgarity and you turn laughter into a smirk ashamed of its own unspoken words. Let the world open all its gates so that with the discovery of corruption and baseness and dishonor may come also the finding of beauty and purity and all things good and noble. Galahad is less chaste than Lancelot, for he knew not evil; and Parsifal is less admirable in his invincible goodness than Amfortas, who lost the guardianship of the Holy Grail because he was too curious about the commanding seductions of the flesh. All that is Rabelais' message and even his praise of strong drink is not a rallying cry to the seamy worship of the god Bacchus, for to him drink seems to typify and symbolize the free rush of the spirit and the acceptance of all the glory and all the lechery of human life. Calvin would never have fattened the calf for the prodigal son or permitted a woman of the streets to wash his feet; and so in his zeal for the joyous brotherhood of sinful man Rabelais comes nearer to the true Christian than the stern ritualist with a mind like a bright sword and a heart like a turning stone.

Along the facades of the Gothic cathedrals you will see angels and gargoyles at good-will in one another's company;

and in the vaulted grandeur of a basilica starred with rose-windows you will find seats carven with obscene imaginations. There was little "selection" in the art of the Middle Ages and the Renaissance any more than there is "selection" in actual existence. Life permits and includes the most fantastic opposition of saint and knave, chimera and ineffable seraphim, sea-blue bird and hideous devil-fish. So long as the mind throws its golden light over the toothed reefs and the gulfs swarming with appalling scaly forms; and so long as the heart eases the corruption of the senses with its wind-taken laughter you may not belong to the children of the elect but you can be sure of decent membership with our common humanity. Rabelais is as modern as life and as ancient as the inexplicable riddle of a universe monstrous and nocturnal in a vasty proliferation of spawning forms; and to all this confusion he brings his most precious gift of a spacious mind echoing with an inextinguishable mirth.

DONALD DOUGLAS.

New York, May, 1928.

The First Book of

RABELAIS

TREATING OF THE HEROIC DEEDS AND SAYINGS
OF GARGANTUA

CHAPTER 1

OF THE GENEALOGY AND ANTIQUITY OF GARGANTUA

I MUST refer you to the great chronicle of Pantagruel for the knowledge of that genealogy and antiquity of race by which Gargantua is come unto us. In it you may understand more at large how the giants were born in this world, and how from them by a direct line issued Gargantua, the father of Pantagruel: and do not take it ill, if for this time I pass by it, although the subject be such, that the oftener it were remembered, the more it would please your worshipful Seniorias; according to which you have the authority of Plato in Philebo and Gorgias; and of Flaccus, who says that there are some kinds of purposes (such as these are without doubt), which, the frequentlier they be repeated, still prove the more delectable.

Would to God everyone had as certain knowledge of his genealogy since the time of the ark of Noah until this age. I think many are at this day emperors, kings, dukes, princes, and popes on the earth, whose extraction is from some porters and pardon-pedlars; as, on the contrary, many are now poor wandering beggars, wretched and miserable, who are descended of the blood and lineage of great kings and emperors, occasioned, as I conceive it, by the transport and revolution of kingdoms and empires, from the Assyrians to the Medes, from the Medes to the Persians, from the Persians to the Macedonians, from the Macedonians to the Romans, from the Romans to the Greeks, from the Greeks to the French.

And to give you some hint concerning myself, who speaks unto you, I cannot think but I am come of the race of some rich king or prince in former times; for never yet saw you any man that had a greater desire to be a king, and to be rich, than I have, and that only that I may make good cheer, do nothing, nor care for anything, and plentifully enrich my friends, and all honest and learned men. But herein do I comfort myself, that in the other world I shall be so, yea and greater too than at this present I dare wish. As for you, with the same or a better conceit consolate yourselves in your distresses, and drink fresh if you can come by it.

To return to our wethers, I say that by the sovereign gift of heaven, the antiquity and genealogy of Gargantua hath been reserved for our use more full and perfect than any other except that of the Messias, whereof I mean not to speak; for it belongs not unto my purpose, and the devils, that is to say, the false accusers and dissembled gospellers, will therein oppose me. This genealogy was found by John Andrew in a meadow, which he had near the pole-arch, under the olive-tree, as you go to Narsay; where, as he was making cast up some ditches, the diggers with their mattocks struck against a great brazen tomb, and unmeasurably long, for they could never find the end thereof, by reason that it entered too far within the sluices of Vienne. Opening this tomb in a certain place thereof, sealed on the top with the mark of a goblet, about which was written in Etrurian letters HIC BIBITUR, they found nine flagons set in such order as they use to rank their kyles in Gascony, of which that which was placed in the middle had under it a big, fat, great, grey, pretty, small, mouldy, little pamphlet, smelling stronger, but no better than roses. In that book the said genealogy was found written all at length, in a chancery hand, not in paper, not in parchment, nor in nax, but in the bark of an elm-tree, yet so worn with the long tract of time, that hardly could three letters together be there perfectly discerned.

I (though unworthy) was sent for thither, and with much help of those spectacles, whereby the art of reading dim writings, and letters that do not clearly appear to the sight, is practised, as Aristotle teacheth it, did translate the book as you may see in your Pantagruelizing, that is to say, in drinking stiffly to your own heart's desire, and reading the dreadful and horrific acts of Pantagruel. At the end of the book there was a little treatise entitled the Antidoted Fanfreluches, or a Galimatia of extravagant conceits. The rats and moths, or (that I may not lie) other wicked beasts, had nibbled off the beginning: the rest I have hereto subjoined, for the reverence I bear to antiquity.

CHAPTER 2

HOW GARGANTUA WAS CARRIED ELEVEN MONTHS IN HIS MOTHER'S BELLY

GRANGOUSIER was a good fellow in his time, and notable jester; he loved to drink neat, as much as any man that then was in the world, and would willingly eat salt meat. To this intent he was ordinarily well furnished with gammons of bacon, both of Westphalia, Mayence and Bayonne, with store of dried neat's tongues, plenty of links, chitterlings and puddings in their season; together with salt beef and mustard, a good deal of hard roes of powdered mullet called botargos, great provision of sausages, not of Bolonia (for he feared the Lombard Boccone), but of Bigorre, Longaulnay, Brene, and Rouargue. In the vigour of his age he married Gargamelle, daughter to the King of the Parpaillons, a jolly pug, and well-mouthed wench. These two did oftentimes do two-backed beast together, in so far, that at

last she became great with child of a fair son, and went with
him unto the eleventh month; for so long, yea longer, may
a woman carry her great belly, especially when it is some
masterpiece of nature, and a person predestinated to the
performance, in his due time, of great exploits. As Homer
says, that the child, which Neptune begot upon the nymph,
was born a whole year after the conception, that is, in the
twelfth month. For, as Aulus Gellius saith, lib. 3, this long
time was suitable to the majesty of Neptune, that in it the
child might receive his perfect form. For the like reason
Jupiter made the night, wherein he lay with Alcmena, last
forty-eight hours, a shorter time not being sufficient for the
forging of Hercules, who cleansed the world of the monsters
and tyrants wherewith it was suppressed. My masters, the
ancient Pantagruelists, have confirmed that which I say,
and withal declared it to be not only possible, but also maintained the lawful birth and legitimation of the infant born
of a woman in the eleventh month after the decease of her
husband. Hypocrates, *lib. de alimento,* Plinius, *lib.* 7 *cap* 5.
Plautus, in his *Cistelleria.* Marcus Varro, in his satire in-
scribed *The Testament,* alleging to this purpose the authority
of Aristotle. Censorinus, *lib. de die natali.* Arist. *lib.* 7, *cap.*
3 *& 4, de natura animalium.* Gellius, *lib.* 3, *cap.* 16. Servius,
in his exposition upon this verse of Virgil's eclogues, *Matri
longa decem, &c.,* and a thousand other fools, whose number
hath been increased by the lawyers, *ff. de suis, et legit l. in-
testato. paragrapho. fin.* and in *Auth. de restitut. et ea quœ
parit in xi mense.* Moreover upon these grounds they have
foisted in their Robidilardic, or Lapiturolive law. Gallus
ff. de lib. et posth. l. sept. ff. de stat. hom., and some other
laws, which at this time I dare not name.

CHAPTER 3

HOW GARGAMELLE, BEING GREAT WITH GARGANTUA, DID EAT A HUGE DEAL OF TRIPES

THE occasion and manner how Gargamelle was brought to bed, and delivered of her child, was thus: on the third day of February, with having eaten at dinner too many godebillios. Godebillios are the fat tripes of coiros. Coiros are beeves fattened at the cratch in ox-stalls, or in the fresh guimo meadows. Guimo meadows are those that for their fruitfulness may be mowed twice a year. Of those fat beeves they had killed three hundred sixty-seven thousand and fourteen, to be salted at Shrovetide, that in the entering of the spring they might have plenty of powdered beef, wherewith to season their mouths at the beginning of their meals, and to taste their wine the better.

They had abundance of tripes, as you have heard, and they were so delicious, that everyone licked his fingers. But the mischief was this, that, for all men could do, there was no possibility to keep them long in that relish; for in a very short while they would have stunk, which had been an undecent thing. It was therefore concluded, that they should be all of them gulched up, without losing anything. To this effect they invited all the burghers of Sainais, of Suillé, of the Roche-Clermaud, of Vaugaudry, without omitting the Coudray, Monpensier, the Gué de Vède, and other their neighbours, all stiff drinkers, brave fellows, and good players at the kyles. The good man Grangousier took great pleasure in their company, and commanded there should be no want nor pinching for anything. Nevertheless he bade his wife eat sparingly, because she was near her time, and that these tripes were no very commendable meat. They would fain, said he, be at the chewing of ordure, that would eat the case

wherein it was. Notwithstanding these admonitions, she did
eat sixteen quarters, two bushels, three pecks and a pipkin
full. O the fair fecality wherewith she swelled, by the in-
grediency of such stuff!

After dinner they all went out in a hurl to the grove of
the willows, where, on the green grass, to the sound of the
merry flutes and pleasant bagpipes, they danced so gallantly, that it was a sweet and heavenly sport to see them so
frolic.

CHAPTER 4

THE DISCOURSE OF THE DRINKERS

THEN did they fall upon the chat of victuals and some
belly furniture to be snatched at in the very same place.
Which purpose was no sooner mentioned, but forthwith began flagons to go, gammons to trot, goblets to fly, great
bowls to ting, glasses to ring. Draw, reach, fill, mix, give it
me without water. So, my friend, so, whip me off this glass
neatly, bring me hither some claret, a full weeping glass till
it run over. A cessation and truce with thirst. Ha, thou false
fever, wilt thou not be gone? By my figgins, godmother, I
cannot as yet enter in the humour of being merry, nor drink
so currently as I would. You have catched a cold, gammer?
Yea, forsooth, sir. By the belly of Sanct Buff, let us talk of
our drink: I never drink but at my hours, like the Pope's
mule. And I never drink but in my breviary, like a fair father
guardian. Which was first, thirst or drinking? Thirst, for
who in the time of innocence would have drunk without
being athirst? Nay, sir, it was drinking; for *privatio præ-
supponit habitum*. I am learned, you see; *Fœcundi calices
quem non fecere disertum?* We poor innocents drink but
too much without thirst. Not I truly, who am a sinner, for I
never drink without thirst, either present or future. To pre-

vent it, as you know, I drink for the thirst to come. I drink eternally. This is to me an eternity of drinking, and drinking of eternity. Let us sing, let us drink, and tune up our roundelays. Where is my funnel? What, it seems I do not drink but by an attorney? Do you wet yourselves to dry, or do you dry to wet you? Pish, I understand not the rhetoric (theoric, I should say), but I help myself somewhat by the practice. *Baste!* enough! I sup, I wet, I humect, I moisten my gullet, I drink, and all for fear of dying. Drink always and you shall never die. If I drink not, I am a-ground, dry, gravelled and spent. I am stark dead without drink, and my soul ready to fly into some marsh amongst frogs; the soul never dwells in a dry place, drouth kills it. O you butlers, creators of new forms, make me of no drinker a drinker, a perennity and everlastingness of sprinkling and bedewing me through these my parched and sinewy bowels. He drinks in vain that feels not the pleasure of it. This entereth into my veins. I would willingly wash the tripes of the calf which I apparelled this morning. I have pretty well now ballasted my stomach and stuffed my paunch. If the papers of my bonds and bills could drink as well as I do, my creditors would not want for wine when they come to see me, or when they are to make any formal exhibition of their rights to what of me they can demand. This hand of yours spoils your nose. O how many other such will enter here before this go out! What, drink so shallow? It is enough to break both girds and petrel. This is called a cup of dissimulation, or flagonal hypocrisy.

What difference is there between a bottle and a flagon. Great difference; for the bottle is stopped and shut up with a stopple, but the flagon with a vice.* Bravely and well played upon the words! Our fathers drank lustily, and emptied their cans. Well cacked, well sung! Come, let us drink;

* La bouteille est fermée à bouchon, et le flaccon à vis.

will you send nothing to the river? Here is one going to wash the tripes. I drink no more than a sponge. I drink like a Templar knight. And I, *tanquam sponsus*. And I, *sicut terra sine aqua*. Give me a synonymon for a gammon of bacon. It is the compulsory of drinkers; it is a pulley. By a pulley-rope wine is let down into a cellar, and by a gammon into the stomach. Hey! now, boys, hither, some drink, some drink. There is no trouble in it. *Respice personam, pone pro duos, bus non est in usu.* If I could get up as well as I can swallow down, I had been long ere now very high in the air.

Thus became Tom Tosspot rich,—thus went in the tailor's stitch. Thus did Bacchus conquer th' Inde—thus Philosophy, Melinde. A little rain allays a great deal of wind; long tippling breaks the thunder. Here, page, fill! I prithee, forget me not when it comes to my turn, and I will enter the election I have made of thee into the very register of my heart. Sup, Guillot, and spare not, there is somewhat in the pot. I appeal from thirst, and disclaim its jurisdiction. Page, sue out my appeal in form. This remnant in the bottom of the glass must follow its leader. I was wont heretofore to drink out all, but now I leave nothing. Let us not make too much haste; it is requisite we carry all along with us. Heyday, here are tripes fit for our sport, and, in earnest, excellent godebillios of the dun ox (you know) with the black streak. O, for God's sake let us lash them soundly, yet thriftily. Drink, or I will,—No, no, drink, I beseech you.* Sparrows will not eat unless you bob them on the tail, nor can I drink if I be not fairly spoke to. The concavities of my body are like another Hell for their capacity. Lagonædatera.† There is not a corner, nor coney-burrow in all my body, where this wine doth not ferret out my thirst. Ho, this will bang it

---

* Ou je vous, je vous prie.
† *Laczn lateris cavitas; aidgs orcus;* and *etepos alter.*

soundly. But this shall banish it utterly. Let us wind our
horns by the sound of flagons and bottles, and cry aloud,
that whoever hath lost his thirst come not hither to seek it.
Long clysters of drinking are to be voided without doors.
The great God made the planets, and we make the platters
neat. I have the word of the gospel in my mouth, Sitio. The
stone called asbestos is not more unquenchable than the
thirst of my paternity. Appetite comes with eating, says
Angeston, but the thirst goes away with drinking. I have a
remedy against thirst, quite contrary to that which is good
against the biting of a mad dog. Keep running after a dog,
and he will never bite you; drink always before the thirst,
and it will never come upon you. There I catch you, I awake
you. Argus had a hundred eyes for his sight, a butler should
have (like Briareus) a hundred hands wherewith to fill us
wine indefatigably. Hey now, lads, let us moisten ourselves,
it will be time to dry hereafter. White wine here, wine, boys!
Pour out all in the name of Lucifer, fill here, you, fill and
fill (peascods on you) till it be full. My tongue peels. Lans
trinque; to thee, countryman, I drink to thee, good fellow,
comrade to thee, lusty, lively! Ha, la, la, that was drunk to
some purpose, and bravely gulped over. *O lachryma Christi*,
it is of the best grape! I'faith, pure Greek, Greek! O the fine
white wine! upon my conscience, it is a kind of taffetas
wine,—hin, hin, it is of one ear, well wrought, and of good
wool. Courage, comrade, up thy heart, billy! We will not be
beasted at this bout, for I have got one trick. *Ex hoc in hoc.*
There is no enchantment nor charm there, every one of you
hath seen it. My 'prenticeship is out, I am a free man at this
trade. I am prester mast.* Prish, Brum! I should say, master past. O the drinkers, those that are a-dry, O poor thirsty
souls! Good page, my friend, fill me here some, and crown

---

* Prestre mace, maistre passe.

the wine, I pray thee. Like a cardinal! *Natura abhorret vacuum.* Would you say that a fly could drink in this? This is after the fashion of Switzerland. Clear off, neat, supernaculum! Come, therefore, blades, to this divine liquor and celestial juice, swill it over heartily, and spare not! It is a decoction of nectar and ambrosia.

CHAPTER 5

HOW GARGANTUA WAS BORN IN A STRANGE MANNER

WHILST they were on this discourse and pleasant tattle of drinking, Gargamelle began to be a little unwell in her lower parts; whereupon Grangousier arose from off the grass, and fell to comfort her very honestly and kindly, suspecting that she was in travail, and told her that it was best for her to sit down upon the grass under the willows, because she was like very shortly to see young feet, and that therefore it was convenient she should pluck up her spirits, and take a good heart of new at the fresh arrival of her baby; saying to her withal, that although the pain was somewhat grievous to her, it would be but of short continuance, and that the succeeding joy would quickly remove that sorrow, in such sort that she should not so much as remember it. On, with a sheep's courage! quoth he. Despatch this boy, and we will speedily fall to work for the making of another. Ha! said she, so well as you speak at your own ease, you that are men! Well, then, in the name of God, I'll do my best, seeing that you will have it so, but would to God that it were cut off from you! What? said Grangousier. Ha, said she, you are a good man indeed, you understand it well enough. What? said he. By the goat's blood, if it please you, that shall be done instantly; cause bring hither a knife. Alas, said she, the Lord forbid, and pray Jesus to forgive me! I did not say it from my heart,

therefore let it alone, and do not do it neither more nor less
any kind of harm for my speaking so to you. But I am like to
have work enough to do to-day and yet God bless you and it.

Courage, courage, said he, take you no care of the matter,
let the four foremost oxen do the work. I will yet go drink
one whiff more, and if in the mean time anything befall you
that may require my presence, I will be so near to you, that,
at the first whistling in your fist, I shall be with you forthwith. A little while after she began to groan, lament, and cry.
Then suddenly came the midwives from all quarters. Whereupon an old ugly trot in the company, who had the repute
of an expert she-physician, and was come from Brisepaille,
near to Saint Genou, three score years before, made her a
restrictive and binding medicine. By this inconvenient the
cotyledons of her matrix were presently loosed, through
which the child sprang up and leaped, and so, entering into
the hollow vein, did climb by the diaphragm even above her
shoulders, where the vein divides itself into two, and from
thence taking his way towards the left side, issued forth at
her left ear. As soon as he was born, he cried not as other
babes use to do, *Miez, miez, micz, miez,* but with a high
sturdy, and big voice shouted about, Some drink, some drink,
some drink, as inviting all the world to drink with him. The
noise hereof was so extremely great, that it was heard in
both the countries at once of Beauce and Bibarois. I doubt
me, that you do not thoroughly believe the truth of this
strange nativity. Though you believe it not, I care not much:
but an honest man, and of good judgment, believeth still
what is told him, and that which he finds written.

Is this beyond our law or our faith—against reason or
the holy Scripture? For my part, I find nothing in the sacred
Bible that is against it. But tell me, if it had been the will
of God, would you say that he could not do it? Ha, for

favour sake, I beseech you, never emberlucock or inpulrega-
fize your spirits with these vain thoughts and idle conceits;
for I tell you, it is not impossible with God, and, if he
pleased, all women henceforth should bring forth their children at the ear. Was not Bacchus engendered out of the very
thigh of Jupiter? Did not Roquetaillade come out at his
mother's heel, and Crocmoush from the slipper of his nurse?
Was not Minerva born of the brain, even through the ear of
Jove? Adonis, of the bark of a myrrh tree; and Castor and
Pollux of the doupe of that egg which was laid and hatched
by Leda? But you would wonder more, and with far greater
amazement, if I should now present you with that chapter of
Plinius, wherein he treateth of strange births, and contrary to
nature, and yet am not I so impudent a liar as he was. Read
the seventh book of his Natural History, chap. 3, and trouble
not my head any more about this.

CHAPTER 6

AFTER WHAT MANNER GARGANTUA HAD HIS NAME GIVEN
    HIM, AND HOW HE TIPPLED, BIBBED AND CURRIED THE
    CAN

THE good man Grangousier, drinking and making merry
with the rest, heard the horrible noise which his son had
made as he entered into the light of this world, when he cried
out, Some drink, some drink, some drink, whereupon he said
in French *Que grand tu as et souple le gousier!* that is to say,
How great and nimble a throat thou hast. Which the company hearing, said that verily the child ought to be called
Gargantua; because it was the first word that after his
birth his father had spoke, in imitation, and at the example
of the ancient Hebrews; whereunto he condescended, and his
mother was very well pleased therewith. In the meanwhile,

to quiet the child, they gave him to drink a tirelaregot, that is, till his throat was like to crack with it; then was he carried to the font, and there baptized, according to the manner of good Christians.

Immediately thereafter were appointed for him seventeen thousand, nine hundred and thirteen cows of the towns of Pautille and Brehemond, to furnish him with milk in ordinary, for it was impossible to find a nurse sufficient for him in all the country, considering the great quantity of milk that was requisite for his nourishment; although there were not wanting some doctors of the opinion of Scotus, who affirmed that his own mother gave him suck, and that she could draw out of her breasts one thousand, four hundred, two pipes, and nine pails of milk at every time.

Which indeed is not probable, and this point hath been found duggishly scandalous and offensive to tender ears, for that it savoured a little of heresy. Thus was he handled for one year and ten months; after which time, by the advice of physicians, they began to carry him, and then was made for him a fine little cart drawn with oxen, of the invention of Jan Denio, wherein they led him hither and thither with great joy; and he was worth the seeing, for he was a fine boy, had a burly physiognomy, and almost ten chins. Yet without a cause did not he sup one drop; for if he happened to be vexed, angry, displeased, or sorry, if he did fret, if he did weep, if he did cry, and what grievous quarter soever he kept, in bringing him some drink, he would be instantly pacified, reseated in his own temper, in a good humour again, and as still and quiet as ever. One of his governesses told me, how he was so accustomed to this kind of way, that, at the sound of pints and flagons, he would on a sudden fall into an ecstasy, as if he had then tasted of the joys of paradise; so that they, upon consideration of this, his divine complexion, would every morning, to cheer him up, play with a knife upon the glasses, on the bottles with their stopples, and on the pottle-pots with their lids and covers, at the sound whereof he became gay, did leap for joy, would loll and rock himself in the cradle, then nod with his head, monochordizing with his fingers.

CHAPTER 7

HOW THEY APPARELLED GARGANTUA

BEING of this age, his father ordained to have clothes made to him in his own livery, which was white and blue. To work then went the tailors, and with great expedition were those clothes made, cut, and sewed, according to the fashion that was then in request. I find by the ancient records or pancarts, to be seen in the chamber of accounts, or court of the exchequer at Montsoreau, that he was accoutred in manner as followeth. To make him every shirt of his were taken up nine hundred ells of Chasteleraud linen, and two hundred for the gussets, in manner of cushions, which they put under his armpits. His shirt was not gathered nor plaited, for the plaiting of shirts was not found out till the seam-stresses (when the point of their needle* was broken) began to work and occupy with the tail. There were taken up for his doublet, eight hundred and thirteen ells of white satin, and for his points fifteen hundred and nine dogs' skins and a half. Then was it that men began to tie their breeches to their doublets, and not their doublets to their breeches: for it is against nature, as hath most amply been showed by Ockham upon the exponibles of Master Haultechaussade.

For his breeches were taken up eleven hundred and five ells and a third of white broadcloth. They were cut in the

* *Besongner du cul*, Englished *The eye of the needle*.

form of pillars, chamfered, channelled and pinked behind that they might not overheat his reins: and were, within the panes, puffed out with the lining of as much blue damask as was needful: and remark, that he had very good leg-harness, proportionable to the rest of his stature.

For his shoes were taken up four hundred and six ells of blue crimson-velvet, and were very neatly cut by parallel lines, joined in uniform cylinders. For the soling of them were made use of eleven hundred hides of brown cows, shapen like the tail of a keeling.

For his coat were taken up eighteen hundred ells of blue velvet, dyed in grain, embroidered in its borders with fair gilliflowers, in the middle decked with silver purl, intermixed with plates of gold and store of pearls, hereby showing that in his time he would prove an especial good fellow and singular whipcan.

His girdle was made of three hundred ells and a half of silken serge, half white and half blue, if I mistake it not. His sword was not of Valentia, nor his dagger of Saragossa, for his father could not endure these *hidalgos borrachos maranisados como diablos;* but he had a fair sword made of wood, and the dagger of boiled leather, as well painted and gilded as any man could wish.

His purse was made of the cod of an elephant, which was given him by Herr Pracontal, proconsul of Lybia.

For his gown were employed nine thousand six hundred ells, wanting two-thirds, of blue velvet, as before, all so diagonally purled, that by true perspective issued thence an unnamed colour, like that you see in the necks of turtle-doves or turkey-cocks, which wonderfully rejoiced the eyes of the beholders. For his bonnet or cap were taken up three hundred, two ells and a quarter of white velvet, and the form thereof was wide and round, of the bigness of his head; for his father said that the caps of the Marrabaise fashion, made like the cover of a pasty, would one time or other bring a mischief on those that wore them. For his plume, he wore a fair great blue feather, plucked from an onocrotal of the country of Hircania the wild, very prettily hanging down over his right ear. For the jewel or brooch which in his cap he carried, he had in a cake of gold, weighing three score and eight marks, a fair piece enamelled, wherein was portrayed a man's body with two heads, looking towards one another, four arms, four feet. To wear about his neck, he had a golden chain, weighing twenty-five thousand and sixty-three marks of gold, the links thereof being made after the manner of great berries, amongst which were set in work green jaspers engraven and cut dragon-like, all environed with beams and sparks, as king Nicepsos of old was wont to wear them; and it reached down to the very bust of the rising of his belly, whereby he reaped great benefit all his life long, as the Greek physicians know well enough. For his gloves were put in work sixteen otters' skins, and three of the loupgarous, or men-eating wolves, for the bordering of them; and of this stuff were they made, by the appointment of the Cabalists of Sanlouand. As for the rings which his father would have him to wear, to renew the ancient mark of nobility, he had on the forefinger of his left hand a carbuncle as big as an ostrich's egg, enchased very daintily in gold of the fineness of a Turkey seraph. Upon the middle finger of the same hand he had a ring made of four metals together, of the strangest fashion that ever was seen; so that the steel did not crash against the gold, nor the silver crush the copper. All this was made by Captain Chappuys, and Alcofribas his good agent. On the medical finger of his right hand he had a ring made spirewise, wherein was set a perfect Balas ruby, a pointed diamond, and a Physon emerald, of an inestimable value. For Hans Carvel, the king of Melinda's jeweller, esteemed them at the rate of threescore nine millions, eight hundred ninety-four thousand, and eighteen French crowns of Berry, and at so much did the Foucres of Augsburg prize them.

CHAPTER 8

THE COLOURS AND LIVERIES OF GARGANTUA

GARGANTUA's colours were white and blue, as I have showed you before, by which his father would give us to understand that his son to him was a heavenly joy; for the white did signify gladness, pleasure, delight, and rejoicing, and the blue, celestial things. I know well enough that, in reading this, you laugh at the old drinker, and hold this exposition of colours to be very extravagant, and utterly disagreeable to reason, because white is said to signify faith, and blue constancy. But without moving, vexing, heating, or putting you in a chafe (for the weather is dangerous), answer me if it please you; for no other compulsory way of arguing will I use towards you, or any else: only now and then I will mention a word or two of my bottle. What is it that induceth you, what stirs you up to believe, or who told you that white signifieth faith, and blue constancy? An old paltry book, say you, sold by the hawking pedlars and ballad-mongers, entitled The Blason of Colours. Who made it? Whoever it was, he was wise in that he did not set his name to it. But, besides, I know not what I should rather admire in him, his presumption or his sottishness. His presumption and overweening, for that he should without reason, without cause, or without any appearance of truth, have dared to prescribe, by his private authority, what things should be denotated and signified by the colour: which is the custom of tyrants, who will have their will to bear sway in stead of equity, and not of the wise and learned, who with the evidence of reason satisfy their readers. His sottishness and want of spirit, in that he thought that, without any other demonstration or sufficient argument, the world would be pleased to make his blockish and ridiculous impositions the rule of their devices. In effect, he hath found, it seems, some simple ninny in those rude times of old, when the wearing of high round bonnets was in fashion, who gave some trust to his writings, according to which they carved and engraved their apophthegms and mottoes, trapped and caparisoned their mules and sumpter-horses, apparelled their pages, quartered their breeches, bordered their gloves, fringed the curtains and valances of their beds, painted their ensigns, composed songs, and, which is worse, placed many deceitful jugglings and unworthy base tricks undiscoveredly amongst the very chastest matrons and most reverend sciences. In the like darkness and mist of ignorance are wrapped up these vainglorious courtiers and name-transposers, who, going about in their impresas to signify *esperance* (that is, hope), have portrayed a sphere—and birds' pennes for pains—*l'ancholie* (which is the flower colombine) for melancholy—a waning moon or crescent, to show the increasing or rising of one's fortune—a bench rotten and broken, to signify bankrupt—*non* and a *corslet* for *non dur habit* (otherwise *non durabit*, it shall not last), *un lit sans ciel,* that is, a bed without a tester, for *un licencie,* a graduated person, as bachelor in divinity or utter barrister-at-law; which are equivocals so absurd and witless, so barbarous and clownish, that a fox's tail should be fastened to the neck-piece of, and a vizard made of a cowsherd given to everyone that henceforth should offer, after the restitution of learning, to make use of any such fopperies in France. Yet do I hope one day to write

more at large of these things, and to show both by philosophical arguments and authorities, received and approved
of by and from all antiquity, what, and how many colours
there are in nature, and what may be signified by every one
of them if God save the mould of my cap, which is my best
wine-pot, as my grandam said.

CHAPTER 9

OF THAT WHICH IS SIGNIFIED BY THE COLOURS WHITE AND BLUE

THE white therefore signifieth joy, solace, and gladness,
and that not at random, but upon just and very good
grounds: which you may perceive to be true, if laying aside
all prejudicate affections, you will but give ear to what
presently I shall expound unto you.

Aristotle saith that, supposing two things contrary in
their kind, as good and evil, virtue and vice, heat and cold,
white and black, pleasure and pain, joy and grief,—and
so of others,—if you couple them in such manner that the
contrary of one kind may agree in reason with the contrary
of the other, it must follow by consequence that the other
contrary must answer to the remanent opposite to that
wherewith it is conferred. As, for example, virtue and vice
are contrary in one kind, so are good and evil. If one of
the contraries of the first kind be consonant to one of those
of the second, as virtue and goodness, for it is clear that virtue is good, so shall the other two contraries, which are evil
and vice, have the same connection, for vice is evil.

This logical rule being understood, take these two contraries, joy and sadness; then these other two, white and
black, for they are physically contrary. If so be, then, that
black do signify grief, by good reason then should white

import joy. Nor is this signification instituted by human imposition, but by the universal consent of the world received, which philosophers call Jus Gentium, the Law of Nations, or an uncontrollable right of force in all countries whatsoever. For you know well enough that all people, and all languages and nations, except the ancient Syracusans and certain Argives, who had cross and thwarting souls, when they mean outwardly to give evidence of their sorrow, go in black; and all mourning is done with black. Which general consent is not without some argument and reason in nature, the which every man may by himself very suddenly comprehend, without the instruction of any—and this we call the law of nature. By virtue of the same natural instinct we know that by white all the world hath understood joy, gladness, mirth, pleasure, and delight. In former times the Thracians and Cretans did mark their good, propitious, and fortunate days with white stones, and their sad, dismal, and unfortunate ones with black. Is not the night mournful, sad, and melancholic? It is black and dark by the privation of light. Doth not the light comfort all the world? And it is more white than anything else. Which to prove I could direct you to the book of Laurentius Valla against Bartolus; but an evangelical testimony I hope will content you. Matth. 17 it is said that, at the transfiguration of our Lord, *Vestimenta ejus facta sunt alba sicut lux,* his apparel was made white like the light. By which lightsome whiteness he gave his three apostles to understand the idea and figure of the eternal joys; for by the light are all men comforted, according to the word of the old woman, who, although she had never a tooth in her head, was wont to say, *Bona lux.* And Tobit, chap. 5, after he had lost his sight, when Raphael saluted him, answered, *What joy can I have, that do not see the light of Heaven?* In that colour did the angels testify the joy of the whole world at the resurrection of our Saviour, John 20, and at his ascension, Acts 1. With the like colour of vesture did St. John the Evangelist, Apoc. 4. 7, see the faithful clothed in the heavenly and blessed Jerusalem.

Read the ancient, both Greek and Latin histories; and you shall find that the town of Alba (the first pattern of Rome) was founded and so named by reason of a white sow that was seen there. You shall likewise find in those stories, that when any man, after he had vanquished his enemies, was by decree of the senate to enter into Rome triumphantly, he usually rode in a chariot drawn by white horses: which in the ovation triumph was also the custom; for by no sign or colour would they so significantly express the joy of their coming as by the white. You shall there also find, how Pericles, the general of the Athenians, would needs have that part of his army unto whose lot befell the white beans, to spend the whole day in mirth, pleasure, and ease, whilst the rest were a-fighting. A thousand other examples and places could I allege to this purpose, but that it is not here where I should do it.

By understanding hereof, you may resolve one problem, which Alexander Aphrodiseus hath accounted unanswerable: why the lion, who with his only cry and roaring affrights all beasts, dreads and feareth only a white cock? For, as Proclus saith, *Libro de Sacrificia et Magia,* it is because the presence of the virtue of the sun, which is the organ and promptuary of all terrestrial and sidereal light, doth more symbolize and agree with a white cock, as well in regard of that colour, as of his property and specifical quality, than with a lion. He saith furthermore, that devils have been often seen in the shape of lions, which at the sight of a white cock have presently vanished. This is the cause why Galli or Gallices (so are the Frenchmen called, because they are naturally white as milk, which the Greeks call Gala,) do willingly wear in their caps white feathers, for by nature they are of a candid disposition, merry, kind, gracious, and well-beloved, and for their cognizance and arms have the whitest flower of any, the Flower de luce or Lily.

If you demand how, by white, nature would have us understand joy and gladness, I answer, that the analogy and uniformity is there. For, as the white doth outwardly disperse and scatter the rays of the sight, whereby the optic spirits are manifestly dissolved, according to the opinion of Aristotle in his problems and perspective treatises; as you may likewise perceive by experience, when you pass over mountains covered with snow, how you will complain that you cannot see well; as Xenophon writes to have happened to his men, and as Galen very largely declareth, *lib.* 10, *de usu partium:* just so the heart with excessive joy is inwardly dilated, and suffereth a manifest resolution of the vital spirits, which may go so far on that it may thereby be deprived of its nourishment, and by consequence of life itself, by this perichary or extremity of gladness, as Galen saith, *lib.* 12, *method, lib.* 5, *de locis affectis, and lib.* 2, *de symptomatum causis.* And as it hath come to pass in former times, witness Marcus Tullius, *lib.* 1, *Quæst. Tuscul.,* Verrius, Aristotle, Titus Livius, in his relation of the battle of Cannæ, Plinius, *lib.* 7, *cap.* 32 *and* 34, A. Gellius, *lib.* 3 *c.* 15, and many other writers,—to Diagoras the Rhodian, Chilon, Sophocles, Dionysius the tyrant of Sicily, Philippides, Philemon, Polycrates, Philistion, M. Juventi, and others who died with joy. And as Avicen speaketh, *in* 2 *canon et lib. de virib. cordis,* of the saffron, that it doth so rejoice the heart that, if you take of it excessively, it will by a superfluous resolution and dilation deprive it altogether of life. Here peruse Alex. Aphrodiseus, *lib.* 1, *Probl., cap.* 19, and that for a cause. But what? It seems I am entered further into this point than I intended at the first. Here, therefore, will I strike sail, referring the rest to that book of mine which handleth this matter to the full.

Meanwhile, in a word I will tell you, that blue doth certainly signify heaven and heavenly things, by the same very tokens and symbols that white signifieth joy and pleasure.

CHAPTER 10

OF THE YOUTHFUL AGE OF GARGANTUA

GARGANTUA, from three years upwards unto five, was brought up and instructed in all convenient discipline by the commandment of his father; and spent that time like the other little children of the country, that is, in drinking, eating, and sleeping: in eating, sleeping, and drinking: and in sleeping, drinking, and eating. Still he wallowed and rolled up and down himself in the mire and dirt—he blurred and sullied his nose with filth—he blotted and smutched his face with any kind of scurvy stuff—he trod down his shoes in the heel—at the flies he did oftentimes yawn, and ran very heartily after the butterflies, the empire whereof belonged to his father. He sharpened his teeth with a top, washed his hands with his broth, and combed his head with a bowl. He would cover himself with a wet sack, and drink in eating of his soup. He did eat his cake sometimes without bread, would bite in laughing, and laugh in biting. Oftentimes he did spit in the basin, and hide himself in the water for fear of rain. He would strike out of the cold iron, be often in the dumps, and frig and wriggle it. He would flay the fox, say the ape's paternoster, return to his sheep, and turn the hogs to the hay. He would beat the dogs before the lion, put the plough before the oxen, and claw where it did not itch. He would pump one to draw somewhat out of him, by griping all would hold fast nothing, and always eat his white bread first. He shoed the geese, kept a self-tickling to make himself laugh, and was very steadable in the kitchen: made a mock at the gods, would cause sing Magnificat at matins, and found it very convenient so to do. He would eat cabbage,—knew flies in a dish of milk, and would make them lose their feet. He would scrape paper, blur parchment, then run away as hard as he could. He would pull at the kid's leather, or vomit up his dinner, then reckon without his host. He would beat the bushes without catching the birds, thought the moon was made of green cheese, and that bladders are lanterns. Out of one sack he would take two moultures or fees for grinding; would act the ass's part to get some bran, and of his fist would make a mallet. He took the cranes at the first leap, and would have the mail-coats to be made link after link. He always looked a given horse in the mouth, leaped from the cock to the ass, and put one ripe between two green. By robbing Peter he paid Paul, he kept the moon from the wolves, and hoped to catch larks if ever the heavens should fall. He did make of necessity virtue, of such bread such pottage, and cared as little for the peeled as for the shaven. Every morning he did cast up his gorge, and his father's little dogs eat out of the dish with him, and he with them. He would bite their ears, and they would scratch his nose.

CHAPTER 11

OF GARGANTUA'S WOODEN HORSES

AFTERWARDS, that he might be all his lifetime a good rider, they made to him a fair great horse of wood, which he did make leap, curvet, jerk out behind, and skip forward, all at a time: to pace, trot, rack, gallop, amble, to play the hobby, the hackney-gelding: go the gait of the camel, and of the wild ass. He made him also change his colour of hair, as the monks of Coultibo (according to the variety of their holidays) use to do their clothes, from bay brown, to sorrel, dapple-grey, mouse-dun, deer-colour, roan, cow-colour, gingio-line, skewed colour, piebald, and the colour of the savage elk.

Himself of a huge big post made a hunting nag, and another for daily service of the beam of a vinepress: and of a great oak made up a mule, with a footcloth, for his chamber. Besides this, he had ten or twelve spare horses, and seven horses for post; and all these were lodged in his own chamber, close by his bedside. One day the Lord of Breadinbag* came to visit his father in great bravery, and with a gallant train: and, at the same time, to see him came likewise the Duke of Freemeal and the Earl of Wetgullet.† The house truly for so many guests at once was somewhat narrow, but especially the stables; whereupon the steward and harbinger of the said Lord Breadinbag, to know if there were any other empty stables in the house, came to Gargantua, a little young lad, and secretly asked him where the stables of the great horses were, thinking that children would be ready to tell all. Then he led them up along the stairs of the castle, passing by the second hall unto a broad great gallery, by which they entered into a large tower, and as they were going up at another pair of stairs, said the harbinger to the steward, This child deceives us, for the stables are never on the top of the house. You may be mistaken, said the steward, for I know some places at Lyons, at the Basmette, at Chaisnon, and elsewhere, which have their stables at the very tops of the houses: so it may be that behind the house there is a way to come to this ascent. But I will

* *Painensac.*   † Francrepas Mouillevent.

question with him further. Then said he to Gargantua, My pretty little boy, whither do you lead us? To the stable, said he, of my great horses. We are almost come to it, we have but these stairs to go up at. Then leading them alongst another great hall, he brought them into his chamber, and opening the door, said unto them, This is the stable you ask for; this is my jennet; this is my gelding; this is my courser, and this is my hackney, and laid on them with a great lever. I will bestow upon you, said he, this Friesland horse; I had him from Frankfort, yet will I give him you; for he is a pretty little nag, and will go very well, with a tessel of goshawks, half a dozen of spaniels, and a brace of greyhounds: thus are you king of the hares and partridges for all this winter. By St. John, said they, now we are paid, he hath gleeked us to some purpose, bobbed we are now forever. I deny it, said he,—he was not here above three days. Judge you now, whether they had most cause, either to hide their heads for shame, or to laugh at the jest. As they were going down again thus amazed, he asked them, Will you have a whimwham?* To-day, said the steward, though we happen to be roasted, we shall not be burnt, for we are pretty well quipped and larded, in my opinion. O my jolly dapper boy, thou hast given us a gudgeon; I hope to see thee Pope before I die. I think so, said he, myself; and then shall you be a puppy, and this gentle popinjay a perfect papelard, that is, dissembler.

CHAPTER 12

HOW GARGANTUA WAS TAUGHT LATIN BY A SOPHISTER

THE good man Grangousier having heard this discourse, was ravished with admiration, considering the high reach and marvellous understanding of his son Gargantua, and

* Aubeliere.

said to his governesses, Philip, king of Macedon, knew the
great wit of his son Alexander by his skilful managing of a
horse; for his horse Bucephalus was so fierce and unruly
that none durst adventure to ride him, after that he had
given to his riders such devilish falls, breaking the neck
of this man, the other man's leg, braining one, and putting
another out of his jawbone. This by Alexander being considered, one day in the hippodrome (which was a place
appointed for the breaking and managing of great horses),
he perceived that the fury of the horse proceeded merely
from the fear he had of his own shadow, whereupon getting
on his back, he run him against the sun, so that the shadow
fell behind, and by that means tamed the horse and brought
him to his hand. Whereby his father, knowing the divine
judgment that was in him, caused him most carefully to be
instructed by Aristotle, who at that time was highly renowned
above all the philosophers of Greece. After the same manner
I tell you, that by this only discourse, which now I have here
had before you with my son Gargantua, I know that his
understanding doth participate of some divinity, and that,
if he be well taught, and have that education which is fitting,
he will attain to a supreme degree of wisdom. Therefore will
I commit him to some learned man, to have him indoctri-
nated according to his capacity, and will spare no cost.
Presently they appointed him a great sophister-doctor, called
Master Tubal Holofernes, who taught him his A B C so well,
that he could say it by heart backwards; and about this he
was five years and three months. Then read he to him Donat,
Le Facet, Theodolet, and Alanus *in parabolis*. About this he
was thirteen years, six months, and two weeks. But you must
remark that in the mean time he did learn to write in Gothic
characters, and that he wrote all his books—for the art of
printing was not then in use—and did ordinarily carry a

great pen and inkhorn, weighing about seven thousand
quintals (that is, 700,000 pound weight), the penner whereof
was as big and as long as the great pillars of Enay, and the
horn was hanging to it in great iron chains, it being of the
wideness of a tun of merchant ware. After that he read unto
him the book *de modis significandi,* with the commentaries
of Hurtbise, of Fasquin, of Tropdieux, of Guallaut, of John
Calf, of Billonio, of Berlinguandus, and a rabble of others;
and herein he spent more than eighteen years and eleven
months, and was so well versed in it that to try masteries
in school disputes with his condisciples he would recite it by
heart backwards, and did some times prove on his finger-
ends to his mother, *quod de modis significandi non erat
scientia.* Then did he read to him the compost for knowing
the age of the moon, the seasons of the year, and tides of the
sea, on which he spent sixteen years and two months, and that
justly at the time that his said preceptor died of the French
pox, which was in the year one thousand four hundred and
twenty. Afterwards he got an old coughing fellow to teach
him, named Master Jobelin Bridé, or muzzled dolt, who read
unto him Hugutio, Hebrard['s] *Grecism,* the Doctrinal, the
Parts, the *Quid est,* the *Supplementum,* Marmotretus, *De
moribus in mensa servandis,* Seneca *de quatuor virtutibus
cardinalibus,* Passavantus *cum commento,* and *Dormi secure*
for the holidays, and some other of such like mealy stuff, by
reading whereof he became as wise as any we ever since
baked in an oven.

CHAPTER 13

HOW GARGANTUA WAS PUT UNDER OTHER SCHOOL MASTERS

At the last his father perceived that indeed he studied
hard, and that, although he spent all his time in it, he did

nevertheless profit nothing, but which is worse, grew thereby foolish, simple, doted, and blockish, whereof making a heavy regret to Don Philip of Marays, Viceroy or Depute King of Papeligosse, he found that it were better for him to learn nothing at all, than to be taught such-like books, under such school masters; because their knowledge was nothing but brutishness, and their wisdom but blunt foppish toys serving only to bastardize good and noble spirits, and to corrupt all the flower of youth. That it is so, take said he, any young boy of this time who hath only studied two years,—if he have not a better judgment, a better discourse, and that expressed in better terms than your son, with a completer carriage and civility to all manner of persons, account me for ever hereafter a very clounch and bacon-slicer of Brene. This pleased Grangousier very well, and he commanded that it should be done. At night at supper, the said Des Marays brought in a young page of his, of Ville-gouges, called Eudemon, so neat, so trim, so handsome in his apparel, so spruce, with his hair in so good order, and so sweet and comely in his behaviour, that he had the resemblance of a little angel more than of a human creature. Then he said to Grangousier, Do you see this young boy? He is not as yet full twelve years old. Let us try, if it pleases you, what difference there is betwixt the knowledge of the doting Mateologians of old time and the young lads that are now. The trial pleased Grangousier, and he commanded the page to begin. Then Eudemon, asking leave of the vice-king his master so to do, with his cap in his hand, a clear and open countenance, beautiful and ruddy lips, his eyes steady, and his looks fixed upon Gargantua with a youthful modesty, standing up straight on his feet, began very gracefully to commend him; first, for his virtue and good manners; secondly, for his knowledge; thirdly, for his nobility; fourthly, for his bodily accomplishments; and, in the fifth place, most sweetly exhorted him to reverence his father with all due observancy, who was so careful to have him well brought up. In the end he prayed him, that he would vouchsafe to admit of him amongst the least of his servants; for other favour at that time desired he none of heaven, but that he might do him some grateful and acceptable service. All this was by him delivered with such proper gestures, such distinct pronunciation, so pleasant a delivery, in such exquisite fine terms, and so good Latin, that he seemed rather a Gracchus, a Cicero, an Æmilius of the time past, than a youth of this age. But all the countenance that Gargantua kept was, that he fell to crying like a cow, and cast down his face, hiding it with his cap, nor could they possibly draw one word from him. Whereat his father was so grievously vexed that he would have killed Master Jobelin, but the said Des Marays withheld him from it by fair persuasions, so that at length he pacified his wrath. Then Grangousier commanded he should be paid his wages, that they should whittle him up soundly, like a sophister, with good drink, and then give him leave to go to all the devils in hell. At least, said he, to-day shall it not cost his host much if by chance he should die as drunk as a Switzer. Master Jobelin being gone out of the house, Grangousier consulted with the Viceroy what school master they should choose for him, and it was betwixt them resolved that Ponocrates, the tutor of Eudemon, should have the charge, and that they should go altogether to Paris, to know what was the study of the young men of France at that time.

CHAPTER 14

HOW GARGANTUA WAS SENT TO PARIS, AND OF THE HUGE
GREAT MARE THAT HE RODE ON; HOW SHE DESTROYED
THE OXFLIES OF THE BEAUCE

IN the same season Fayoles, the fourth King of Numidia, sent out of the country of Africa to Grangousier the most hideously great mare that ever was seen and of the strangest form, for you know well enough how it is said that Africa always is productive of some new thing. She was as big as six elephants, and had her feet cloven into fingers, like Julius Cæsar's horse, with slouch-hanging ears, like the goats in Languedoc, and a little horn on her buttock. She was of a burnt sorrel hue, with a little mixture of dapple-grey spots, but above all she had a horrible tail; for it was little more or less than every whit as great as the steeple-pillar of St. Mark beside Langes: and squared as that is, with tuffs and en-nicroches or hair-plaits wrought within one another, no otherwise than as the beards are upon the ears of corn.

If you wonder at this, wonder rather at the tails of the Scythian rams, which weighed above thirty pounds each; and of the Suiran sheep, who need, if Tenard say true, a little cart at their heels to bear up their tail, it is so long and heavy. You female lechers in the plain countries have no such tails. And she was brought by sea in three carricks and a brigantine unto the harbour of Olone in Thalmondois. When Grangousier saw her, Here is, said he, what is fit to carry my son to Paris. So now, in the name of God, all will be well. He will in times coming be a great scholar. If it were not, my masters, for the beasts, we should live like clerks. The next morning—after they had drunk, you must under-stand—they took their journey; Gargantua, his pedagogue Ponocrates, and his train, and with them Eudemon, the young page. And because the weather was fair and temperate, his father caused to be made for him a pair of dun boots,— Babin calls them buskins. Thus did they merrily pass their time in travelling on their high way, always making good cheer, and were very pleasant till they came a little above Orleans, in which place there was a forest of five-and-thirty leagues long, and seventeen in breadth, or thereabouts. This forest was most horribly fertile and copious in dorflies, hornets, and wasps, so that it was a very purgatory for the poor mares, asses, and horses. But Gargantua's mare did avenge herself handsomely of all the outrages therein committed upon beasts of her kind, and that by a trick whereof they had no suspicion. For as soon as they were entered into the said forest, and that the wasps had given the assault, she drew out and unsheathed her tail, and therewith skirmishing, did so sweep them that she overthrew all the wood alongst and athwart, here and there, this way and that way, longwise and sidewise, over and under, and felled everywhere the wood with as much ease as a mower doth the grass, in such sort that never since hath there been there neither wood nor dorflies: for all the country was thereby reduced to a plain champaign field. Which Gargantua took great pleasure to behold, and said to his company no more but this: *Je trouve beau ce* (I find this pretty); whereupon that country hath been ever since that time called Beauce. But all the breakfast the mare got that day was but a little yawning and gaping, in memory whereof the gentlemen of Beauce do as yet to this day break their fast with gaping, which they find to be very good, and do spit the better for it. At last they came to Paris, where Gargantua refreshed himself two or three days, making very merry with his folks, and inquiring what men of learning there were then in the city, and what wine they drunk there.

CHAPTER 15

HOW GARGANTUA PAID HIS WELCOME TO THE PARISIANS, AND
  HOW HE TOOK AWAY THE GREAT BELLS OF OUR LADY'S
  CHURCH

SOME few days after that they had refreshed themselves,
he went to see the city; and was beheld of everybody there
with great admiration; for the people of Paris are so sottish,
so badot, so foolish and fond by nature, that a juggler, a
carrier of indulgencies, a sumpter-horse, or mule with cymbals or tinkling bells, a blind fiddler in the middle of a cross
lane, shall draw a greater confluence of people together than
an evangelical preacher. And they pressed so hard upon him
that he was constrained to rest himself upon the towers of
Our Lady's Church. At which place, seeing so many about
him, he said with a loud voice, I believe that these buzzards
will have me to pay them here my welcome hither, and my
Proficiat. It is but good reason. I will now give them their
wine, but it shall be only in sport. This done, he considered
the great bells, which were in the said towers, and made them
sound very harmoniously. Which whilst he was doing, it came
into his mind that they would serve very well for tingling
tantans and ringing campanels to hang about his mare's neck
when she should be sent back to his father, as he intended to
do, loaded with Brie cheese and fresh herring. And indeed he
forthwith carried them to his lodging. In the meanwhile
there came a master beggar of the friars of St. Anthony to
demand in his canting way the usual benevolence of some
hoggish stuff, who, that he might be heard afar off, and to
make the bacon he was in quest of shake in the very chim-
neys, made account to filch them away privily. Nevertheless,
he left them behind very honestly, not for that they were too
hot, but that they were somewhat too heavy for his carriage.

This was not he of Bourg, for he was too good a friend of mine. All the city was risen up in sedition, they being, as you know, upon any slight occasion, so ready to uproars and insurrections, that foreign nations wonder at the patience of the kings of France, who do not by good justice restrain them from such tumultuous courses, seeing the manifold inconveniences which thence arise from day to day. Would to God I knew the shop wherein are forged these divisions, and factious combinations, that I might bring them to light in the confraternities of my parish! Believe for a truth, that the place wherein the people gathered together, were thus sulphured, hopurymated, moiled, was called Nesle, where then was, but now is no more, the oracle of Leucotia. There was the case proposed, and the inconvenience showed of the transporting of the bells. After they had well ergoted pro and con, they concluded in baralipton, that they should send the oldest and most sufficient of the faculty unto Gargantua, to signify unto him the great and horrible prejudice they sustain by the want of those bells. And notwithstanding the good reasons given in by some of the university why this charge was fitter for an orator than a sophister, there was chosen for this purpose our Master Janotus de Bragmardo.

CHAPTER 16

HOW JANOTUS DE BRAGMARDO WAS SENT TO GARGANTUA TO RECOVER THE GREAT BELLS

MASTER JANOTUS, with his hair cut round like a dish à la Cæsarine, in his most antique accoutrement liripipionated with a graduate's hood, and having sufficiently antidoted his stomach with oven-marmalades, that is, bread and holy water of the cellar, transported himself to the lodging of Gargantua, driving before him three red-muzzled beadles, and dragging after him five or six artless masters, all thoroughly bedaggled with the mire of the streets. At their entry Ponocrates met them, who was afraid, seeing them so disguised, and thought they had been some masquers out of their wits, which moved him to inquire of one of the said artless masters of the company what this mummery meant. It was answered him, that they desired to have their bells restored to them. As soon as Ponocrates heard that, he ran in all haste to carry the news unto Gargantua, that he might be ready to answer them, and speedily resolve what was to be done. Gargantua being advertised hereof, called apart his school master Ponocrates, Philotimus, steward of his house, Gymnastes, his esquire, and Eudemon, and very summarily conferred with them, both of what he should do and what answer he should give. They were all of opinion that they should bring them unto the goblet-office, which is the buttery, and there make them drink like roysters and line their jackets soundly. And that this cougher might not be puffed up with vain-glory by thinking the bells were restored at his request, they sent, whilst he was chopining and plying the pot, for the mayor of the city, the rector of the faculty, and the vicar of the church, unto whom they resolved to deliver the bells before the sophister had propounded his commission.

CHAPTER 17

THE STUDY OF GARGANTUA, ACCORDING TO THE DISCIPLINE OF HIS SCHOOL MASTERS THE SOPHISTERS

THE first day being thus spent, and the bells put up again in this own place, the citizens of Paris, in acknowledgment of this courtesy, offered to maintain and feed his mare as long as he pleased, which Gargantua took in good part, and they sent her to graze in the forest of Biere. I think she is not there now. This done, he with all his heart submitted his study to the discretion of Ponocrates; who for the beginning appointed that he should do as he was accustomed, to the end he might understand by what means, in so long time, his old masters had made him so sottish and ignorant. He disposed therefore of his time in such fashion, that ordinarily he did awake betwixt eight and nine o'clock, whether it was day or not, for so had his ancient governors ordained, alleging that which David saith, *Vanum est vobis ante lucem surgere.* Then did he tumble and toss, wag his legs, and wallow in the bed some time, the better to stir up and rouse his vital spirits, and apparelled himself according to the season: but willingly he would wear a great long gown of thick frieze, furred with fox-skins. Afterwards he combed his head with an Almain comb, which is the four fingers and the thumb. For his preceptor said that to comb himself otherwise, to wash and make himself neat, was to lose time in this world. Then he cracked, yawned, spitted, coughed, yexed, sneezed and, to suppress the dew and bad air, went to breakfast, having some good fried tripes, fair rashers on the coals, excellent gammons of bacon, store of fine minced meat, and a great deal of sippet brewis, made up of the fat of the beef-pot, laid upon bread, cheese, and chopped parsley strewed together. Ponocrates showed him that he ought not to eat so soon after rising out of his bed, unless he had performed some exercise beforehand. Gargantua answered, What! have not I sufficiently well exercised myself? I have wallowed and rolled myself six or seven turns in my bed before I rose. Is not that enough? Pope Alexander did so, by the advice of a Jew his physician, and lived till his dying day in despite of his enemies. My first masters have used me to it, saying that to breakfast made a good memory, and therefore they drank first. I am very well after it, and dine but the better. And Master Tubal, who was the first licenciate at Paris, told me that it was not enough to run apace, but to set forth betimes: so doth not the total welfare of our humanity depend upon perpetual drinking in a ribble rabble, like ducks, but on drinking early in the morning; *unde versus,*

> To rise betimes is no good hour,
> To drink betimes is better sure.

After that he had thoroughly broke his fast, he went to church, and they carried to him, in a great basket, a huge impantoufled or thick-covered breviary, weighing, what in grease, clasps, parchment and cover, little more or less than eleven hundred and six pounds. There he heard six-and-twenty or thirty masses. This while, to the same place came his orison-mutterer impaletocked, or lapped up about the chin like a tufted whoop, and his breath pretty well antidoted with store of the vine-tree-syrup. With him he mumbled all his kiriels and dunsicals breborions, which he so curiously thumbed and fingered, that there fell not so much as one grain to the ground. As he went from the church, they brought him, upon a dray drawn with oxen, a confused heap of paternosters and aves of St. Claude, every one of them being of the bigness of a hat-block; and thus walking through the cloisters, galleries, or garden, he said more in turning them over than sixteen hermits would have done. Then did he study some paltry half-hour with his eyes fixed upon his book; but, as the comic saith, his mind was in the kitchen. He sat down at table; and because he was naturally phlegmatic, he began his meal with some dozens of gammons, dried neat's tongues, hard roes of mullet, called botargos, andouilles or sausages, and such other forerunners of wine. In the meanwhile, four of his folks did cast into his mouth one after another continually mustard by whole shovelfuls. Immediately after that, he drank a horrible draught of white wine for the ease of his kidneys. When that was done, he ate according to the season meat agreeable to his appetite, and then left off eating when his belly began to strout, and was like to crack for fullness. As for his drinking, he had in that neither end nor rule. For he was wont to say, That the limits and bounds of drinking were, when the cork of the shoes of him that drinketh swelleth up half a foot high.

CHAPTER 18

THE GAMES OF GARGANTUA

THEN blockishly mumbling with a set on countenance a piece of scurvy grace, he washed his hands in fresh wine, picked his teeth with the foot of a hog, and talked jovially with his attendants. Then the carpet being spread, they brought plenty of cards, many dice, with great store and abundance of chequers and chessboards.

There he played.

At flush.	At the fib.
At primero.	At the pass ten.
At the beast.	At one-and-thirty.
At the rifle.	At post and pair, or even
At trump.	and sequence.
At the prick and spare not.	At three hundred.
At the hundred.	At the unlucky man.
At the peeny.	At the last couple in hell.
At the unfortunate woman.	

At love.

At the chess.

At Reynard the fox.

At the squares.

At the cows.

At the lottery.

At the chance or mum-chance.

At three dice or manifest

At the hock.

At the surly.

At the lansquenet.

At the cuckoo.

At puff, or let him speak that hath it.

At take nothing and throw out.

At the marriage.

At the frolic or jackdaw.

At the opinion.

At who doth the one, doth the other.

At the sequences.

At the ivory bundles.

At the tarots.

At losing load him.

At he's gulled and *esto*.

At the torture.

At the handruff.

At the click.

At the French trictrac.

At feldown.

bleaks.

At the tables.

At nivinivinack.

At the lurch.

At doublets or queen's game.

At the faily.

At the long tables or fer-keering.

At honours.

At pinch without laughing.

At prickle me tickle me.

At the unshoeing of the ass.

At the cocksess.

At hari hohi.

At I set me down.

At earl beardy.

At the old mode.

At draw the spit.

At put out.

At gossip lend me your sack.

At the ramcod ball.

At thrust out the harlot.

At Marseilles figs.

At nicknamry.

At stick and hole.

At boke or him, or flaying the fox.

At the branching it.

At the magatapies.

At the horn.

At tod's body.

At needs must.

At the dames or draughts.

At bob and mow.

At primus secundus.

At mark-knife.

At the keys.

At span-counter.

At even or odd.

At cross or pile.

At ball and huckle-bones.

At ivory balls.

At the billiards.

At bob and hit.

At the owl.

At the charming of the hare.

At pull yet a little.

At trudgepig.

At trill madam, or grapple my lady.

At the cat selling.

At blow the coal.

At the re-wedding.

At the quick and dead judge.

At unoven the iron.

At the false clown.

At the flints, or at the nine stones.

At the crutch hulch

At the flowered or Shrove-tide ox.

At the madge-owlet.

At tilt at weeky.

At ninepins.

At the cock quintin.

At tip and hurl.

At the flat bowls.

At the veer and turn.

At rogue and ruffian.

At bumbatch touch.

At the mysterious trough.

At the short bowls.

At the dapple-grey.

At cock and crank it.

At break-pot.

At my desire.

At twirly whirlytrill.

At the dales or straths.

At the twigs.

At the quoits.

At I'm for that.

At I take you napping.

At fair and softly passeth Lent.

At the forked oak.

At truss.

At the wolf's tail.

At bum to buss, or nose in breech.

back.

At the Sanct is found.

At hinch, pinch and laugh not.

At the leek.

At bumdockdousse.

At the loose gig.

At the hoop.

At the sow.

At belly to belly.

At the rush bundles.

At the short staff.

At the whirling gig.

At hide and seek, or are you all hid?

At the picket.

At the blank.

At the pilferers.

At the caveson.

At prison bars.

At have at the nuts.

At cherry-pit.

At rub and rice.

At whiptop.

At the casting top.

At the hobgoblins.

At the O wonderful.

At the soily smutchy.

At fast and loose.

At scutchbreech.

At the broom-besom.

At Geordie, give me my lance.

At swaggy, waggy or shoggy-shou.

At stook and rook, shear and threave.

At the birch.

At the muss.

At the dilly dilly darling.

At St. Cosme, I come to adore thee.

At the lusty brown boy.

At greedy glutton.

At the morris dance.

At feeby.

At the whole frisk and gambol.

At battabum, or riding of the wild mare.

At Hind the ploughman.

At the good mawkin.

At the dead beast.

At climb the ladder, Billy.

At the dying hog.

At the salt doup.

At the pretty pigeon.

At barley break.

At the bavine.

At the bush leap.

At ox moudy.

At purpose in purpose.

At nine less.

At blind-man-buff.

At the fallen bridges.

At bridled nick.

At the white at butts.

At thwack swinge him.

At apple, pear, plum.

At mumgi.

At the toad.

At Greedy Glutton.

At the morris dance.

At feeby.

At the whole frisk and gambol.

At the good mawkin.

At the dead beast.

At the climb of the ladder, Billy.

At the dying hog.

At crossing.

At bo-peep.

At the harrower's nest.

At forward hey.

At the fig.

At gunshot crack.

At mustard peel.

At the gome.

At the relapse.

At jog breech, or prick him forward.

At cricket.

At the pounding stick.

At jack and the box.

At the queens.

At the trades.

At heads and points.

At the vine-tree hug.

At the bolting cloth.

At Joan Thomson.

At the oat's seed.

At black be thy fall.

At battabum, or riding of the wild mare.

At Hind the ploughman.

At the salt doup.

At the pretty pigeon.

At barley break.

At the bavine.

At the bush leap.

At knockpate.

At the Cornish c[h]ough.

At the crane-dance.

At slash and cut.

At bobbing, or the flirt on the nose.

At the larks.

At fillipping.

At ho the distaff.

After he had thus well played, revelled, past and spent his time, it was thought fit to drink a little, and that was eleven glassfuls the man, and, immediately after making good cheer again, he would stretch himself upon a fair bench, or a good large bed, and there sleep two or three hours together, without thinking or speaking any hurt. After he was awakened he would shake his ears a little. In the mean time they brought him fresh wine. There he drank better than ever. Ponocrates showed him that it was an ill diet to drink so after sleeping. It is, answered Gargantua, the very life of the patriarchs and holy fathers; for naturally I sleep, salt and my sleep hath been to me in stead of so many gammons of bacon. Then began he to study a little, and out came the paternosters or rosary of beads, which the better and more formally to despatch, he got upon an old mule, which had served nine kings, and so mumbling with his mouth, nodding and dodding his head, would go see a coney ferreted or caught in a gin. At his return he went into the kitchen to know what roast meat was on the spit, and what otherwise was to be dressed for supper. And supped very well, upon my conscience, and commonly did invite some of his neighbours that were good drinkers, with whom carousing and drinking merrily, they told stories of all sorts from the old to the new. Amongst others he had for domestics the Lords of Fou, of Gourville, of Griniot, and of Marigny. After supper were brought in upon the place the fair wooden gospels and the books of the four kings, that is to say, many pairs of tables and cards—or the fair flush, one, two, three— or at all, to make short work; or else they went to see the wenches thereabouts, with little small banquets, intermixed with collations and rear-suppers. Then did he sleep, without unbridling, until eight o'clock in the next morning.

CHAPTER 19

HOW GARGANTUA WAS INSTRUCTED BY PONOCRATES AND IN
SUCH SORT DISCIPLINATED, THAT HE LOST NOT ONE
HOUR OF THE DAY

WHEN Ponocrates knew Gargantua's vicious manner of
living, he resolved to bring him up in another kind; but for
a while he bore with him, considering that nature cannot
endure a sudden change, without great violence. Therefore,
to begin his work the better, he requested a learned physician of that time, called Master Theodorus, seriously to
perpend, if it were possible, how to bring Gargantua into a
better course. The said physician purged him canonically
with Anticyrian hellebore, by which medicine he cleansed
all the alteration and perverse habitude of his brain. By
this means also Ponocrates made him forget all that he had
learned under his ancient preceptors, as Timotheus did to
his disciples, who had been instructed under other musicians.
To do this the better, they brought him into the company
of learned men, which were there, in whose imitation he had
a great desire and affection to study otherwise, and to improve his parts. Afterwards he put himself into such a road
and way of studying, that he lost not any one hour in the
day, but employed all his time in learning and honest knowledge. Gargantua awaked, then, about four o'clock in the
morning. Whilst they were in rubbing of him, there was read
unto him some chapter of the holy Scripture aloud and
clearly, with a pronunciation fit for the matter, and hereunto was appointed a young page born in Basche, named
Anagnostes. According to the purpose and argument of that
lesson, he oftentimes gave himself to worship, adore, pray,
and send up his supplications to that good God, whose Word
did show his majesty and marvellous judgment. Then his

master repeated what had been read, expounding unto him
the most obscure and difficult points.

They considered the face of the sky, if it was such as they
had observed it the night before, and into what signs the sun
was entering, as also the moon for that day. This done, he
was apparelled, combed, curled, trimmed, and perfumed,
during which time they repeated to him the lessons of the
day before. He himself said them by heart, and upon them
would ground some practical cases concerning the estate of
man, which he would prosecute sometimes two or three
hours, but ordinarily they ceased as soon as he was fully
clothed. Then for three good hours he had a lecture read
unto him. This done, they went forth, still conferring of the
substance of the lecture, either unto a field near the university called the Brack, or unto the meadows, where they
played at the ball, the long-tennis, and at the piletrigone
(which is a play wherein we throw a triangular piece of iron
at a ring, to pass it), most gallantly exercising their bodies,
as formerly they had done their minds. All their play was
but in liberty, for they left off when they pleased, and that
was commonly when they did sweat over all their body, or
were otherwise weary. Then were they very well wiped and
rubbed, shifted their shirts, and, walking soberly, went to
see if dinner was ready. Whilst they stayed for that, they
did clearly and eloquently pronounce some sentences that
they had retained of the lecture. In the meantime Master
Appetite came, and then very orderly sat they down at
table. At the beginning of the meal there was read some
pleasant history of the warlike actions of former times, until
he had taken a glass of wine. Then, if they thought good,
they continued reading, or began to discourse merrily together; speaking first of the virtue, propriety, efficacy, and
nature of all that was served in at the table: of bread, of

wine, of water, of salt, of fleshes, fishes, fruits, herbs, roots, and of their dressing. By means whereof he learned in a little time all the passages competent for this, that were to be found in Pliny, Athenæus, Dioscorides, Julius Pollux, Galen, Porphyry, Oppian, Polybius, Heliodore, Aristotle, Ælian, and others. Whilst they talked of these things, many times, to be the more certain, they caused the very books to be brought to the table, and so well and perfectly did he in his memory retain the things above said, that in that time there was not a physician that knew half so much as he did. Afterwards they conferred of the lessons read in the morning, and, ending their repast with some conserve or marmalade of quinces, he picked his teeth with mastic toothpickers, washed his hands and eyes with fair fresh water, and gave thanks unto God in some fine cantiques, made in praise of the divine bounty and munificence. This done, they brought in cards, not to play, but to learn a thousand pretty tricks and new inventions, which were all grounded upon arithmetic. By this means he fell in love with that numerical science, and every day after dinner and supper he passed his time in it pleasantly as he was wont to do at cards and dice; so that at last he understood so well both the theory and practical part thereof, that Tunstall the Englishman, who had written very largely of that purpose, confessed that verily in comparison of him he had no skill at all. And not only in that, but in the other mathematical sciences, as geometry, astronomy, music, &c. For in waiting on the concoction and attending the digestion of his food, they made a thousand pretty instruments and geometrical figures, and did in some measure practise the astronomical canons.

After this they recreated themselves with singing musically, in four or five parts, or upon a set theme or ground at random, as it best pleased them. In matter of musical in-

struments, he learned to play upon the lute, the virginals,
the harp, the Almain flute with nine holes, the viol, and the
sackbut. This hour thus spent, and digestion finished, he
did purge his body of natural excrements, then betook himself to his principal study for three hours together, or more,
as well to repeat his matutinal lectures as to proceed in the
book wherein he was, as also to write handsomely, to draw
and form the antique and Roman letters. This being done,
they went out of their house, and with them a young gentleman of Touraine, named the Esquire Gymnast, who taught
him the art of riding. Changing then his clothes, he rode a
Naples courser, a Dutch roussin, a Spanish jennet, a barded
or trapped steed, then a light fleet horse, unto whom he gave
a hundred carriers, made him go the high saults, bounding
in the air, free the ditch with a skip, leap over a style or
pale, turn short in a ring both to the right and left hand.
There he broke not his lance; for it is the greatest foolery in
the world to say, I have broken ten lances at tilts or in fight.
A carpenter can do even as much. But it is a glorious and
praiseworthy action with one lance, to break and overthrow
ten enemies. Therefore, with a sharp, stiff, strong, and well-
steeled lance would he usually force up a door, pierce a
harness, beat down a tree, carry away the ring, lift up a
cuirassier saddle, with the mail-coat and gauntlet. All this
he did in complete arms from head to foot. As for the prancing flourishes and smacking popisms for the better cherish-
ing of the horse, commonly used in riding, none did them
better than he. The cavallerize of Ferrara was but as an ape
compared to him. He was singularly skilful in leaping nimbly
from one horse to another without putting foot to ground,
and these horses were called desultories. He could likewise
from either side, with a lance in his hand, leap on horseback
without stirrups, and rule the horse at his pleasure without

a bridle, for such things are useful in military engagements. Another day he exercised the battle-axe, which he so dexterously wielded, both in the nimble, strong, and smooth management of that weapon, and that in all the feats practicable by it, that he passed knights of arms in the field, and at all essays.

Then tossed he the pike, played with the two-handed sword, with the backsword, with the Spanish tuck, the dagger, poniard, armed, unarmed, with a buckler, with a cloak, with a target. Then would he hunt the hart, the roebuck, the bear, the fallow deer, the wild boar, the hare, the pheasant, the partridge, and the bustard. He played at the balloon, and made it bound in the air, both with fist and foot. He wrestled, ran, jumped—not at three steps and a leap, called the hops, nor at clochepied, called the hare's leap, nor yet at the Almains; for, said Gymnast, these jumps are for the wars altogether unprofitable, and of no use—but at one leap he would skip over a ditch, spring over a hedge, mount six paces upon a wall, ramp and grapple after this fashion up against a window of the full height of his lance. He did swim in deep waters on his belly, on his back, sideways, with all his body, with his feet only, with one hand in the air, wherein he held a book, crossing thus the breadth of the river of Seine without wetting it, and dragged along his cloak with his teeth, as did Julius Cæsar; then with the help of one hand he entered forcibly into a boat, from whence he cast himself again headlong into the water, sounded the depths, hollowed the rocks, and plunged into the pits and gulfs. Then turned he the boat about, governed it, led it swiftly or slowly with the stream and against the stream, stopped it in his course, guided it with one hand, and with the other laid hard about him with a huge great oar, hoisted the sail, hied up along the mast by the shrouds, ran upon the edge of the decks, set the compass in order, tackled the bowlines, and steered the helm. Coming out of the water, he ran furiously up against a hill, and with the same alacrity and swiftness ran down again. He climbed up at trees like a cat, and leaped from the one to the other like a squirrel. He did pull down the great boughs and branches like another Milo; then with two sharp well-steeled daggers and two tried bodkins would he run up by the wall to the very top of a house like a rat; then suddenly came down from the top to the bottom, with such an even composition of members that by the fall he would catch no harm.

He did cast the dart, throw the bar, put the stone, practise the javelin, the boar-spear or partisan, and the halbert. He broke the strongest bows in drawing, bended against his breast the greatest crossbows of steel, took his aim by the eye with the hand-gun, and shot well, traversed and planted the cannon, shot at butt-marks, at the papgay from below upwards, or to a height from above downwards, or to a descent; then before him, sideways, and behind him, like the Parthians. They tied a cable-rope to the top of a high tower, by one end whereof hanging near the ground he wrought himself with his hands to the very top; then upon the same track came down so sturdily and firm that you could not on a plain meadow have run with more assurance. They set up a great pole fixed upon two trees. There would he hang by his hands, and with them alone, his feet touching at nothing, would go back and fore along the foresaid rope with so great swiftness that hardly could one overtake him with running; and then, to exercise his breast and lungs, he would shout like all the devils in hell. I heard him once call Eudemon from St. Victor's gate to Montmartre. Stentor had never such a voice at the siege of Troy. Then for the strengthening of his nerves or sinews they made him two great sows of lead, each of them weighing eight thousand and seven hundred quintals, which they called alteres. Those he took up from the ground, in each hand one, then lifted them up over his head, and held them so without stirring three quarters of an hour and more, which was an inimitable force. He fought at barriers with the stoutest and most vigorous companions; and when it came to the cope, he stood so sturdily on his feet that he abandoned himself unto the strongest, in case they could remove him from his place, as Milo was wont to do of old. In whose imitation, likewise, he held a pomegranate in his hand, to give it unto him that could take it from him. The time being thus bestowed, and himself rubbed, cleansed, wiped, and refreshed with other clothes, he returned fair and softly; and passing through certain meadows, or other grassy places, beheld the trees and plants, comparing them with what is written of them in the books of the ancients, such as Theophrast, Dioscorides, Marinus, Pliny, Nicander, Macer, and Galen, and carried home to the house great handfuls of them, whereof a young page called Rizotomas had charge; together with little mattocks, pickaxes, grubbing-hooks, cabbies, pruning-knives, and other instruments requisite for herborizing. Being come to their lodging, whilst supper was making ready, they repeated certain passages of that which hath been read, and sat down to table. Here remark, that his dinner was sober and thrifty, for he did then eat only to prevent the gnawings of his stomach, but his supper was copious and large, for he took then as much as was fit to maintain and nourish him; which, indeed, is the true diet prescribed by the art of good and sound physic, although a rabble of loggerheaded physicians, nuzzeled in the brabbling shop of sophisters, counsel the contrary. During that repast was continued the lesson read at dinner as long as they thought good; the rest was spent in good discourse, learned and profitable. After that they had given thanks, he set himself to sing vocally, and play upon harmonious instruments, or otherwise passed his time at some pretty sports, made with cards or dice, or in practising the feats of legerdemain with cups and balls. There they stayed some nights in frolicking thus, and making themselves merry till it was time to go to bed; and on other nights they would go make visits unto learned men, or to such as had been travellers in strange and remote countries. When it was full night before they retired themselves, they went unto the most open place of the house to see the face of the sky, and there beheld the comets, if any were, as likewise the figures, situations, aspects, oppositions, and conjunctions of both the fixed stars and planets.

Then with his master did he briefly recapitulate, after the manner of the Pythagoreans, that which he had read, seen, learned, done, and understood in the whole course of that day.

Then prayed they unto God the Creator, in falling down before him, and strengthening their faith towards him, and glorifying him for his boundless bounty; and, giving thanks unto him for the time that was past, they recommended themselves to his divine clemency for the future. Which being done, they went to bed, and betook themselves to their repose and rest.

CHAPTER 20

HOW GARGANTUA SPENT HIS TIME IN RAINY WEATHER

IF it happened that the weather were anything cloudy, foul, and rainy, all the forenoon was employed, as before specified, according to custom, with this difference only, that they had a good clear fire lighted to correct the distempers of the air. But after dinner, instead of their wonted exercitations, they did abide within, and, by way of apotherapy (that is, a making the body healthful by exercise), did recreate themselves in bottling up of hay, in cleaving and sawing of wood, and in threshing sheaves of corn at the barn. Then they studied the art of painting or carving; or brought into use the antique play of tables, as Leonicus hath written of it, and as our good friend Lascaris playeth at it. In playing they examined the passages of ancient authors wherein the said play is mentioned or any metaphor drawn from it. They went likewise to see the drawing of metals, or the casting of great ordnance; how the lapidaries did work; as also the goldsmiths and cutters of precious stones. Nor did they omit to visit the alchemists, money-coiners, upholsters, weavers, velvet-workers, watchmakers, looking-glass framers, printers, organists, and other such kind of artificers, and, everywhere giving them somewhat to drink, did learn and consider the industry and invention of the trades. They went also to hear the public lectures, the solemn commencements, the repetitions, the acclamations, the pleadings of the gentle lawyers, and sermons of evangelical preachers. He went through the halls and places appointed for fencing, and there played against masters themselves at all weapons, and showed them by experience that he knew as much in it as, yea more than, they. And, instead of herborizing, they visited the shops of druggists, herbalists, and apothecaries, and diligently considered the fruits, roots, leaves, gums, seeds, the grease and ointments of some foreign parts, as also how they did adulterate them. He went to see the jugglers, tumblers, mountebanks, and quacksalvers, and considered their cunning, their shifts, their somersaults and smooth tongue, especially of those of Chauny in Picardy, who are naturally great praters, and brave givers of fibs, in matter of green apes.

At their return they did eat more soberly at supper than at other times, and meats more desiccative and extenuating; to the end that the intemperate moisture of the air, communicated to the body by a necessary confinitive, might by this means be corrected, and that they might not receive any prejudice for want of their ordinary bodily exercise. Thus was Gargantua governed, and kept on in this course of education, from day to day profiting, as you may understand such a young man of his age may, of a pregnant judgment, with good discipline well continued. Which, although at the beginning it seemed difficult, became a little after, so sweet, so easy, and so delightful, that it seemed rather the recreation of a king than the study of a scholar. Nevertheless Ponocrates, to divert him from his vehement intension of the spirits, thought fit, once a month, in upon some fair and clear day, to go out of the city betimes in the morning, either towards Gentilly, or Boulogne, or to Montrouge, or Charanton bridge, or to Vanves, or St. Clou, and there spend all the day long in making the greatest cheer that could be devised, sporting, making merry, drinking healths, playing, singing, dancing, tumbling in some fair meadow, unnestling of sparrows, taking of quails, and fishing for frogs and crabs. But although that day was passed without books or lecture, yet was it not spent without profit; for in the said meadows they usually repeated certain pleasant verses of Virgil's agriculture, of Hesiod and of Politian's husbandry, would set a-broach some witty Latin epigrams, then immediately turned them into roundelays and songs for dancing in the French language. In their feasting they would sometimes separate the water from the wine that was therewith mixed, as Cato teacheth, *De re rustica*, and Pliny with an ivy cup would wash the wine in a basinful of water, then take it out again with a funnel as pure as ever. They made the water go from one glass to another, and contrived a thousand little automatory engines, moving of themselves.

CHAPTER 21

HOW THERE WAS A GREAT STRIFE AND DEBATE RAISED BETWIXT THE CAKE-BAKERS OF LERNÉ, AND THOSE OF GARGANTUA'S COUNTRY, WHEREUPON WERE WAGED GREAT WARS

AT that time, which was the season of vintage, in the beginning of harvest, when the country shepherds were set to keep the vines, and hinder the starlings from eating up the grapes, as some cake-bakers of Lerné happened to pass along the broad highway driving into the city ten or twelve horses loaded with cakes, the said shepherds courteously entreated them to give them some for their money, as the price then ruled in the market. For here it is to be remarked, that it is a celestial food to eat for breakfast hot fresh cakes with grapes, especially the frail clusters, the great red grapes, the muscadine, the verjuice grape, and the laskard, for those that are costive in their belly, whereupon they are commonly called the vintage thinkers. The bun-sellers or cake-makers were in nothing inclinable to their request; but, which was worse, did injure them most outrageously, calling them prattling gabblers, lickorous gluttons, freckled bittors, mangy rascals, shite-a-bed scoundrels, drunken roysters, sly knaves, drowsy loiterers, slapsauce fellows, slabberdegullion druggels, lubberly louts, cozening foxes, ruffian rogues, paltry customers, sycophant varlets, drawlatch hoydens, flouting milksops, jeering companions, staring clowns, forlorn snakes, ninny lobcocks, scurvy sneaksbies, fondling fops, base loons, saucy coxcombs, idle lusks, scoffing braggarts, noddy meacocks, blockish grutnols, doddipol-joltheads, jobbernol goose-caps, foolish loggerheads, flutch calf-lollies, grouthead gnat-snappers, lob-dotterels, gaping changelings, codshead loobies, woodcock slangams, ninny-hammer flycatchers, noddypeak simpletons, and other suchlike defamatory epithets; saying further, that it was not for them to eat of these dainty cakes, but might very well content themselves with the coarse unranged bread, or to eat of the great brown household loaf. To which provoking words, one amongst them, called Forgier, an honest fellow of his person and a notable springal, made answer very calmly thus: How long is it since you have got horns, that you are become so proud? Indeed formerly you were wont to give us some freely, and will you not now let us have any for our money? This is not the part of good neighbours, neither do we serve you thus when you come thither to buy our good corn, whereof you make your cakes and buns. Besides that, we would have given you to the bargain some of our grapes, but, by his zounds, you may chance to repent it, and possibly have need of us at another time, when we shall use you after the like manner, and therefore remember it. Then Marquet, a prime man in the confraternity of the cake-bakers, said unto him, Yea, sir, thou art pretty well crest risen this morning, thou didst eat yesternight too much millet and bolymong. Come hither, sirrah, come hither, I will give thee some cakes. Whereupon Forgier, dreading no harm, in all simplicity went towards him, and drew a six-pence out of his leather satchel, thinking that Marquet would have sold him some of his cakes. But, instead of cakes, he gave him with his whip such a rude lash overthwart the legs, that the marks of the whipcord knots were apparent in them, then would have fled away; but Forgier cried out loud, as he could, O, murder, murder, help, help, help! and in the meantime threw a great cudgel after him, which he carried under his arm, wherewith he hit him in the coronal joint of his head, upon the crotaphic artery of the right side thereof, so forcibly, that Marquet fell down from his mare more like a dead than a living man. Meanwhile the farmers and country swains, that were watching their walnuts near to that place, came running with their great poles and long staves, and laid such a load on these cake-bakers, as if they had been to thresh upon green rye. The other shepherds and shepherdesses, hearing the lamentable shout of Forgier, came with their slings and slackies following them, and throwing great stones at them, as thick as if it had been hail. At last they overtook them, and took from them about four or five dozen of their cakes. Nevertheless they paid for them the ordinary price, and gave them over and above one hundred eggs and three baskets full of mulberries. Then did the cake-bakers help to get up to his mare Marquet, who was most shrewdly wounded, and forthwith returned to Lerné, changing the resolution they had to go to Pareille, threatening very sharp and boisterously the cowherds, shepherds, and farmers of Sevillé and Sinays. This done, the shepherds and shepherdesses made merry with these cakes and fine grapes, and sported themselves together at the sound of the pretty small pipe, scoffing and laughing at those vainglorious cake-bakers, who had that day met with a mischief for want of crossing themselves with a good hand in the morning. Nor did they forget to apply to Forgier's leg some fair great red medicinal grapes, and so handsomely dressed it and bound it up that he was quickly cured.

CHAPTER 22

HOW THE INHABITANTS OF LERNÉ, BY THE COMMANDMENT
OF PICROCHOLE THEIR KING, ASSAULTED THE SHEPHERDS
OF GARGANTUA UNEXPECTEDLY AND ON A SUDDEN

THE cake-bakers, being returned to Lerné, went presently,
before they did either eat or drink, to the Capitol, and there
before their king, called Picrochole, the third of that name,
made their complaint, showing their panniers broken, their
caps all crumpled, their coats torn, their cakes taken away,
but, above all, Marquet most enormously wounded, saying
that all that mischief was done by the shepherds and herds-
men of Grangousier, near the broad highway beyond Sevillé.
Picrochole incontinent grew angry and furious; and, without
asking any further what, how, why, or wherefore, commanded the ban and arriere ban to be sounded throughout
all his country, that all his vassals of what condition soever
should, upon pain of the halter, come, in the best arms they
could, unto the great place before the castle, at the hour of
noon, and, the better to strengthen his design, he caused the
drum to be beat about the town. Himself, whilst his dinner
was making ready, went to see his artillery mounted upon
the carriage, to display his colours, and set up the great royal
standard, and loaded wains with store of ammunition both
for the field and the belly, arms and victuals. At dinner he
despatched his commissions, and by his express edict my
Lord Shagrag was appointed to command the vanguard,
wherein were numbered sixteen thousand and fourteen arquebusiers or firelocks, together with thirty thousand and eleven
volunteer adventurers. The great Touquedillon, master of the
horse, had the charge of the ordnance, wherein were reckoned
nine hundred and fourteen brazen pieces, in cannons, double
cannons, basilisks, serpentines, culverins, bombards or mur-

derers, falcons, bases or passevolins, spirols, and other sorts
of great guns. The rear-guard was committed to the Duke
of Scrapegood. In the main battle was the king and the
princes of his kingdom. Thus being hastily furnished, before
they would set forward, they sent three hundred light horsemen, under the conduct of Captain Swillwind, to discover
the country, clear the avenues, and see whether there was
any ambush laid for them. But, after they had made diligent
search, they found all the land round about in peace and
quiet, without any meeting or convention at all; which
Picrochole understanding, commanded that everyone should
march speedily under his colours. Then immediately in all
disorder, without keeping either rank or file, they took the
fields one amongst another, wasting, spoiling, destroying, and
making havoc of all wherever they went, not sparing poor
nor rich, privileged or unprivileged places, church nor laity,
drove away oxen and cows, bulls, calves, heifers, wethers,
ewes, lambs, goats, kids, hens, capons, chickens, geese,
ganders, goslings, hogs, swine, pigs, and such like; beating
down the walnuts, plucking the grapes, tearing the hedges,
shaking the fruit-trees, and committing such incomparable
abuses, that the like abomination was never heard of. Nevertheless, they met with none to resist them, for everyone submitted to their mercy, beseeching them that they might be
dealt with courteously in regard that they had always carried
themselves as became good and loving neighbours, and that
they had never been guilty of any wrong or outrage done
upon them, to be thus suddenly surprised, troubled, and disquieted, and that, if they would not desist, God would punish
them very shortly. To which expostulations and remon-
strances no other answer was made, but that they would
teach them to eat cakes.

CHAPTER 23

HOW A MONK OF SEVILLÉ SAVED THE CLOSE OF THE ABBEY FROM BEING RANSACKED BY THE ENEMY

So much they did, and so far they went pillaging and stealing, that at last they came to Sevillé, where they robbed both
men and women, and took all they could catch: nothing was
either too hot or too heavy for them. Although the plague
was there in the most part of all the houses, they nevertheless entered everywhere, then plundered and carried away
all that was within, and yet for all this not one of them took
any hurt, which is a most wonderful case. For the curates,
vicars, preachers, physicians, chirurgeons, and apothecaries,
who went to visit, to dress, to cure, to heal, to preach unto
and admonish those that were sick, were all dead of the infection, and these devilish robbers and murderers caught
never any harm at all. Whence comes this to pass, my masters? I beseech you think upon it. The town being thus pil-
laged, they went unto the abbey with a horrible noise and
tumult, but they found it shut and made fast against them.
Whereupon the body of the army marched forward towards
a pass or ford called the Gué de Vède, except seven companies of foot and two hundred lancers, who, staying there,
broke down the walls of the close, to waste, spoil, and make
havoc of all the vines and vintage within that place. The
monks (poor devils) knew not in that extremity to which of
all their sancts they should vow themselves. Nevertheless, at
all adventures, they rang the bells *ad capitulum capitulantes.*
There it was decreed that they should make a fair procession,
stuffed with good lectures, prayers, and litanies *contra hostium insidias,* and jolly responses *pro pace.*

There was then in the abbey a claustral monk, called Friar
John of the funnels and gobbets, in French *des entoumeures,*

young, gallant, frisk, lusty, nimble, quick, active, bold, adventurous, resolute, tall, lean, wide-mouthed, long-nosed, a fair despatcher of morning prayers, unbridler of masses, and runner over of vigils; and, to conclude summarily in a word, a right monk, if ever there was any, since the monking world monked a monkery; for the rest, a clerk even to the teeth in matter of breviary. This monk, hearing the noise that the enemy made within the enclosure of the vineyard, went out to see what they were doing; and perceiving that they were cutting and gathering the grapes, whereon was grounded the foundation of all their next year's wine, returned unto the choir of the church where the other monks were, all amazed and astonished like so many bell-melters. Whom when he heard sing, ini, nim, pe, ne, ne, ne, ne, nene, tum, ne, num, num, im, i, mi, co, o, no, o, o, neno, ne, no, no, no, rum, nenum, num: It is well sung, said he. By the virtue of God, why do not you sing, Panniers, farewell, vintage is done? The devil snatch me, if they be not already within the middle of our close, and cut so well both vines and grapes, that, by Cod's body, there will not be found for these four years to come so much as a gleaning in it. By the belly of Sanct James, what shall we poor devils drink the while? Lord God, *da mihi potum*. Then said the prior of the convent: What should this drunken fellow do here? let him be carried to prison for troubling the divine service. Nay, said the monk, the wine service, let us behave ourselves so that it be not troubled; for you yourself, my lord prior, love to drink of the best, and so doth every honest man. Never yet did a man of worth dislike good wine; it is a monastical apophthegm. But these responses that you chant here, by G—, are not in season. Wherefore is it, that our devotions were instituted to be short in the time of harvest and vintage, and long in the advent, and all the winter? The late friar,

Massepelosse, of good memory, a true zealous man, or else
I give myself to the devil, of our religion, told me, and I
remember it well, how the reason was, that in this season we
might press and make the wine, and in winter whiff it up.
Hark you, my masters, you that love the wine, Cop's body,
follow me; for Sanct Anthony burn me as freely as a faggot,
if they get leave to taste one drop of the liquor that will not
now come and fight for relief of the wine. Hog's belly, the
goods of the church! Ha, no, no. What the devil, Sanct
Thomas of England was well content to die for them; if I
died in the same cause, should not I be a sanct likewise?
Yes. Yet shall not I die there for all this, for it is I that must
do it to others and send them a-packing.

As he spake this he threw off his great monk's habit, and
laid hold upon the staff of the cross, which was made of
the heart of a sorbapple-tree, it being of the length of a
lance, round, of a full grip, and a little powdered with lilies
called flower de luce, the workmanship whereof was almost
all defaced and worn out. Thus went he out in a fair long-
skirted jacket, putting his frock scarfwise athwart his breast,
and in this equipage, with his staff, shaft or truncheon of the
cross, laid on so lustily, brisk, and freely upon his enemies,
who, without any order, or ensign, or trumpet, or drum, were
busied in gathering the grapes of the vineyard. For the
cornets, guidons, and ensign-bearers had laid down their
standards, banners, and colours by the wall sides; the drum-
mers had knocked out the heads of their drums on one end
to fill them with grapes; the trumpeters were loaded with
great bundles of bunches and huge knots of clusters; in sum,
everyone of them was out of array, and all in disorder. He
hurried therefore, upon them so rudely, without crying gare
or beware, that he overthrew them like hogs, tumbled them
over like swine, striking athwart and alongst, and by one

means or other laid so about him, after the old fashion of
fencing, that to some he beat out their brains, to others he
crushed their arms, battered their legs, and bethwacked their
sides till their ribs cracked with it. To others again he un-
jointed the spondyles or knuckles of the neck, disfigured their
chaps, gashed their faces, made their cheeks hang flapping
on their chin, and so swinged and belammed them that they
fell down before him like hay before a mower. To some others
he spoiled the frame of their kidneys, marred their backs,
broke their thigh-bones, pashed in their noses, poached out
their eyes, cleft their mandibles, tore their jaws, dung in their
teeth into their throat, shook asunder their omoplates or
shoulder blades, sphacelated their shins, mortified their
shanks, inflamed their ankles, heaved off the hinges their
ishies, their sciatica or hip-gout, dislocated the joints of
their knees, squattered into pieces the boughts or pestles of
their thighs, and so thumped, mauled and belaboured them
everywhere, that never was corn so thick and threefold
threshed upon by ploughmen's flails as were the pitifully
disjointed members of their mangled bodies under the merciless baton of the cross. If any offered to hide himself amongst
the thickest of the vines, he laid him squat as a flounder,
bruised the ridge of his back, and dashed his reins like a
dog. If any thought by flight to escape, he made his head to
fly in pieces by the lamdoidal commissure, which is a seam
in the hinder part of the skull. If anyone did scramble up
into a tree, thinking there to be safe, he rent up his perinee,
and impaled him in the fundament. If any of his old acquaintance happened to cry out, Ha, Friar John, my friend
Friar John, quarter, quarter, I yield myself to you, to you
I render myself! So thou shalt, said he, and must, whether
thou wouldst or no, and withal render and yield up thy
soul to all the devils in hell; then suddenly gave them dronos,

that is, so many knocks, thumps, raps, dints, thwacks, and bangs, as sufficed to warn Pluto of their coming and despatch them a-going. If any was so rash and full of temerity as to resist him to his face, then was it he did show the strength of his muscles, for without more ado he did transpierce him, by running him in at the breast, through the mediastine and the heart. Others, again, he so quashed and bethumped, that, with a sound bounce under the hollow of their short ribs, he overturned their stomachs so that they died immediately. To some, with a smart souse on the epigaster, he would make their midriff swag, then, redoubling the blow, gave them such a homepush on the navel that he made their puddings to gush out. Believe, that it was the most horrible spectacle that ever one saw. Some cried unto Sanct Barbe, others to St. George. O the holy Lady Nytouch, said one, the good Sanctess; O our Lady of Succours, said another, help, help! Others cried, Our Lady of Cunaut, of Loretto, of Good Tidings, on the other side of the water St. Mary Over. Some vowed a pilgrimage to St. James, and others to the holy handkerchief of Chamberry, which three months after that burnt so well in the fire that they could not get one thread of it saved. Others sent up their vows to St. Cadouin, others to St. John d'Angely, and to St. Eutropiius of Xaintes. Others again invoked St. Mesmes of Cinon, St. Martin of Candes, St. Cloüaud of Sinays, the holy relics of Laurezay, with a thousand other jolly little sancts and santrels. Some died without speaking, others spoke without dying; some died in speaking, others spoke in dying. Others shouted as loud as they could Confession, Confession, *Confiteor, Miserere, In manus!* So great was the cry of the wounded, that the prior of the abbey with all his monks came forth, who, when they saw these poor wretches so slain amongst the vines, and wounded to death, confessed some of them. But

whilst the priests were busied in confessing them, the little
monkies ran all to the place where Friar John was, and asked
him wherein he would be pleased to require their assistance.
To which he answered that they should cut the throats of
those he had thrown down upon the ground. They presently,
leaving their outer habits and cowls upon the rails, began to
throttle and make an end of those whom he had already
crushed. Can you tell with what instruments they did it?
With fair gullies, which are little hulch-backed demi-knives,
the iron tool whereof is two inches long, and the wooden
handle one inch thick, and three inches in length, wherewith
the little boys in our country cut ripe walnuts in two while
they are yet in the shell, and pick out the kernel, and they
found them very fit for the expediting of that weasand-slit-
ting exploit. In the meantime Friar John, with his formidable
baton of the cross, got to the breach which the enemies had
made, and there stood to snatch up those that endeavoured
to escape. Some of the monkitos carried the standards, banners, ensigns, guidons, and colours into their cells and chambers to make garters of them. But when those that had been
shriven would have gone out at the gap of the said breach,
the sturdy monk quashed and felled them down with blows,
saying, These men have had confession and are penitent
souls; they have got their absolution and gained the pardons:
they go into paradise as straight as a sickle, or as the way is
to Faye (like Crooked-Lane at Eastcheap). Thus by his
prowess and valour were discomfited all those of the army
that entered into the close of the abbey, unto the number
of thirteen thousand, six hundred, twenty and two, besides
the women and little children, which is always to be understood. Never did Maugis the Hermit bear himself more
valiantly with his bourbon or pilgrim's staff against the
Saracens, of whom it is written in the Acts of the four sons

of Aymon, than did this monk against his enemies with the staff of the cross.

CHAPTER 24

HOW PICROCHOLE STORMED AND TOOK BY ASSAULT THE ROCK CLERMOND, AND OF GRANGOUSIER'S UNWILLINGNESS AND AVERSION FROM THE UNDERTAKING OF WAR

WHILST the monk did thus skirmish, as we have said, against those which were entered within the close, Picrochole in great haste passed the ford of Vède—a very especial pass —with all his soldiers, and set upon the rock Clermond, where there was made him no resistance at all; and, because it was already night, he resolved to quarter himself and his army in that town, and to refresh himself of his pugnative choler. In the morning he stormed and took the bulwarks and the castle, which afterwards he fortified with rampiers, and furnished with all ammunition requisite, intending to make his retreat there, if he should happen to be otherwise worsted; for it was a strong place, both by art and nature, in regard of the stance and situation of it. But let us leave them there, and return to our good Gargantua, who is at Paris very assiduous and earnest at the study of good letters and athletical exercitations, and to the good old man Grangousier his father, who after supper warmeth his ballocks by a good, clear, great fire, and, waiting upon the broiling of some chestnuts, is very serious in drawing scratches on the hearth, with a stick burnt at the one end, wherewith they did stir up the fire, telling to his wife and the rest of the family pleasant old stories and tales of former times.

Whilst he was thus employed one of the shepherds which did keep the vines, named Pillot, came towards him, and to full related the enormous abuses which were committed,

and the excessive spoil that was made by Picrochole, King of
Lerné, upon his lands and territories, and how he had pil-
laged, wasted, and ransacked all the country, except the enclosure at Sevillé which Friar John des Entoumeures to his
great honour had preserved; and that at the same present
time the said king was in the rock Clermond, and there, with
great industry and circumspection, was strengthening himself and his whole army. Halas, halas, alas! said Grangousier,
what is this, good people? Do I dream, or is it true that they
tell me? Picrochole, my ancient friend of old time, of my
kindred and alliance, comes he to invade me? What moves
him? What provokes him? What sets him on? What drives
him to it? Who hath given him this counsel? Ho, ho, ho, ho,
ho, my God, my Saviour, help me, inspire me, and advise me
what I shall do! I protest, I swear before thee, so be thou
favourable to me, if ever I did him or his subjects any
damage or displeasure, or committed any the least robbery
in his country; but, on the contrary, I have succoured and
supplied him with men, money, friendship, and counsel, upon
any occasion wherein I could be steadable for the improve-
ment of his good. That he hath therefore at this nick of time
so outraged and wronged me, it cannot be but the malevolent
and wicked spirit. Good God, thou knowest my courage, for
nothing can be hidden from thee. If perhaps he be grown
mad, and that thou hast sent him hither to me for the better
recovery and re-establishment of his brain, grant me power
and wisdom to bring him to the yoke of thy holy will by good
discipline. Ho, ho, ho, ho, my good people, my friends and
my faithful servants, must I hinder you from helping me?
Alas, my old age required henceforward nothing else but rest,
and all the days of my life I have laboured for nothing so
much as peace; but now I must, I see it well, load with arms
my poor weary, and feeble shoulders, and take in my trem-

bling hands the lance and horseman's mace, to succour and protect my honest subjects. Reason will have it so; for by their labour am I entertained, and with their sweat am I nourished, I, my children and my family. This notwithstanding, I will not undertake war, until I have first tried all the ways and means of peace; that I resolve upon.

Then assembled he his council, and proposed the matter as it was indeed. Whereupon it was concluded that they should send some discreet man unto Picrochole to know wherefore he had thus suddenly broken the peace and invaded those lands unto which he had no right or title. Furthermore, that they should send for Gargantua, and those under his command, for the preservation of the country, and defence thereof now at need. All this pleased Grangousier very well, and he commanded that so it should be done. Presently therefore he sent the Basque his lackey to fetch Gargantua with all diligence, and wrote to him as followeth:

CHAPTER 25

THE TENOUR OF THE LETTER WHICH GRANGOUSIER WROTE TO HIS SON GARGANTUA

THE fervency of thy studies did require that I should not in a long time recall thee from that philosophical rest thou now enjoyest, if the confidence reposed in our friends and ancient confederates had not at this present disappointed the assurance of my old age. But seeing such is my fatal destiny, that I should be now disquieted by those in whom I trusted most, I am forced to call thee back to help the people and goods which by the right of nature belong unto thee. For even as arms are weak abroad, if there be not counsel at home, so is that study vain and counsel unprofitable which in a due and convenient time is not by virtue executed and put in effect. My deliberation is not to provoke but to appease—not to assault, but to defend—not to conquer, but to preserve my faithful subjects and hereditary dominions, into which Picrochole is entered in a hostile manner without any ground or cause, and from day to day pursueth his furious enterprise with that height of insolence that is intolerable to freeborn spirits. I have endeavoured to moderate his tyrannical choler, offering him all that which I thought might give him satisfaction; and oftentimes have I sent lovingly unto him to understand wherein, by whom, and how he found himself to be wronged. But of him could I obtain no other answer but a mere defiance, and that in my lands he did pretend only to the right of a civil correspondency and good behaviour, whereby I knew that the eternal God hath left him to the disposure of his own free will and sensual appetite—which cannot choose but be wicked, if by divine grace it be not continually guided—and to contain him within his duty, and bring him to know himself, hath sent him hither to me by a grievous token. Therefore, my beloved son, as soon as thou canst, upon sight of these letters, repair hither with all diligence, to succour not me so much, which nevertheless by natural piety thou oughtest to do, as thine own people, which by reason thou mayest save and preserve. The exploit shall be done with as little effusion of blood as may be. And, if possible, by means far more expedient, such as military policy, devices, and stratagems of war, we shall save all the souls, and send them home as merry as crickets unto their own houses. My dearest son, the peace of Jesus Christ our Redeemer be with thee. Salute from me Ponocrates, Gymnastes, and Eudemon. The twentieth of September.

THY FATHER GRANGOUSIER.

CHAPTER 26

HOW ULRIC GALLET WAS SENT UNTO PICROCHOLE

THE letters being dictated, signed, and sealed, Grangousier ordained that Ulric Gallet, master of the requests, a very wise and discreet man, of whose prudence and sound judgment he had made trial in several difficult and debateful matters, [should] go unto Picrochole, to show what had been decreed amongst them. At the same hour departed the good man Gallet, and having passed the ford, asked at the miller that dwelt therein what condition Picrochole was: who answered him that his soldiers had left him neither cock nor hen, that they were retired and shut up into the rock Clermond, and that he would not advise him to go any further for fear of the scouts, because they were enormously furious. Which he easily believed, and therefore lodged that night with the miller.

The next morning he went with a trumpeter to the gate of the castle, and required the guards he might be admitted to speak with the king of somewhat that concerned him. These words being told unto the king, he would by no means consent that they should open the gate, but, getting upon the top of the bulwark, said unto the ambassador, What is the news, what have you to say? Then the ambassador began to speak as followeth.

CHAPTER 27

THE SPEECH MADE BY GALLET TO PICROCHOLE

THERE cannot arise amongst men a juster cause of grief than when they receive hurt and damage, where they may justly expect for favour and good will; and not without cause, though without reason, have many, after they had fallen into such a calamitous accident, esteemed this indignity less supportable than the loss of their own lives, in such sort that, if they have not been able by force of arms nor any other means, by reach of wit or subtlety, to stop them in their course and restrain their fury, they have fallen into desperation, and utterly deprived themselves of this light. It is therefore no wonder if King Grangousier, my master, be full of high displeasure and much disquieted in mind upon thy outrageous and hostile coming; but truly it would be a marvel if he were not sensible of and moved with the incomparable abuses and injuries perpetrated by thee and thine upon those of his country, towards whom there hath been no example of inhumanity omitted. Which in itself is to him so grievous, for the cordial affection wherewith he hath always cherished his subjects, that more it cannot be to any mortal man; yet in this, above human apprehension, is it to him the more grievous that these wrongs and sad offences have been committed by thee and thine, who, time out of mind, from all antiquity, thou and thy predecessors have been in a continual league and amity with him and all his ancestors; which, even until this time, you have as sacred together inviolably preserved, kept, and entertained, so well, that not he and his only, but the very barbarous nations of the Poictevins, Bretons, Manceaux, and those that dwell beyond the isles of the Canaries, and that of Isabella, have thought it as easy to pull down the firmament, and to set up the depths above the clouds, as to make a breach in your alliance; and have been so afraid of it in their enterprises that they never dared to provoke, incense, or endamage the one for fear of the other. Nay, which is more, this sacred league hath so filled the world, that there are few nations at this day inhabiting throughout all the continent and isles of the ocean, who have not ambitiously aspired to be received

into it, upon your own covenants and conditions, holding
your joint confederacy in as high esteem as their own territories and dominions, in such sort, that from the memory of
man there hath not been either prince or league so wild and
proud that durst have offered to invade, I say not your countries, but not so much as those of your confederates. And if,
by rash and heady counsel, they have attempted any new
design against them, as soon as they heard the name and
title of your alliance, they have suddenly desisted from their
enterprises. What rage and madness, therefore doth now in-
cite thee, all old alliance infringed, all amity trod under foot,
and all right violated, thus in a hostile manner to invade his
country, without having been by him or his in anything
prejudiced, wronged, or provoked? Where is faith? Where
is law? Where is reason? Where is humanity? Where is the
fear of God? Dost thou think that these atrocious abuses
are hidden from the eternal spirit and the supreme God who
is the just rewarder of all our undertakings? If thou so think
thou deceivest thyself, for all things shall come to pass as
in his incomprehensible judgment he hath appointed. Is it
thy fatal destiny, or influences of the stars, that would put
an end to thy so long enjoyed ease and rest? For that all
things have their end and period, so as that, when they are
come to the superlative point of their greatest height, they
are in a trice tumbled down again, as not being able to abide
long in that state. This is the conclusion and end of those
who cannot by reason and temperance moderate their fortunes and prosperities. But if it be predestinated that thy
happiness and ease must now come to an end, must it needs
be by wronging my king,—him by whom thou wert established? If thy house must come to ruin, should it therefore
in its fall crush the heels of him that set it up? The matter
is so unreasonable, and so dissonant from common sense,

that hardly can it be conceived by human understanding, and altogether incredible unto strangers, till by the certain and undoubted effects thereof, it be made apparent that nothing is either sacred or holy to those who, having emancipated themselves from God and reason, do merely follow the perverse affections of their own depraved nature. If any wrong had been done by us to thy subjects and dominions—if we had favoured the ill-willers—if we had not assisted thee in thy need—if thy name and reputation had been wounded by us—or, to speak more truly, if the calumniating spirit, tempting to induce thee to evil, had, by the false illusions and deceitful fantasies put into thy conceit the impression of a thought that we had done unto thee anything unworthy of our ancient correspondence and friendship, thou oughtest first to have inquired out the truth, and afterwards by a seasonable warning to admonish us thereof; and we should have so satisfied thee, according to thine own heart's desire, that thou shouldst have had occasion to be contented. But, O eternal God, what is thy enterprise? Wouldst thou, like a perfidious tyrant, thus spoil and lay waste thy master's kingdom? Hast thou found him so silly and blockish, that he would not—or so destitute of men and money, of counsel and skill in military discipline, that he cannot withstand thy unjust invasion? March hence presently, and to-morrow, some time of the day, retreat unto thine own country, without doing any kind of violence or disorderly act by the way: and pay withal a thousand besans of gold (which, in English money, amounteth to five thousand pounds), for reparation of the damages thou hast done in this country. Half thou shalt pay to-morrow, and the other half at the ides of May next coming, leaving with us in the meantime, for hostages, the Dukes of Turnbank

Lowbuttock, and Smalltrash, together with the Prince of
Itches and Viscount of Snatchbit.*

CHAPTER 28

HOW GRANGOUSIER, TO BUY PEACE, CAUSED THE CAKES TO BE RESTORED

WITH that the good man Gallet held his peace but Picrochole to all his discourse answered nothing but Come and
fetch them, come and fetch them,—they will knead and provide some cakes for you. Then returned he to Grangousier,
whom he found upon his knees bareheaded, crouching in a
little corner of his cabinet, and humbly praying unto God
that he would vouchsafe to assuage the choler of Picrochole,
and bring him to the rule of reason without proceeding by
force. When the good man came back, he asked him, Ha, my
friend, my friend, what news do you bring me? There is
neither hope nor remedy, said Gallet; the man is quite out
of his wits, and forsaken of God. Yea, but, said Grangousier,
my friend, what cause doth he pretend for his outrages? He
did not show me any cause at all, said Gallet, only that in a
great anger he spoke some words of cakes. I cannot tell if
they have done any wrong to his cake-bakers. I will know,
said Grangousier, the matter thoroughly, before I resolve any
more upon what is to be done. Then sent he to learn concerning that business, and found by true information that
his men had taken violently some cakes from Picrochole's
people, and that Marquet's head was broken with a slacky or
short cudgel that, nevertheless, all was well paid, and that
the said Marquet had first hurt Forgier with a stroke of his
whip across the legs. And it seemed good to his whole council, that he should defend himself with all his might. Not-

* Tournemoule, Bas-de-fesses, Menuail, Gratelles, Morpiaille.

withstanding all this, said Grangousier, seeing the question
is but about a few cakes, I will labour to content him, for I
am very unwilling to wage war against him. He inquired then
what quantity of cakes they had taken away, and understanding that it was but some four or five dozen, he commanded five cart-loads of them to be baked that same night;
and that there should be one full of cakes made with fine
butter, fine yolks of eggs, fine saffron, and fine spice, to be
bestowed upon Marquet, unto whom likewise he directed to
be given seven hundred thousand and three Philips [that is,
at three shillings the piece, one hundred five thousand pounds
and nine shillings of English money], for reparation of his
losses and hindrances, and for satisfaction of the chirurgeon
that had dressed his wound; and furthermore settled upon
him and his forever in freehold the apple-orchard called La
Pomardiere. For the conveyance and passing of all which
was sent to Gallet, who by the way as they went made them
gather near the willow-trees great store of boughs, canes, and
reeds, wherewith all the carriers were enjoined to garnish and
deck their carts, and each of them to carry one in his hand,
as himself likewise did thereby to give all men to understand
that they demanded but peace, and that they came to buy it.

Being come to the gate, they required to speak with
Picrochole from Grangousier. Picrochole would not so much
as let them in, nor go to speak with them, but sent them
word that he was busy, and that they should deliver their
mind to Captain Touquedillon, who was then planting a
piece of ordnance upon the wall. Then said the good man
unto him, My lord, to ease you of all this labour, and to take
away all excuses why you may not return unto our former
alliance, we do here presently restore unto you the cakes
upon which the quarrel arose. Five dozen did our people
take away; they were well paid for: we love peace so well

that we restore unto you five cartloads, of which this cart shall be for Marquet, who doth most complain. Besides, to content him entirely, here are seven hundred thousand and three Philips, which I deliver to him, and, for the losses he may pretend to have sustained, I resign for ever the farm of the Pomardiere, to be possessed in fee-simple by him and his forever, without the payment of any duty, or acknowledgment of homage, fealty, fine, or service whatsoever; and here is the tenour of the deed. And, for God's sake, let us live henceforward in peace, and withdraw yourselves merrily into your own country from within this place, unto which you have no right at all, as yourselves must needs confess, and let us be good friends as before. Touquedillon related all this to Picrochole, and more and more exasperated his courage, saying to him, These clowns are afraid to some purpose. By G—, Grangousier conskites himself for fear, the poor drinker. He is not skilled in warfare, nor hath he any stomach for it. He knows better how to empty the flagons,—that is his art. I am of opinion that it is fit we send back the carts and the money, and, for the rest, that very speedily we fortify ourselves here, then prosecute our fortune. But what! Do they think to have to do with a ninny-whoop, to feed you thus with cakes? You may see what it is. The good usage and great familiarity which you have had with them heretofore hath made you contemptible in their eyes. Anoint a villain, he will prick you: prick a villain, and he will anoint you.*

Sa, sa, sa, said Picrochole, by St. James, you have given a true character of them. One thing I will advise you, said Touquedillon. We are here but badly victualled, and furnished with mouth harness very slenderly. If Grangousier should come to besiege us, I would go presently, and pluck out of all your soldiers' heads and mine own all the teeth, ex-

* Ungentem, pungit, pungentem rusticus ungit.

cept three to each of us, and with them alone we should make an end of our provision but too soon. We shall have, said Picrochole, but too much sustenance and feeding stuff. Came we hither to eat or to fight? To fight, indeed, said Touquedillon; yet from the paunch comes the dance, and where famine rules force is exiled. Leave off your prating, said Picrochole, and forthwith seize upon what they have brought. Then took they money and cakes, oxen and carts, and sent them away without speaking one word, only that they would come no more so near for a reason that they would give them the morrow after. Thus, without doing anything, returned they to Grangousier, and related the whole matter unto him, subjoining that there was no hope left to draw them to peace but by sharp and fierce wars.

CHAPTER 29

HOW SOME STATESMEN OF PICROCHOLE, BY HAIRBRAINED COUNSEL, PUT HIM IN EXTREME DANGER

THE carts being unloaded, and the money and cakes secured, there came before Picrochole the Duke of Smalltrash, the Earl Swashbuckler, and Captain Dirt-tail* who said unto him, Sir, this day we make you the happiest, the most warlike, and chivalrous prince that ever was since the death of Alexander of Macedonia. Be covered, be covered, said Picrochole. Gramercy, said they, we do but our duty. The manner is this. You shall leave some captain here to have the charge of this garrison, with a party competent for keeping of the place, which, besides its natural strength, is made stronger by the rampiers and fortresses of your devising. Your army you are to divide into two parts, as you know very well how to do. One part thereof shall fall upon Gran-

* Menuail, Spadassin, Merdaille.

zousier and his forces. By it shall he be easily at the very
first shock routed, and then shall you get money by heaps,
for the clown hath store of ready coin. Clown we call him,
because a noble and generous prince hath never a penny, and
that to hoard up treasure is but a clownish trick. The other
part of the army, in the meantime, shall draw towards Onys,
Xaintonge, Angomois, and Gascony. Then march to Perigot,
Medoc, and Elanes, taking wherever you come, without resistance towns, castles, and forts; afterwards to Bayonne, St.
John de Luc, to Fontarabia, where you shall seize upon all
the ships, and coasting along Galicia and Portugal, shall
pillage all the maritime places, even unto Lisbon, where you
shall be supplied with all necessaries befitting a conqueror.
By copsody, Spain will yield, for they are but a race of
boobies. Then are you to pass by the Straits of Gibraltar,
where you shall erect two pillars more stately than those of
Hercules, to the perpetual memory of your name, and the
narrow entrance there shall be called the Picrocholinal sea.

Having passed the Picrocholinal sea, behold, Barbarossa
yields himself your slave. I will, said Picrochole, give him
fair quarter and spare his life. Yea, said they, so that he be
content to be christened. And you shall conquer the kingdoms of Tunis, of Hippo, Argier, Bomine [Bona], Corone,
yea, all Barbary. Furthermore, you shall take into your hands
Majorca, Minorca, Sardinia, Corsica, with the other islands
of the Ligustic and Balearian seas. Going alongst on the left
hand, you shall rule all Gallia Narbonensis, Provence, the
Allobrogians, Genoa, Florence, Lucca, and then God b' w'
ye, Rome. [Our poor Monsieur the Pope dies now for fear.]
By my faith, said Picrochole, I will not then kiss his pan-
toufle.

Italy being thus taken, behold Naples, Calabria, Apulia,
and Sicily, all ransacked, and Malta too. I wish the pleasant

Knights of the Rhodes heretofore would but come to resist
you, that we might see their urine. I would, said Picrochole,
very willingly go to Loretto. No, no, said they, that shall
be at our return. From thence we will sail eastwards, and
take Candia, Cyprus, Rhodes, and the Cyclade Islands, and
set upon [the] Morea. It is ours, by St. Trenian. The Lord
preserve Jerusalem; for the great Soldan is not comparable
to you in power. I will then, said he, cause Solomon's temple
to be built. No, said they, not yet, have a little patience,
stay awhile, be never too sudden in your enterprises. Can
you tell what Octavian Augustus said? *Festina lente*. It is
requisite that you first have the Lesser Asia, Caria, Lycia,
Pamphilia, Cilicia, Lydia, Phrygia, Mysia, Bithnia, Carazia,
Satalia, Samagaria, Castamena, Luga, Savasta, even unto
Euphrates. Shall we see, said Picrochole, Babylon and Mount
Sinai? There is no need, said they, at this time. Have we not
hurried up and down, travelled and toiled enough, in having
transfretted and passed over the Hircanian sea, marched
alongst the two Armenias and the three Arabias? Ay, by my
faith, said he, we have played the fools, and are undone. Ha,
poor souls! What's the matter? said they. What shall we
have, said he, to drink in these deserts? For Julian Augustus
with his whole army died there for thirst, as they say. We
have already, said they, given order for that. In the Syriac
sea you have nine thousand and fourteen great ships laden
with the best wines in the world. They arrived at Port Joppa.
There they found two-and-twenty thousand camels and sixteen hundred elephants, which you shall have taken at one
hunting about Sigelmes, when you entered into Lybia; and,
besides this, you had all the Mecca caravan. Did not they
furnish you sufficiently with wine? Yes, but, said he, we did
not drink it fresh. By the virtue, said they, not of a fish, a
valiant man, a conqueror, who pretends and aspires to the

monarchy of the world, cannot always have his wine. God be thanked that you and your men are come safe and sound unto the banks of the river Tigris. But, said he, what doth that part of our army in the meantime which overthrows that unworthy swillpot Grangousier? They are not idle, said they. We shall meet with them by-and-by. They shall have won you Brittany, Normandy, Flanders, Hainault, Brabant, Artois, Holland, Zealand; they have passed the Rhine over the bellies of the Switzers and lansquenets, and a party of those hath subdued Luxemburg, Lorraine, Champagne, and Savoy, even to Lyons, in which place they have met with your forces returning from the naval conquests of the Mediterranean sea; and have rallied again in Bohemia, after they had plundered and sacked Suevia, Wittemberg, Bavaria, Austria, Moravia, and Styria. Then they set fiercely together upon Lubeck, Norway, Swedeland, Rie, Denmark, Gitland, Greenland, the Sterlins, even unto the frozen sea. This done, they conquered the Isles of Orkney and subdued Scotland, England, and Ireland. From thence sailing through the sandy sea and by the Sarmates, they have vanquished and over- come Prussia, Poland, Lithuania, Russia, Wallachia, Tran- sylvania, Hungary, Bulgaria, Turkzeland, and are now at Constantinople. Come, said Picrochole, let us go join with them quickly, for I will be Emperor of Trebizond also. Shall we not kill all these dogs, Turks and Mahometans? What a devil should we do else? said they. And you shall give their goods and lands to such as shall have served you honestly. Reason, said he, will have it so, that is but just. I give unto you the Caramania, Suria, and all the Palestine. Ha, sir, said they, it is out of your goodness; gramercy, we thank you. God grant you may always prosper. There was there present at that time an old gentleman well experienced in the wars, a stern soldier and who had been in many great hazards,

named Echephron, who, hearing this discourse, said, I do
greatly doubt that all this enterprise will be like the tale
or interlude of the pitcher full of milk wherewith a shoe
maker made himself rich in conceit; but, when the pitcher
was broken, he had not whereupon to dine. What do you
pretend by these large conquests? What shall be the end of
so many labours and crosses? Thus it shall be, said Pic
rochole, that when we are returned we shall sit down, rest
and be merry. But, said Echephron, if by chance you should
never come back, for the voyage is long and dangerous, were
it not better for us to take our rest now, than unnecessarily
to expose ourselves to so many dangers? Oh, said Swash
buckler, by G—, here is a good dotard; come, let us go
hide ourselves in the corner of a chimney, and there spend
the whole time of our life amongst ladies, in threading of
pearls, or spinning like Sardanapalus. He that nothing ven
tures hath neither horse nor mule, says Solomon. He who
adventureth too much, said Echephron, loseth both horse
and mule, answered Malchon. Enough, said Picrochole, go
forward. I fear nothing but that these devilish legions of
Grangousier whilst we are in Mesopotamia, will come on
our backs and charge up our rear. What course shall we
then take? What shall be our remedy? A very good one,
said Dirt-tail; a pretty little commission, which you must
send unto the Muscovites, shall bring you into the field in
an instant four hundred and fifty thousand choice men of
war. Oh that you would but make me your lieutenant-general,
I should for the lightest faults of any inflict great punish
ments. I fret, I charge, I strike, I take, I kill, I slay, I play
the devil. On, on, said Picrochole, make haste, my lads, and
let him that loves me follow me.

CHAPTER 30

HOW GARGANTUA LEFT THE CITY OF PARIS TO SUCCOUR HIS
COUNTRY, AND HOW GYMNAST ENCOUNTERED WITH THE
ENEMY

IN this same very hour Gargantua, who was gone out of
Paris as soon as he had read his father's letters, coming upon
his great mare, had already passed the Nunnery-bridge, himself, Ponocrates, Gymnast, and Eudemon, who all three, the
better to enable them to go along with him, took post-horses.
The rest of his train came after him by even journeys at a
slower pace, bringing with them all his books and philosophical instruments. As soon as he had alighted at Parillé, he
was informed by a farmer of Gouguet how Picrochole had
fortified himself within the rock Clermond, and had sent
Captain Tripet with a great army to set upon the wood of
Vède and Vaugaudry, and that they had already plundered
the whole country, not leaving cock nor hen, even as far as
to the winepress of Billard. These strange and almost incredible news of the enormous abuses thus committed over
all the land, so affrighted Gargantua that he knew not what
to say nor do. But Ponocrates counselled him to go unto
the Lord of Vauguyon, who at all times had been their
friend and confederate, and that by him they should be
better advised in their business. Which they did incontinently, and found him very willing and fully resolved to
assist them, and therefore was of opinion that they should
send some one of his company to scout along and discover
the country, to learn in what condition and posture the
enemy was, that they might take counsel, and proceed according to the present occasion. Gymnast offered himself to
go. Whereupon it was concluded, that for his safety and the
better expedition, he should have with him someone that

knew the ways, avenues, turnings, windings, and rivers thereabouts. Then away went he and Prelingot, the equerry or
gentleman of Vauguyon's horse, who scouted and espied as
narrowly as they could upon all quarters without any fear.
In the meantime Gargantua took a little refreshment, ate
somewhat himself, the like did those who were with him,
and caused to give to his mare a picotine of oats, that is, three
score and fourteen quarters and three bushels. Gymnast and
his comrade rode so long, that at last they met with the
enemy's forces, all scattered and out of order, plundering,
stealing, robbing, and pillaging all they could lay their hands
on. And, as far off as they could perceive him, they ran
thronging upon the back of one another in all haste towards
him, to unload him of his money, and untruss his port-
mantles. Then cried he out unto them, My masters, I am a
poor devil, I desire you to spare me. I have yet one crown
left. Come, we must drink it, for it is *aurum potabile*, and
this horse here shall be sold to pay my welcome. Afterwards
take me for one of your own, for never yet was there any
man that knew better how to take, lard, roast, and dress, yea,
by G——, to tear asunder and devour a hen, than I that am
here: and for my *proficiat* I drink to all good fellows. With
that he unscrewed his borracho (which was a great Dutch
leathern bottle), and without putting in his nose drank very
honestly. The maroufle rogues looked upon him, opening
their throats a foot wide, and putting out their tongues like
greyhounds, in hopes to drink after him; but Captain Tripet,
in the very nick of that their expectation, came running to
him to see who it was. To him Gymnast offered his bottle,
saying, Hold, captain, drink boldly and spare not; I have
been thy taster, it is wine of La Faye Monjau. What! said
Tripet, this fellow gibes and flouts us? Who art thou? said
Tripet. I am, said Gymnast, a poor devil (*pauvre diable*).

Ha, said Tripet, seeing thou art a poor devil, it is reason
that thou shouldst be permitted to go whithersoever thou wilt,
for all poor devils pass everywhere without toll or tax. But
it is not the custom of poor devils to be so well mounted;
therefore, sir devil, come down, and let me have your horse,
and if he do not carry me well, you, master devil, must do it:
for I love a life that such a devil as you should carry me
away.

CHAPTER 31

HOW GYMNAST VERY NIMBLY AND CUNNINGLY KILLED CAP-
TAIN TRIPET AND OTHERS OF PICROCHOLE'S MEN

WHEN they heard these words, some amongst them began
to be afraid, and blessed themselves with both hands, thinking indeed that he had been a devil disguised, insomuch that
one of them, named Good John, captain of the trained bands
of the country bumpkins, took his psalter out of his codpiece, and cried out aloud, *Hagios ho theos*. If thou be of
God, speak; if thou be of the other spirit, avoid hence, and
get thee going. Yet he went not away. Which words being
heard by all the soldiers that were there, divers of them
being a little inwardly terrified, departed from the place.
All this did Gymnast very well remark and consider, and
therefore making as if he would have alighted from off his
horse, as he was poising himself on the mounting side, he
most nimbly, with his short sword by his thigh, shifting his
foot in the stirrup, performed a stirrup-leather feat, whereby,
after the inclining of his body downwards, he forthwith
launched himself aloft in the air, and placed both his feet
together on the saddle, standing upright with his back turned
towards the horse's head. Now, said he, my case goes backward. Then suddenly in the same very posture wherein he

was, he fetched a gambol upon one foot, and, turning to
the left hand, failed not to carry his body perfectly round,
just into its former stance, without missing one jot. Ha, said
Tripet, I will not do that at this time, and not without
cause. Well, said Gymnast, I have failed, I will undo this
leap. Then with a marvellous strength and agility, turning
towards the right hand, he fetched another frisking gambol
as before, which done, he set his right hand thumb upon
the hind-bow of the saddle, raised himself up, and sprung
in the air, poising and upholding his whole body upon the
muscle and nerve of the said thumb, and so turned and
whirled himself about three times. At the fourth, revers-
ing his body, and overturning it upside down and fore-
side back, without touching anything, he brought himself
betwixt the horse's two ears, springing with all his body into
the air, upon the thumb of his left hand, and in that posture,
turning like a windmill, did most actively do that trick
which he called the miller's pass. After this, clapping his
right hand flat upon the middle of the saddle, he gave himself such a jerking swing that he thereby seated himself upon
the crupper, after the manner of gentlewomen sitting on
horseback. This done, he easily passed his right leg over the
saddle, and placed himself like one that rides in croup. But,
said he, it were better for me to get into the saddle; then
putting the thumbs of both hands upon the crupper before
him, and thereupon leaning himself as upon the only sup-
porters of his body, he incontinently turned heels over head
in the air, and straight found himself betwixt the bow of the
saddle in a good settlement. Then with a somersault springing into the air again, he fell to stand with both his feet
close together upon the saddle, and there made above a
hundred frisks, turns, and demipommads, with his arms held
out across, and in so doing cried out aloud, I rage, I rage,

devils, I am stark mad, devils, I am mad, hold me, devils, hold me, hold, devils, hold, hold!

Whilst he was thus vaulting, the rogues in great astonishment said to one another, By cock's death, he is a goblin or a devil thus disguised, *Ab hoste maligno libera nos, Domine*, and ran away in a full flight, as if they had been routed, looking now and then behind them, like a dog that carryeth away a goose-wing in his mouth. Then Gymnast, spying his advantage, alighted from his horse, drew his sword, and laid on great blows upon the thickest and highest crested among them, and overthrew them in great heaps, hurt, wounded, and bruised, being resisted by nobody, they thinking he had been a starved devil, as well in regard of his wonderful feats in vaulting, which they had seen, as for the talk Tripet had with him, calling him poor devil! Only Tripet would have traitorously cleft his head with his horseman's sword, or lance-knight falchion; but he was well armed, and felt nothing of the blow but the weight of the stroke. Whereupon, turning suddenly about, he gave Tripet a home-thrust, and upon the back of that whilst he was about to ward his head from a slash, he ran him in at the breast with a hit, which at once cut his stomach, the fifth gut called the colon, and the half of his liver, wherewith he fell to the ground, and in falling gushed forth above four pottles of pottage, and his soul mingled with the pottage.

This done, Gymnast withdrew himself, very wisely considering that a case of great adventure and hazard should not be pursued unto its utmost period, and that it becomes all cavaliers modestly to use their good fortune without troubling or stretching it too far. Wherefore, getting to horse, he gave him the spur, taking the right way unto Vauguyon, and Prelingot with him.

CHAPTER 32

HOW GARGANTUA DEMOLISHED THE CASTLE AT THE FORD OF
VÈDE, AND HOW THEY PASSED THE FORD

As soon as he came, he related the estate and condition
wherein they had found the enemy, and the stratagem which
he alone had used against all their multitude, affirming that
they were but rascally rogues, plunderers, thieves, and robbers, ignorant of all military discipline, and that they might
boldly set forward unto the field; it being an easy matter to
fell and strike them down like beasts. Then Gargantua
mounted his great mare, accompanied as we have said before, and finding in his way a high and great tree, which commonly was called by the name of St. Martin's tree, because
heretofore St. Martin planted a pilgrim's staff there, which
in tract of time grew to that height and greatness, said, This
is that which I lacked; this tree shall serve me both for a
staff and lance. With that he pulled it up easily, plucked off
the boughs, and trimmed it at his pleasure. Gargantua,
being come to the place of the wood of Vède, was informed
by Eudemon that there was some remainder of the enemy
within the castle, which to know, Gargantua cried out as
loud as he was able, Are you there or are you not there?
If you be there, be there no more; and if you are not there,
I have no more to say. But a ruffian gunner, whose charge
was to attend the portcullis over the gate, let fly a cannon-
ball at him, and hit him with that shot most furiously on
the right temple of his head, yet did him no more hurt than
if he had but cast a prune or kernel of a wine-grape at him.
What is this? said Gargantua; do you throw at us grape-
kernels here? The vintage shall cost you dear; thinking
indeed that the bullet had been the kernel of a grape, or
raisin-kernel.

Those who were within the castle, being till then busy at
the pillage, when they heard this noise ran to the towers
and fortresses, from whence they shot at him above nine
thousand and five-and-twenty falconshot and arquebusades,
aiming all at his head, and so thick did they shoot at him
that he cried out, Ponocrates, my friend, these flies here are
like to put out mine eyes; give me a branch of those willow-
trees to drive them away, thinking that the bullets and stones
shot out of the great ordnance had been but dunflies. Ponocrates looked and saw that there were no other flies but
great shot which they had shot from the castle. Then was it
that he rushed with his great tree against the castle, and with
mighty blows overthrew both towers and fortresses, and laid
all level with the ground, by which means all that were within
were slain and broken in pieces. Going from thence, they
came to the bridge at the mill, where they found all the ford
covered with dead bodies, so thick that they had choked up
the mill and stopped the current of its water, and these were
those that were destroyed in the urinal deluge of the mare.
There they were at a stand, consulting how they might pass
without hindrance by these dead carcasses. But Gymnast
said, If the devils have passed there, I will pass well enough.
The devils have passed there, said Eudemon, to carry away
the damned souls. By St. Treignan! said Ponocrates, then
by necessary consequence he shall pass there. Yes, yes, said
Gymnastes, or I shall stick in the way. Then setting spurs
to his horse, he passed through freely, his horse not fearing
nor being anything affrighted at the sight of the dead bodies;
for he had accustomed him, according to the doctrine of
Ælian, not to fear armour, nor the carcasses of dead men;
and that not by killing men as Diomedes did the Thracians,
or as Ulysses did in throwing the corpses of his enemies at
his horse's feet, as Homer saith, but by putting a Jack-a-lent

amongst his hay, and making him go over it ordinarily when he gave him his oats. The other three followed him very close, except Eudemon only, whose horse's foreright or far forefoot sank up to the knee in the paunch of a great fat chuff who lay there upon his back drowned, and could not get it out. There was he pestered, until Gargantua, with the end of his staff, thrust down the rest of the villain's tripes into the water whilst the horse pulled out his foot; and, which is a wonderful thing in hippiatry, the said horse was thoroughly cured of a ringbone which he had in that foot by this touch of the burst guts of that great looby.

CHAPTER 33

HOW GARGANTUA, IN COMBING HIS HEAD, MADE THE GREAT CANNON-BALLS FALL OUT OF HIS HAIR

BEING come out of the river of Vède, they came very shortly after to Grangousier's castle, who waited for them with great longing. At their coming they were entertained with many congees, and cherished with embraces. Never was seen a more joyful company, for *Supplementum Supplementi Chronicorum* saith that Gargamelle died there with joy; for my part, truly I cannot tell, neither do I care very much for her, nor for anybody else. The truth was, that Gargantua, in shifting his clothes, and combing his head with a comb, which was nine hundred foot long of the Jewish cane measure, and whereof the teeth were great tusks of elephants, whole and entire, he made fall at every rake above seven balls of bullets, at a dozen the ball, that stuck in his hair at the razing of the castle of the wood of Vède. Which his father Grangousier seeing, thought they had been lice, and said unto him, What, my dear son, hast thou brought us this far some short-winged hawks of the college of Montague? I did not mean that thou shouldst reside there. Then answered Ponocrates, My sovereign lord, think not that I have placed him in that lousy college which they call Montague; I had rather have put him amongst the gravediggers of Sanct Innocent, so enormous is the cruelty and villainy that I have known there: for the galley-slaves are far better used amongst the Moors and Tartars, the murderers in the criminal dungeons, yea, the very dogs in your house, than the poor wretched students in the aforesaid college. And if I were King of Paris, the devil take me if I would not set it on fire, and burn both principal and regents, for suffering this inhumanity to be exercised before their eyes. Then, taking up one of these bullets, he said, These are cannonshot, which your son Gargantua hath lately received by the treachery of your enemies, as he was passing before the wood of Vède.

But they have been so rewarded, that they are all destroyed in the ruin of the castle, as were the Philistines by the policy of Samson, and those whom the tower of Silohim slew, as it is written in the thirteenth of Luke. My opinion is, that we pursue them whilst the luck is on our side; for occasion hath all her hair on her forehead; when she is passed, you may not recall her,—she hath no tuft whereby you can lay hold on her, for she is bald in the hind part of her head, and never returneth again. Truly, said Grangousier, it shall not be at this time; for I will make you a feast this night, and bid you welcome.

This said, they made ready supper, and, of extraordinary besides his daily fare, were roasted sixteen oxen, three heifers, two and thirty calves, three score and three fat kids, four score and fifteen wethers, three hundred farrow pigs or shoats soused in sweet wine or must, eleven score partridges, seven hundred snipes and woodcocks, four hundred Loudun and

Cornwall capons, six thousand pullets, and as many pigeons, six hundred crammed hens, fourteen hundred leverets, or young hares and rabbits, three hundred and three buzzards, and one thousand and seven hundred cockerels. For venison, they could not so suddenly come by it, only eleven wild boars, which the Abbot of Turpenay sent, and eighteen fallow deer which the Lord of Gramount bestowed; together with seven score pheasants, which were sent by the Lord of Essars; and some dozens of quests, coushats, ringdoves, and woodculvers; river-fowl, teals and awteals, bitterns, courtes, plovers, francolins, briganders, tyrasons, young lapwings, tame ducks, shovellers, woodlanders, herons, moorhens, criels, storks, canepetiers, oranges, flamans, which are phœnicopters, or crimson-winged sea-fowls, terrigoles, turkeys, arbens, coots, solan-geese, curlews, termagants, and water-wagtails, with a great deal of cream, curds, and fresh cheese, and store of soup, pottages, and brewis, with great variety. Without doubt there was meat enough, and it was handsomely dressed by Snapsauce, Hotchpot, and Brayverjuice, Grangousier's cooks. Jenkin Trudgeapace and Cleanglass were very careful to fill them drink.

CHAPTER 34

HOW GARGANTUA DID EAT UP SIX PILGRIMS IN A SALAD

THE story requireth that we relate that which happened unto six pilgrims who came from Sebastian near to Nantes, and who for shelter that night, being afraid of the enemy, had hid themselves in the garden upon the chichling peas, among the cabbages and lettuces. Gargantua finding himself somewhat dry, asked whether they could get any lettuce to make him a salad; and hearing that there was the greatest and fairest in the country, for they were as great as plum-trees or as walnut-trees, he would go thither himself, and brought thence in his hand what he thought good, and withal carried away the six pilgrims, who were in so great fear that they did not dare to speak nor cough.

Washing them, therefore, first at the fountain, the pilgrims said one to another softly, What shall we do? We are almost drowned here amongst these lettuce, shall we speak? But if we speak, he will kill us for spies. And, as they were thus deliberating what to do, Gargantua put them with the lettuce into a platter of the house, as large as the huge tun of the White Friars of the Cistercian order; which done, with oil, vinegar, and salt, he ate them up, to refresh himself a little before supper, and had already swallowed up five of the pilgrims, the sixth being in the platter, totally hid under a lettuce, except his bourbon or staff that appeared, and nothing else. Which Grangousier seeing, said to Gargantua, I think that is the horn of a shell-snail, do not eat it. Why not, said Gargantua, they are good all this month: which he no sooner said, but, drawing up the staff, and therewith taking up the pilgrim, he ate him very well, then drank a terrible draught of excellent white wine. The pilgrims thus devoured, made shift to save themselves as well as they could, by withdrawing their bodies out of the reach of the grinders of his teeth, but could not escape from thinking they had been put in the lowest dungeon of a prison. And when Gargantua whiffed the great draught, they thought to have been drowned in his mouth, and the flood of wine had almost carried them away into the gulf of his stomach. Nevertheless, skipping with their bourbons, as St. Michael's palmers use to do, they sheltered themselves from the danger of that inundation under the banks of his teeth. But one of them by chance, groping or sounding the country with his staff, to try whether they were in safety or no, struck hard against the cleft of a hollow tooth, and hit the mandibulary sinew or nerve of the jaw, which put Gargantua to very great pain, so that he began to cry for the rage that he felt. To ease himself therefore of his smarting ache, he called for his toothpicker, and rubbing towards a young walnut-tree, where they lay skulking, unnestled you my gentlemen pilgrims.

For he caught one by the legs, another by the script, another by the pocket, another by the scarf, another by the band of the breeches, and the poor fellow that had hurt him with the bourbon, him he hooked to him by the codpiece, which snatch nevertheless did him a great deal of good, for it pierced unto him a pocky botch he had in the groin, which grievously tormented him ever since they were past Ancenis. The pilgrims, thus dislodged, ran away athwart the plain a pretty pace, and the pain ceased, even just at the time when by Eudemon he was called to supper, for all was ready.

CHAPTER 35

HOW THE MONK WAS FEASTED BY GARGANTUA, AND OF THE JOVIAL DISCOURSE THEY HAD AT SUPPER

WHEN Gargantua was set down at table, after all of them had somewhat stayed their stomachs by a snatch or two of the first bits eaten heartily, Grangousier began to relate the source and cause of the war raised between him and Picrochole; and came to tell how Friar John of the Funnels had triumphed at the defence of the close of the abbey, and extolled him for his valour above Camillus, Scipio, Pompey, Cæsar, and Themistocles. Then Gargantua desired that he might be presently sent for, to the end that with him they might consult of what was to be done. Whereupon, by a joint consent, his steward went for him, and brought him along merrily, with his staff of the cross, upon Grangousier's mule. When he was come, a thousand huggings, a thousand embracements, a thousand good days were given. Ha, Friar John, my friend Friar John, my brave cousin Friar John from the devil! Let me clip thee, my heart, about the neck; to me an armful. I must grip thee, my ballock, till thy back crack with it. Come, my cod, let me coll thee till I kill thee. And Friar John, the gladdest man in the world, never was man made welcomer, never was any more courteously and graciously received than Friar John. Come, come, said Gargantua, a stool here close by me at this end. I am content, said the monk, seeing you will have it so. Some water, page; fill, my boy, fill; it is to refresh my liver. Give me some, child, to gargle my throat withal. *Deposita cappa,* said Gymnast, let us pull off this frock. Ho, by G——, gentlemen, said the monk, there is a chapter *in Statutis Ordinis* which opposeth my laying of it down. Pish! said Gymnast, a fig for your chapter! This frock breaks both your shoulders, put it off. My friend, said the monk, let me alone with it; for, by G——, I'll drink the better that it is on. It makes all my body jocund. If I should lay it aside, the waggish pages would cut to themselves garters out of it, as I was once served at Coulaines. And, which is worse, I shall lose my appetite. But if in this habit I sit down at table, I will drink, by G——, both to thee and to thy horse, and so courage, frolic, God save the company! I have already supped, yet will I eat never a whit the less for that; for I have a paved stomach, as hollow as a butt of malvoisie or St. Benedictus' boot, and always open like a lawyer's pouch. Of all fishes but the tench, take the wing of a partridge or the thigh of a nun. Doth not he die like a good fellow that dies with a stiff catso? Our prior loves exceedingly the white of a capon. In that, said Gymnast, he doth not resemble the foxes; for of the capons, hens, and pullets which they carry away they never eat the white. Why? said the monk. Because, said Gymnast, they have no cooks to dress them; and, if they be not competently made ready, they remain red and not white; the redness of meats being a token that they have not got enough of the fire, whether by boiling, roasting, or otherwise, except the shrimps, lobsters, crabs, and crayfishes, which are cardinalized with boiling. By God's feast-gazers, said the monk, the porter of our abbey then hath not his head well boiled, for his eyes are as red as a mazer made of an alder-tree. The thigh of this leveret is good for those that have the gout. And lusty, my lads. Some bousing liquor, page! So! crack, crack, crack. O how good is God, that gives us of this excellent juice! I call him to witness, if I had been in the time of Jesus Christ, I would have kept him from being taken by the Jews in the garden of Olivet. And the devil fail me, if I should have failed to cut off the hams of these gentlemen apostles who ran away so basely after they had well supped, and left their good master in the lurch. I hate that man worse than poison that offers to run away when he should fight and lay stoutly about him. Oh that I were but King of France for fourscore or a hundred years! By G——, I should whip like curtail-dogs these runaways of Pavia. A plague take them; why did they not choose rather to die there than to leave their good prince in that pinch and necessity? Is it not better and more honourable to perish in fighting valiantly than to live in disgrace by a cowardly running away? We are like to eat no great store of goslings this year; therefore, friend, reach me some of that roasted pig there.

Diavolo, is there no more must? No more sweet wine? *Germinavit radix Jesse. Je renie ma vie, je meurs de soif;* I renounce my life, I rage for thirst. This wine is none of the worst. What wine drink you at Paris? I give myself to the devil, if I did not once keep open house at Paris for all comers six months together. Do you know Friar Claude of the high kilderkins? Oh the good fellow that he is! But I do not know what fly hath stung him of late, he is become so hard a student. For my part, I study not at all. In our abbey we never study for fear of the mumps, which disease in horses is called the mourning in the chine. Our late abbot was wont to say that it is a monstrous thing to see a learned monk. By G——, master, my friend, *Magis magnos clericos non sunt magis magnos sapientes.* You never saw so many hares as there are this year. I could not anywhere come by a goshawk nor tassel of falcon. My Lord Belloniere promised me a lanner, but he wrote to me not long ago that he was become pursy. The partridges will so multiply henceforth, that they will go near to eat up our ears. I take no delight in the stalking-horse, for I catch such cold that I am like to founder myself at that sport. If I do not run, toil, travel, and trot about, I am not well at ease. True it is that in leaping over the hedges and bushes my frock leaves always some of its wool behind it. I have recovered a dainty greyhound; I give him to the devil, if he suffer a hare to escape him. A groom was leading him to my Lord Huntlittle, and I robbed him of him. Did I ill? No, Friar John, said Gymnast, no, by all the devils that are, no! So, said the monk, do I attest these same devils so long as they last, or rather, virtue [of] G——, what could that gouty limpard have done with so fine a dog? By the body of G——, he is better pleased when one presents him with a good yoke of oxen. How now, said Ponocrates, you swear, Friar John. It is only, said the monk, but to grace and adorn my speech. They are colours of a Ciceronian rhetoric.

CHAPTER 36

WHY MONKS ARE THE OUTCASTS OF THE WORLD; AND WHEREFORE SOME HAVE BIGGER NOSES THAN OTHERS

By the faith of a Christian, said Eudemon, I do wonderfully dote and enter in a great ecstasy when I consider the honesty and good fellowship of this monk, for he makes us here all merry. How is it, then, that they exclude the monks from all good companies, calling them feast-troublers, marrers of mirth, and disturbers of all civil conversation, as the bees drive away the drones from their hives? *Ignavum cucos pecus*, said Maro, *a præsepibus arcent*. Hereunto, answered Gargantua, there is nothing so true as that the frock and cowl draw unto itself the opprobries, injuries, and maledictions of the world, just as the wind called Cecias attracts the clouds. The peremptory reason is, because they eat the ordure and excrements of the world, that is to say, the sins of the people, and, like dung-chewers and excrementitious eaters, they are cast into the privies and secessive places, that is, the convents and abbeys, separated from political conversation, as the jakes and retreats of a house are. But if you conceive how an ape in a family is always mocked and provokingly incensed, you shall easily apprehend how monks are shunned of all men, both young and old. The ape keeps not the house as a dog doth, he draws not in the plough as the ox, he yields neither milk nor wool as the sheep, he carrieth no burden as a horse doth. That which he doth, is only to conskite, spoil, and defile all, which is the cause wherefore he hath of all men mocks, frumperies, and bastinadoes.

After the same manner a monk—I mean those little, idle, lazy monks—doth not labour and work as do the peasant and artificer; doth not ward and defend the country, as doth the man of war; cureth not the sick and diseased, as the physician doth; doth neither preach nor teach, as do the evangelical doctors and school masters; doth not import commodities and things necessary for the commonwealth, as the merchant doth. Therefore is it that by and of all men they are hooted at, hated, and abhorred. Yea, but, said Grangousier, they pray to God for us. Nothing less, answered Gargantua. True it is, that with a tingle tangle jangling of bells they trouble and disquiet all their neighbours about them. Right, said the monk; a mass, a matin, a vesper well rung, are half said. They mumble out great store of legends and psalms, by them not at all understood; they say many paternosters interlarded with Ave-Maries, without thinking upon or apprehending the meaning of what it is they say, which truly I call mocking of God, and not prayers. But so help them God, as they pray for us, and not for being afraid to lose their victuals, their manchots, and good fat pottage. All true Christians, of all estates and conditions, in all places and at all times, send up their prayers to God, and the Mediator prayeth and intercedeth for them, and God is gracious to them. Now such a one is our good Friar John; therefore every man desireth to have him in his company. He is no bigot or hypocrite; he is not torn and divided betwixt reality and appearance; no wretch of a rugged and peevish disposition, but honest, jovial, resolute, and a good fellow. He travels, he labours, he defends the oppressed, comforts the afflicted, helps the needy, and keeps the close of the abbey. Nay, said the monk, I do a great deal more than that; for whilst we are in despatching our matins and anniversaries in the choir, I make withal some crossbow-strings, polish glass bottles and bolts, I twist lines and weave purse nets wherein to catch coneys. I am never idle. But

now, hither come, some drink, some drink here! Bring the
fruit. These chestnuts are of the wood of Estrox, and with
good new wine are able to make you a fine cracker and
composer of bumsonnets. You are not as yet, it seems, well
moistened in this house with the sweet wine and must. By
G—, I drink to all men freely, and at all fords, like a proctor
or promoter's horse. Friar John, said Gymnast, take away
the snot that hangs at your nose. Ha, ha, said the monk,
am not I in danger of drowning, seeing I am in water even
to the nose? No, no, *Quare? Quia,* though some water come
out from thence, there never goes in any; for it is well
antidoted with pot-proof armour and syrup of the vine-leaf.

Oh, my friend, he that hath winter-boots made of such
leather may boldly fish for oysters, for they will never take
water. What is the cause, said Gargantua, that Friar John
hath such a fair nose? Because, said Grangousier, that God
would have it so, who frameth us in such form and for such
end as is most agreeable with his divine will, even as a potter
fashioneth his vessels. Because, said Ponocrates, he came
with the first to the fair of noses, and therefore made choice
of the fairest and the greatest. Pish, said the monk, that is
not the reason of it, but, according to the virtue monastical
philosophy, it is because my nurse had soft teats, by virtue
whereof, whilst she gave me suck, my nose did sink in as in
so much butter. The hard breasts of nurses make children
short-nosed. But hey, gay, *Ad formam nasi cognoscitur ad
te levavi.* I never eat any confections, page, whilst I am at the
bibbery. Item, bring me rather some toasts.

CHAPTER 37

HOW THE MONK MADE GARGANTUA SLEEP, AND OF HIS HOURS AND BREVIARIES

SUPPER being ended, they consulted of the business in hand, and concluded that about midnight they should fall unawares upon the enemy, to know what manner of watch and ward they kept, and that in the meanwhile they should take a little rest the better to refresh themselves. But Gargantua could not sleep by any means, on which side soever he turned himself. Whereupon the monk said to him, I never sleep soundly but when I am at sermon or prayers. Let us therefore begin, you and I, the seven penitential psalms, to try whether you shall not quickly fall asleep. The conceit pleased Gargantua very well, and, beginning the first of these psalms, as soon as they came to the words *Beati quorum* they fell asleep, both the one and the other. But the monk, for his being formerly accustomed to the hour of claustral matins, failed not to awake a little before midnight, and, being up himself, awaked all the rest, in singing aloud, and with a full clear voice, the song:

Awake, O Reinian, ho, awake!
   Awake, O Reinian, ho!
Get up, you no more sleep must take;
   Get up, for we must go.

When they were all roused and up, he said, My masters, it is a usual saying, that we begin matins with coughing and supper with drinking. Let us now, in doing clean contrarily, begin our matins with drinking, and at night before supper we shall cough as hard as we can. What, said Gargantua, to drink so soon after sleep? This is not to live according to the diet and prescript rule of the physicians, for you ought first

to scour and cleanse your stomach of all its superfluities and
excrements. Oh, well physicked, said the monk; a hundred
devils leap into my body, if there be not more old drunkards than old physicians! I have made this paction and
covenant with my appetite, that it always lieth down and
goes to bed with myself, for to that I every day give very
good order; then the next morning it also riseth with me and
gets up when I am awake. Mind you your charges, gentlemen, or tend your cures as much as you will. I will get me
to my drawer; in terms of falconry, my tiring. What drawer
or tiring do you mean? said Gargantua. My breviary, said
the monk, for just as the falconers, before they feed their
hawks, do make them draw at a hen's leg to purge their
brains of phlegm and sharpen them to a good appetite, so,
by taking this merry little breviary in the morning, I scour
all my lungs and am presently ready to drink.

After what manner, said Gargantua, do you say these
fair hours and prayers of yours? After the manner of Whip-
field,* said the monk, by three psalms and three lessons,
or nothing at all, he that will. I never tie myself to hours,
prayers, and sacraments; for they are made for the man
and not the man for them. Therefore is it that I make my
prayers in fashion of stirrup-leathers; I shorten or lengthen
them when I think good. *Brevis oratio penetrat cœlos et
longa potatio evacuat scyphos.* Where is that written? By
my faith, said Ponocrates, I cannot tell, my pillicock, but
thou art more worth than gold. Therein, said the monk, I
am like you; but, *venite, apotemus.* Then made they ready
store of carbonadoes, or rashers on the coals, and good fat
soups, or brewis with sippets; and the monk drank what he
pleased. Some kept him company, and the rest did forbear,
for their stomachs were not as yet opened. Afterwards every

---

* Fessecamp, and corruptly Fecan.

man began to arm and befit himself for the field. And they armed the monk against his will; for he desired no other armour for back and breast but his frock, nor any other weapon in his hand but the staff of the cross. Yet at their pleasure was he completely armed cap-à-pie, and mounted upon one of the best horses in the kingdom, with a good lashing sabre by his side, together with Gargantua, Ponocrates, Gymnast, Eudemon, and five-and-twenty more of the resolute and adventurous of Grangousier's house, all armed at proof with their lances in their hands, mounted like St. George, and everyone of them having an arquebusier behind him.

CHAPTER 38

HOW THE MONK ENCOURAGED HIS FELLOW-CHAMPIONS, AND HOW HE HANGED UPON A TREE

THUS went out those valiant champions on their adventure, in full resolution to know what enterprise they should undertake and what to take heed of, and look well to in the day of the great and horrible battle. And the monk encouraged them, saying, My children, do not fear nor doubt, I will conduct you safely. God and Sanct Benedict be with us! If I had strength answerable to my courage, by 'sdeath, I would plume them for you like ducks. I fear nothing but the great ordnance; yet I know of a charm by way of prayer, which the sub-sexton of our abbey taught me, that will preserve a man from the violence of guns and all manner of fire-weapons and engines; but it will do me no good, because I do not believe it. Nevertheless, I hope my staff of the cross shall this day play devilish pranks amongst them. By G—, whoever of our party shall offer to play the duck, and shrink when blows are a-dealing, I give myself to the devil, if I do not make a monk of him in my stead, and hamper him within my frock, which is a sovereign cure against cowardice. Did you never hear of my Lord Meurles his greyhound, which was not worth a straw in the fields? He put a frock about his neck: by the body of G—, there was neither hare nor fox that could escape him, and, which is more, he lined all the bitches in the country, though before that he was feeble-reined and *ex frigidis et maleficiatis*.

The monk uttering these words in choler, as he passed under a walnut-tree, in his way towards the causey, he broached the visor of his helmet on the stump of a great branch of the said tree. Nevertheless, he set his spurs so fiercely to the horse, who was full of mettle and quick on the spur, that he bounded forwards, and the monk going about to ungrapple his visor, let go his hold of the bridle, and so hanged by his hand upon the bough, whilst his horse stole away from under him. By this means was the monk left hanging on the walnut-tree, and crying for help, murder, murder, swearing also that he was betrayed. Eudemon perceived him first, and calling Gargantua said, Sir, come and see Absalom hanging. Gargantua, being come, considered the countenance of the monk, and in what posture he hanged; wherefore he said to Eudemon, You were mistaken in comparing him to Absalom; for Absalom hung by his hair, but this shaveling monk hangeth by the ears. Help me, said the monk, in the devil's name; is this a time for you to prate? You seem to me to be like the decretalist preachers, who say that whosoever shall see his neighbour in the danger of death, ought, upon pain of trisulk excommunication, rather choose to admonish him to make his confession to a priest, and put his conscience in the state of peace, than otherwise to help and relieve him.

And therefore when I shall see them fallen into a river, and ready to be drowned, I shall make them a fair long sermon *de contemptu mundi, et fuga seculi,* and when they are

stark dead, shall then go to their aid and succour in fishing
after them. Be quiet, said Gymnast, and stir not, my minion.
I am now coming to unhang thee and to set thee at freedom,
for thou art a pretty little gentle monachus. *Monachus in
claustro non valet ova duo; sed quando esta extra, bene valet
triginta.* I have seen about five hundred hanged, but I never
saw any have a better countenance in his dangling and pendi-
latory swagging. Truly, if I had so good a one, I would willingly hang thus all my lifetime. What, said the monk, have
you almost done preaching? Help me, in the name of God,
seeing you will not in the name of the other spirit, or, by the
habit which I wear, you shall repent it, *tempore et loco
prælibatis.*

Then Gymnast alighted from his horse, and, climbing up
the walnut-tree, lifted up the monk with one hand by the
gussets of his armour under the armpits, and with the other
undid his visor from the stump of the broken branch; which
done, he let him fall to the ground and himself after. As soon
as the monk was down, he put off all his armour, and threw
away one piece after another about the field, and, taking to
him again his staff of the cross, remounted up to his horse,
which Eudemon had caught in his running away. Then went
they on merrily, riding along on the highway.

CHAPTER 39

HOW THE SCOUTS AND FORE-PARTY OF PICROCHOLE WERE
MET WITH BY GARGANTUA, AND HOW THE MONK SLEW
CAPTAIN DRAWFORTH,* AND THEN WAS TAKEN PRISONER
BY HIS ENEMIES

PICROCHOLE, at the relation of those who had escaped out
of the broil and defeat wherein Tripet was untriped, grew
very angry that the devils should have so run upon his men,

* Tirevant.

and held all that night a council of war, at which Rashcalf
and Touchfaucet * concluded his power to be such that he
was able to defeat all the devils of hell if they should come
to jostle with his forces. This Picrochole did not fully believe,
though he doubted not much of it. Therefore sent he under
the command and conduct of the Count Drawforth, for discovering of the country, the number of sixteen hundred
horsemen, all well mounted upon light horses for skirmish
and thoroughly besprinkled with holy water; and everyone
for their fieldmark or cognizance had the sign of a star in his
scarf, to serve at all adventures in case they should happen
to encounter with devils, that by the virtue, as well of that
Gregorian water as of the stars which they wore, they might
make them disappear and evanish.

In this equipage they made an excursion upon the country
till they came near to the Vauguyon, which is the valley of
Guyon, and to the spital, but could never find anybody to
speak unto; whereupon they returned a little back, and took
occasion to pass above the aforesaid hospital to try what
intelligence they could come by in those parts. In which
resolution riding on, and by chance in pastoral lodge or shepherd's cottage near to Coudray hitting upon the five pilgrims,
they carried them way-bound and manacled, as if they had
been spies, for all the exclamations, adjurations, and requests
that they could make. Being come down from thence towards
Sevillé, they were heard by Gargantua, who said then unto
those that were with him, Comrades and fellow-soldiers, we
have here met with an encounter, and they are ten times in
number more than we. Shall we charge them or no? What a
devil, said the monk, shall we do else? Do you esteem men
by their number rather than by their valour and prowess?
With this he cried out, Charge, devils, charge! Which when

* Hastiveau Touquedillon.

he enemies heard, they thought certainly that they had been
very devils, and therefore even then began all of them to run
away as hard as they could drive, Drawforth only excepted,
who immediately settled his lance on his rest, and therewith
hit the monk with all his force on the very middle of his
breast, but, coming against his horrific frock, the point of
the iron being with the blow either broke off or blunted, it
was in matter of execution as if you had struck against an
anvil with a little wax-candle.

Then did the monk with his staff of the cross give him such
a sturdy thump and whirret betwixt his neck and shoulders
upon the acromion bone, that he made him lose both sense
and motion, and fall down stone dead at his horse's feet; and
seeing the sign of the star which he wore scarfwise, he said
unto Gargantua, These men are but priests, which is but the
beginning of a monk; by St. John, I am a perfect monk, I
will kill them to you like flies. Then he ran after them at a
swift and full gallop till he overtook the rear, and felled them
down like tree-leaves, striking athwart and alongst and every
way. Gymnast presently asked Gargantua if they should pursue them. To whom Gargantua answered, By no means; for
according to the right of military discipline, you must never
drive your enemy unto despair, for that such a strait doth
multiply his force and increase his courage, which was before
broken and cast down; neither is there any better help or
outgate of relief for men that are amazed, out of heart, toiled,
and spent, than to hope for no favour at all. How many victories have been taken out of the hands of the victors by the
vanquished, when they would not rest satisfied with reason,
but attempt to put all to the sword, and totally to destroy
their enemies, without leaving so much as one to carry home
news of the defeat of his fellows. Open, therefore, unto your
enemies, all the gates and ways, and make them a bridge of

silver rather than fail, that you may be rid of them. Yea, but, said Gymnast, they have the monk. Have they the monk? said Gargantua. Upon mine honour, then, it will prove to their cost. But to prevent all dangers, let us not yet retreat, but halt here quietly as in an ambush; for I think I do already understand the policy and judgment of our enemies. They are truly more directed by chance and mere fortune than by good advice and counsel. In the meanwhile, whilst these made a stop under the walnut-trees, the monk pursued on the chase, charging all he overtook, and giving quarter to none, until he met with a trooper who carried behind him one of the poor pilgrims, and there would have rifled him. The pilgrim, in hope of relief at the sight of the monk, cried out, Ha, my lord prior, my good friend, my lord prior, save me, I beseech you, save me! Which words being heard by those that rode in the van, they instantly faced about, and seeing that there was nobody but the monk that made this great havoc and slaughter among them, they loaded him with blows as thick as they use to do an ass with wood. But of all this he felt nothing, especially when they struck upon his frock, his skin was so hard. Then they committed him to two of the marshal's men to keep, and, looking about, saw nobody coming against them, whereupon they thought that Gargantua and his party were fled. Then was it that they rode as hard as they could towards the walnut-trees to meet with them, and left the monk there all alone, with his two foresaid men to guard him. Gargantua heard the noise and neighing of the horses, and said to his men, Comrades, I hear the track and beating of the enemy's horse-feet, and withal perceive that some of them come in a troop and full body against us. Let us rally and close here, then set forward in order, and by this means we shall be able to receive their charge to their loss and our honour.

CHAPTER 40

HOW THE MONK RID HIMSELF OF HIS KEEPERS, AND HOW
PICROCHOLE'S FORLORN HOPE WAS DEFEAT

THE monk, seeing them break off thus without order, con-
jectured that they were to set upon Gargantua and those that
were with him, and was wonderfully grieved that he could
not succour them. Then considered he the countenance of the
two keepers in whose custody he was, who would have willingly run after the troops to get some booty and plunder,
and were always looking towards the valley unto which they
were going. Farther, he syllogized, saying, These men are
but badly skilled in matters of war, for they have not required my parole, neither have they taken my sword from
me. Suddenly hereafter he drew his brackmard or horseman's
sword, wherewith he gave the keeper which held him on the
right side such a sound slash that he cut clean through the
jugulary veins and the sphagitid or transparent arteries of
the neck, with the fore-part of the throat called the gar-
gareon, even unto the two adenes, which are throat kernels;
and, redoubling the blow, he opened the spinal marrow betwixt the second and third vertebræ. There fell down that
keeper stark dead to the ground. Then the monk, reining his
horse to the left, ran upon the other, who seeing his fellow
dead, and the monk to have the advantage of him, cried in a
loud voice, Ha, my lord prior, quarter; I yield, my lord
prior; quarter; quarter, my good friend, my lord prior. And
the monk cried likewise, My lord posterior, my friend, my
lord posterior, you shall have it upon your posteriorums.
Ha, said the keeper, my lord prior, my minion, my gentle
lord prior, I pray God make you an abbot. By the habit, said
the monk, which I wear, I will here make you a cardinal.
What! do you use to pay ransoms to religious men? You

shall therefore have by-and-by a red hat of my giving. And
the fellow cried, Ha, my lord prior, my lord prior, my lord
abbot that shall be, my lord cardinal, my lord all! Ha, ha,
hes, no, my lord prior, my good little lord, the prior I yield
render and deliver myself up to you. And I deliver thee, said
the monk, to all the devils in hell. Then at one stroke he cut
off his head, cutting his scalp upon the temple-bones, and
lifting up in the upper part of the skull the two triangulary
bones called cincipital, or the two bones bregmatis, together
with the sagittal commissure or dartlike seam which distin-
guisheth the right side of the head from the left, as also a
great part of the coronal or forehead bone, by which terrible
blow he likewise cut the two meninges or films which enwrap
the brain, and made a deep wound in the brain's two posterior ventricles, and the cranium or skull abode hanging
upon his shoulders by the skin of the pericranium behind, in
form of a doctor's bonnet, black without and red within.
Thus fell he down also to the ground stark dead.

And presently the monk gave his horse the spur, and kept
the way that the enemy held, who had met with Gargantua
and his companions in the broad highway, and were so diminished of their number for the enormous slaughter that Gargantua had made with his great tree amongst them, as also
Gymnast, Ponocrates, Eudemon, and the rest, that they began to retreat disorderly and in great haste, as men altogether
affrighted and troubled in both sense and understanding,
and as if they had seen the very proper species and form of
death before their eyes; or rather, as when you see an ass
with a brizze or gadbee under his tail, or fly that stings him,
run hither and thither without keeping any path or way,
throwing down his load to the ground, breaking his bridle
and reins, and taking no breath nor rest, and no man can tell
what ails him, for they see not anything touch him. So fled

hese people destitute of wit, without knowing any cause of
lying, only pursued by a panic terror which in their minds
hey had conceived. The monk, perceiving that their whole
intent was to betake themselves to their heels, alighted from
his horse and got upon a big large rock which was in the way,
and with his great brackmard sword laid such loan upon
hose runaways, and with main strength fetching a compass
with his arm without feigning or sparing, slew and over-
hrew so many that his sword broke in two pieces. Then
hought he within himself that he had slain and killed suffi-
iently, and that the rest should escape to carry news. There-
ore he took up a battle-axe of those that lay there dead, and
got upon the rock again, passing his time to see the enemy
hus flying and to tumble himself amongst the dead bodies,
nly that he suffered none to carry pike, sword, lance nor
gun with him, and those who carried the pilgrims bound he
made to alight, and gave their horses unto the said pilgrims,
keeping them there with him under the hedge, and also
Touchfaucet, who was then his prisoner.

CHAPTER 41

HOW THE MONK CARRIED ALSO WITH HIM THE PILGRIMS, AND OF THE GOOD WORDS THAT GRANGOUSIER GAVE THEM

THIS skirmish being ended, Gargantua retreated with his
men, excepting the monk, and about the dawning of the day
hey came unto Grangousier, who in his bed was praying to
God for their safety and victory. And seeing them all safe
and sound, he embraced them lovingly, and asked what was
become of the monk. Gargantua answered him that without
doubt the enemies had the monk. Then have they mischief
and ill luck, said Grangousier; which was very true. There-
ore is it a common proverb to this day, to give a man the

monk, or, as in the French, *lui bailler le moine,* when they
would express the doing unto one a mischief. Then commanded he a good breakfast to be provided for their refreshment. When all was ready, they called Gargantua, but he
was so aggrieved that the monk was not to be heard of, that
he would neither eat nor drink. In the meanwhile the monk
comes, and from the gate of the outer court cries out aloud,
Fresh wine, fresh wine, Gymnast, my friend! Gymnast went
out and saw that it was Friar John, who brought along with
him five pilgrims, and Touchfaucet prisoners; whereupon
Gargantua likewise went forth to meet him, and all of them
made him the best welcome that possibly they could, and
brought him before Grangousier, who asked him of all his
adventures. The monk told him all, both how he was taken,
how he rid himself of his keepers, of the slaughter he had
made by the way, and how he had rescued the pilgrims and
brought along with him Captain Touchfaucet. Then did they
altogether fall to banqueting most merrily. In the meantime
Grangousier asked the pilgrims what countrymen they were,
whence they came, and whither they went. Sweer-to-go in the
name of the rest answered, My sovereign lord, I am of Saint
Genou in Berry, this man is of Palvau, this other is of Onzay,
this of Argy, this of St. Nazarand, and this man of Ville-
brenin. We come from Saint Sebastian near Nantes, and are
now returning, as we best may, by easy journeys. Yea, but,
said Grangousier, what went you to do at Saint Sebastian?
We went, said Sweer-to-go, to offer up unto that sanct our
vows against the plague. Ah, poor men! said Grangousier,
do you think that the plague comes from Saint Sebastian?
Yes, truly, answered Sweer-to-go, our preachers tell us so,
indeed. But is it so, said Grangousier, do the false prophets
teach you such abuses? Do they thus blaspheme the sancts
and holy men of God, as to make them like unto the devils,

who do nothing but hurt unto mankind,—as Homer writeth, that the plague was sent into the camp of the Greeks by Apollo, and as the poets feign a great rabble of Vejoves and mischievous gods. So did a certain cafard or dissembling religionary preach at Sinay, that Saint Anthony sent the fire into men's legs, that Saint Eutropius made men hydropic, Saint Clidas, fools, and that Saint Genou made them goutish. But I punished him so exemplarily, though he called me heretic for it, that since that time no such hypocritical rogue durst set his foot within my territories. And truly I wonder that your king should suffer them in their sermons to publish such scandalous doctrine in his dominions; for they deserve to be chastised with greater severity than those who, by magical art, or any other device, have brought the pestilence into a country. The pest killeth but the bodies, but such abominable impostors empoison our very souls. As he spake these words, in came the monk very resolute, and asked them, Whence are you, you poor wretches? Of Saint Genou, said they. And how, said the monk, does the Abbot Gulligut, the good drinker,—and the monks, what cheer make they? By G— body, they'll have a fling at your wives, and breast them to some purpose, whilst you are upon your roaming rant and gadding pilgrimage. Hin, hin, said Sweer-to-go, I am not afraid of mine, for he that will see her by day will never break his neck to come to her in the night-time. Yea, marry, said the monk, now you have hit it. Let her be as ugly as ever was Proserpina, she will once, by the Lord G—, be overturned, and get her skin-coat shaken, if there dwell any monks near to her; for a good carpenter will make use of any kind of timber. Let me be peppered with the pox, if you find not all your wives with a child at your return; for the very shadow of the steeple of an abbey is fruitful. It is, said Gargantua, like the water of Nilus in Egypt, if you be-

lieve Strabo and Pliny, *Lib*. 7, *cap*. 3. What virtue will there
be then, said the monk, in their bullets of concupiscence,
their habits and their bodies?

Then, said Grangousier, go your ways, poor men, in the
name of God the Creator, to whom I pray to guide you perpetually, and henceforward be not so ready to undertake
these idle and unprofitable journeys. Look to your families,
labour every man in his vocation, instruct your children,
and live as the good apostle St. Paul directeth you; in doing
whereof, God, his angels and sancts, will guard and protect
you, and no evil or plague at any time shall befall you. Then
Gargantua led them into the hall to take their refection; but
the pilgrims did nothing but sigh, and said to Gargantua, O
how happy is that land which hath such a man for their lord!
We have been more edified and instructed by the talk which
he had with us, than by all the sermons that ever were
preached in our town. This is, said Gargantua, that which
Plato saith, *Lib*. 5 *de Republ*., that those commonwealths are
happy whose rulers philosophate, and whose philosophers
rule.

Then caused he their wallets to be filled with victuals and
their bottles with wine, and gave unto each of them a horse
to ease them upon the way, together with some pence to
live by.

CHAPTER 42

HOW GRANGOUSIER DID VERY KINDLY ENTERTAIN TOUCH FAUCET HIS PRISONER

TOUCHFAUCET was presented unto Grangousier, and by
him examined upon the enterprise and attempt of Picrochole,
what it was he could pretend to, or aim at, by the rustling
stir and tumultuary coil of this his sudden invasion. Whereunto he answered that his end and purpose was to conquer

all the country, if he could, for the injury done to his cake-bakers. It is too great an undertaking, said Grangousier; and, as the proverb is, He that grips too much, holds fast but little. The time is not now as formerly to conquer the kingdoms of our neighbour princes, and to build up our own greatness upon the loss of our nearest Christian brother. The imitation of the ancient Herculeses, Alexanders, Hannibals, Scipios, Cæsars, and other such heroes, is quite contrary to the profession of the gospel of Christ, by which we are commanded to preserve, keep, rule, and govern every man his own country and lands, and not in a hostile manner to invade others; and that which heretofore the Barbars and Saracens called prowess and valour, we do now call robbing, thievery and wickedness. It would have been more commendable in him to have contained himself within the bounds of his own territories, royally governing them, than to insult and domineer in mine, pillaging and plundering everywhere like a most unmerciful enemy; for by ruling his own with discretion, he might have increased his greatness, but by robbing me he cannot escape destruction. Go your ways in the name of God, prosecute good enterprises, show your king what is amiss, and never counsel him with regard to your own particular profit for the public loss will swallow up the private benefit. As for your ransom, I do freely remit it to you, and will that your arms and horse be restored to you; so should good neighbours do, and ancient friends, seeing this our difference is not properly war. As Plato, *Lib. 5 de Repub.*, would not have it called war, but sedition, when the Greeks took up arms against one another, and that therefore, when such combustions should arise amongst them, his advice was to behave themselves in the managing of them with all discretion and modesty. Although you call it war, it is but superficial; it entereth not into the closet and inmost cabinet of our hearts. For neither of us hath been wronged in his honour, nor is there any question betwixt us in the main, but only how to redress, by the bye, some petty faults committed by our men,—I mean both yours and ours, which although you knew, you ought to let pass; for these quarrelsome persons deserve rather to be contemned than mentioned, especially seeing I offered them satisfaction according to the wrong. God shall be the just judge of our variances, whom I beseech by death rather to take me out of this life, and to permit my goods to perish and be destroyed before mine eyes, than that by me or mine he should in any sort be wronged. These words uttered, he called the monk, and before them all thus spoke unto him, Friar John, my good friend, it is you that took prisoner the Captain Touchfaucet here present? Sir, said the monk, seeing himself is here, and that he is of the years of discretion, I had rather you should know it by his confession than by any words of mine. Then said Touchfaucet, My sovereign lord, it is he indeed that took me, and I do therefore most freely yield myself his prisoner. Have you put him to any ransom? said Grangousier to the monk. No, said the monk, of that I take no care. How much would you have for having taken him? Nothing, nothing, said the monk; I am not swayed by that, nor do I regard it. Then Grangousier commanded that, in presence of Touchfaucet, should be delivered to the monk for taking him the sum of three score and two thousand saluts (in English money fifteen thousand and five hundred pounds), which was done, whilst they made a collation or little banquet to the said Touchfaucet, of whom Grangousier asked if he would stay with him, or if he loved rather to return to his king. Touchfaucet answered that he was content to take whatever course he would advise him to. Then, said Grangousier, return unto your king, and God be with you

Then he gave him an excellent sword of a Vienne blade, with a golden scabbard wrought with vine-branch-like flourishes, of fair goldsmith's work, and a collar or neck-chain of gold, weighing seven hundred and two thousand marks (at eight ounces each), garnished with precious stones of the finest sort, esteemed at a hundred and sixty thousand ducats, and ten thousand crowns more, as an honourable donative, by way of present.

After this talk Touchfaucet got to his horse, and Gargantua for his safety allowed him the guard of thirty men-at-arms and six score archers to attend him, under the conduct of Gymnast, to bring him even unto the gate of the rock Clermond, if there were need. As soon as he was gone the monk restored unto Grangousier the three score and two thousand saluts which he had received, saying, Sir, it is not as yet the time for you to give such gifts; stay till this war be at an end, for none can tell what accidents may occur, and war begun without good provision of money beforehand for going through with it, is but as a breathing of strength, and blast that will quickly pass away. Coin is the sinews of war. Well then, said Grangousier, at the end I will content you by some honest recompense, as also all those who shall do me good service.

CHAPTER 43

HOW GRANGOUSIER SENT FOR HIS LEGIONS, AND HOW TOUCHFAUCET SLEW RASHCALF, AND WAS AFTERWARDS EXECUTED BY THE COMMAND OF PICROCHOLE

ABOUT this same time those of Besse of the Old Market, of St. James' Bourg, of the Draggage, of Parillé, of the Rivers, of the rocks of St. Pol, of the Vaubreton, of Pautillé, of the Brehemont, of Clainbridge, of Cravant, of Grammont, of the

town at the Badgerholes, of Huymes, of Segré, of Husse, of
St. Lovant, of Panzoust, of the Coldraux, of Verron, of Coulaines, of Chose, of Varenes, of Bourgueil, of the Bouchard
Island, of the Croullay, of Narsay, of Cande, of Montsoreau,
and other bordering places, sent ambassadors unto Grangousier, to tell him that they were advised of the great
wrongs which Picrochole had done him, and in regard of
their ancient confederacy, offered him what assistance they
could afford both in men, money, victuals, and ammunition,
and other necessaries for war. The money which by the joint
agreement of them all was sent unto him, amounted to six
score and fourteen millions, two crowns and a half of pure
gold. The forces wherewith they did assist him did consist in
fifteen thousand cuirassiers, two-and-thirty thousand light
horsemen, four score and nine thousand dragoons, and a
hundred-and-forty thousand volunteer adventurers. These
had with them eleven thousand and two hundred cannons,
double cannons, long pieces of artillery called basilisks, and
smaller sized ones known by the name of spirols, besides
the mortar pieces and grenadoes. Of pioneers they had seven-
and-forty thousand, all victualled and paid for six months
and four days of advance. Which offer Gargantua did not
altogether refuse, nor wholly accept of; but giving them
hearty thanks, said that he would compose and order the
war by such a device, that there should not be found great
need to put so many honest men to trouble in the managing
of it; and therefore was content at that time to give order
only for bringing along the legions which he maintained in
his ordinary garrison towns of the Deviniere, of Chavigny,
of Gravrot, and of the Quinquenais, amounting to the number of two thousand cuirassiers, three score and six thousand
foot-soldiers, six-and-twenty thousand dragoons, attended
by two hundred pieces of great ordnance, two-and-twenty

thousand pioneers, and six thousand light horsemen, all drawn up in troops, so well befitted and accommodated with their commissaries, sutlers, farriers, harness-makers, and other such like necessary members in a military camp, so fully instructed in the art of warfare, so perfectly knowing and following their colours, so ready to hear and obey their captains, so nimble to run, so strong at their charging, so prudent in their adventures, and every day so well disciplined, that they seemed rather to be a concert of organ pipes, or mutual concord of the wheels of a clock, than an infantry and cavalry, or army of soldiers.

Touchfaucet immediately after his return presented himself before Picrochole, and related unto him at large all that he had done and seen, and at last endeavoured to persuade him with strong and forcible arguments to capitulate and make an agreement with Grangousier, whom he found to be the honestest man in the world; saying further, that it was neither right nor reason thus to trouble his neighbours, of whom they had never received anything but good. And in regard of the main point, that they should never be able to go through stitch with that war, but to their great damage and mischief; for the forces of Picrochole were not so considerable but that Grangousier could easily overthrow them.

He had not well done speaking when Rashcalf said out loud, Unhappy is that prince which is by such men served, who are so easily corrupted, as I know Touchfaucet is. For I see his courage so changed that he had willingly joined with our enemies to fight against us and betray us, if they would have received him; but as virtue is of all, both friends and foes, praised and esteemed, so is wickedness soon known and suspected, and although it happen, the enemies to make use thereof, for their profit, yet have they always the wicked and the traitors in abomination.

Touchfaucet being at these words very impatient, drew out his sword, and therewith ran Rashcalf through the body, a little under the nipple of his left side, whereof he died presently, and pulling back his sword out of his body said boldly, So let him perish that shall a faithful servant blame. Picrochole incontinently grew furious, and seeing Touchfaucet's new sword and his scabbard so richly diapered with flourishes of most excellent workmanship, said, Did they give thee this weapon so feloniously therewith to kill before my face my so good friend Rashcalf? Then immediately commanded he his guard to hew him in pieces, which was instantly done, and that so cruelly that the chamber was all dyed with blood. Afterwards he appointed the corpse of Rashcalf to be honourably buried, and that of Touchfaucet to be cast over the walls into the ditch.

The news of these excessive violences were quickly spread through all the army; whereupon many began to murmur against Picrochole, in so far that Pinchpenny said to him, My sovereign lord, I know not what the issue of this enterprise will be. I see your men much dejected, and not well resolved in their minds, by considering that we are here very ill provided of victual, and that our number is already much diminished by three or four sallies. Furthermore, great supplies and recruits come daily in to your enemies; but we so moulder away that, if we be once besieged, I do not see how we can escape a total destruction. Tush, pish, said Picrochole, you are like the Melun eels, you cry before they come to you. Let them come, let them come, if they dare.

CHAPTER 44

HOW GARGANTUA SET UPON PICROCHOLE WITHIN THE ROCK
CLERMOND, AND UTTERLY DEFEATED THE ARMY OF THE
SAID PICROCHOLE

GARGANTUA had the charge of the whole army, and his
father Grangousier stayed in his castle, who, encouraging
them with good words, promised great rewards unto those
that should do any notable service. Having thus set forward,
as soon as they had gained the pass at the ford of Vède, with
boats and bridges speedily made they passed over in a trice.
Then considering the situation of the town, which was on a
high and advantageous place, Gargantua thought fit to call
his council, and pass that night in deliberation upon what
was to be done. But Gymnast said unto him, My sovereign
lord, such is the nature and complexion of the French, that
they are worth nothing but at the first push. Then are they
more fierce than devils. But if they linger a little and be
wearied with delays, they'll prove more faint and remiss
than women. My opinion is therefore, that now presently,
after your men have taken breath and some small refection,
you give order for a resolute assault, and that we storm
them instantly. His advice was found very good, and for
effectuating thereof he brought forth his army into the plain
field, and placed the reserves on the skirt or rising of a little
hill. The monk took along with him six companies of foot
and two hundred horsemen well armed, and with great diligence crossed the marsh, and valiantly got upon the top of
the green hillock even unto the highway which leads to London. Whilst the assault was thus begun, Picrochole's men
could not tell well what was best, to issue out and receive
the assailants or keep within the town and not to stir. Himself in the meantime, without deliberation, sallied forth in a

rage with the cavalry of his guard, who were forthwith received and royally entertained with great cannon-shot that fell upon them like hail from the high grounds upon which the artillery was planted. Whereupon the Gargantuists betook themselves unto the valleys, to give the ordnance leave to play and range with the larger scope.

Those of the town defended themselves as well as they could, but their shot passed over us without doing us any hurt at all. Some of Picrochole's men that had escaped our artillery set most fiercely upon our soldiers, but prevailed little; for they were all let in betwixt the files, and there knocked down to the ground, which their fellow-soldiers seeing, they would have retreated, but the monk having seized upon the pass by the which they were to return, they ran away and fled in all the disorder and confusion that could be imagined.

Some would have pursued after them and followed the chase, but the monk withheld them, apprehending that in the pursuit the pursuer might lose their ranks, and so give occasion to the besieged to sally out of the town upon them. Then staying there some space and none coming against him, he sent the Duke Phrontist to advise Gargantua to advance towards the hill upon the left hand to hinder Picrochole's retreat at that gate; which Gargantua did with all expedition, and sent thither four brigades under the conduct of Sebast, which had no sooner reached the top of the hill, but they met Picrochole in the teeth, and those that were with him scattered.

Then charged they upon them stoutly, yet were they much endamaged by those that were upon the walls, who galled them with all manner of shot, both from the great ordnance, small guns and bows. Which Gargantua perceiving, he went with a strong party to their relief, and with his ar-

tillery began to thunder so terribly upon that canton of the
wall, and so long, that all the strength within the town, to
maintain and fill up the breach, was drawn thither. The
monk, seeing that quarter which he kept besieged void of
men and competent guards, and in a manner altogether naked
and abandoned, did most magnanimously on a sudden lead
up his men towards the fort, and never left it till he had got
up upon it, knowing that such as come to the reserve in a
conflict bring with them always more fear and terror than
those that deal about them with their hands in the fight.

Nevertheless, he gave no alarm till all his soldiers had
got within the wall, except the two hundred horsemen, whom
he left without to secure his entry. Then did he give a most
horrible shout, so did all these who were with him, and immediately thereafter, without resistance, putting to the edge of
the sword the guard that was at that gate, they opened it to
the horsemen, with whom most furiously they altogether ran
towards the east gate, where all the hurlyburly was, and
coming close upon them in the rear overthrew all their forces.

The besieged, seeing that the Gargantuists had won the
town upon them, and that they were like to be secure in no
corner of it, submitted themselves unto the mercy of the
monk, and asked for quarter, which the monk very nobly
granted to them, yet made them lay down their arms; then
shutting them up within churches, gave order to seize upon
all the staves of the crosses, and placed men at the doors to
keep them from coming forth. Then opening that east gate,
he issued out to succour and assist Gargantua. But Picrochole, thinking it had been some relief coming to him from
the town, adventured more forwardly than before, and was
upon the giving of a most desperate home-charge, when
Gargantua cried out, Ha, Friar John, my friend Friar John,
you are come in a good hour. Which unexpected accident so

affrighted Picrochole and his men, that, giving all for lost, they betook themselves to their heels, and fled on all hands. Gargantua chased them till they came near to Vaugaudry, killing and slaying all the way, and then sounded the retreat.

CHAPTER 45

HOW PICROCHOLE IN HIS FLIGHT FELL INTO GREAT MISFOR-TUNES, AND WHAT GARGANTUA DID AFTER THE BATTLE

PICROCHOLE thus in despair fled towards the Bouchard Island, and in the way to Riviere his horse stumbled and fell down, whereat he on a sudden was so incensed, that he with his sword without more ado killed him in his choler; then, not finding any that would remount him, he was about to have taken an ass at the mill that was thereby; but the miller's men did so baste his bones and so soundly bethwack him that they made him both black and blue with strokes; then stripping him of all his clothes, gave him a scurvy old canvas jacket wherewith to cover his nakedness. Thus went along this poor choleric wretch, who, passing the water of Port-Huaulx, and relating his misadventurous disasters, was foretold by an old Lourpidon hag that his kingdom should be restored to him at the coming of the Cocklicranes, which she called Coquecigrues. What is become of him since we cannot certainly tell, yet was I told that he is now a porter at Lyons, as testy and pettish in humour as ever he was before, and would be always with great lamentation inquiring at all strangers of the coming of the Cocklicranes, expecting assuredly, according to the old woman's prophecy, that at their coming he shall be re-established in his kingdom. The first thing Gargantua did after his return into the town was to call the muster-roll of his men, which when he had done, he found that there were very few either killed or wounded, only

some few foot of Captain Tolmere's company, and Ponocrates, who was shot with a musket-ball through the doublet.
Then he caused them all, at and in their several posts and
divisions, to take a little refreshment, which was very plen-
teously provided for them in the best drink and victuals that
could be had for money, and gave order to the treasurers and
commissaries of the army to pay for and defray that repast,
and that there should be no outrage at all nor abuse committed in the town, seeing it was his own. And furthermore
commanded, that, immediately after the soldiers had done
with eating and drinking for that time sufficiently and to their
own heart's desire, a gathering should be beaten, for bringing
them altogether, to be drawn up on the piazza before the
castle, there to receive six months' pay completely. All which
was done. After this, by his direction, were brought before
him in the said place all those that remained of Picrochole's
party, unto whom, in the presence of the princes, nobles, and
officers of his court and army, he spoke as followeth.

CHAPTER 46

GARGANTUA'S SPEECH TO THE VANQUISHED

OUR forefathers and ancestors of all times have been of
this nature and disposition, that, upon the winning of a
battle, they have chosen rather, for a sign and memorial of
their triumphs and victories, to erect trophies and monuments in the hearts of the vanquished by clemency than by
architecture in the lands which they had conquered. For
they did hold in greater estimation the lively remembrance
of men purchased by liberality than the dumb inscription of
arches, pillars and pyramids, subject to the injury of storms
and tempests, and the envy of everyone. You may very well
remember of the courtesy which by them was used towards

the Bretons in the battle of St. Aubin of Cormier and the demolishing of Partenay. You have heard, and hearing admire, their gentle comportment towards those at the barriers [the barbarians] of Spaniola, who had plundered, wasted and ransacked the maritime borders of Olone and Thalmondois. All this hemisphere of the world was filled with the praises and congratulations which yourselves and your fathers made, when Alpharbal, King of Canarre, not satisfied with his own fortunes, did most furiously invade the land of Onyx, and with cruel piracies molest all the Armoric Islands and confine regions of Brittany. Yet was he in a set naval fight justly taken and vanquished by my father, whom God preserve and protect. But what? Whereas other kings and emperors, yea, those who entitle themselves Catholics, would have dealt roughly with him, kept him a close prisoner, and put him to an extreme high ransom, he entreated him very courteously, lodged him kindly with himself in his own palace, and out of his incredible mildness and gentle disposition sent him back with a safe conduct, laden with gifts, laden with favours, laden with all offices of friendship. What fell out upon it? Being returned into his country, he called a parliament, where all the princes and states of his kingdom being assembled, he showed them the humanity which he had found in us, and therefore wished them to take such course by way of compensation therein as that the whole world might be edified by the example, as well of their honest graciousness to us as of our gracious honesty towards them. The result hereof was, that it was voted and decreed by an unanimous consent, that they should offer up entirely their land, dominions and kingdoms, to be disposed of by us according to our pleasure.

Alpharbal in his own person presently returned with nine thousand and thirty-eight great ships of burden, bringing with him the treasures, not only of his house and royal lineage, but almost of all the country besides. For he embarking himself, to set sail with a west-northeast wind, everyone in heaps did cast into the ship gold, silver, rings, jewels, spices, drugs, and aromatical perfumes, parrots, pelicans, monkeys, civet cats, black-spotted weasels, porcupines, &c. He was accounted no good mother's son that did not cast in all the rare and precious things he had.

Being safely arrived, he came to my said father, and would have kissed his feet. That action was found too submissively low, and therefore was not permitted, but in exchange he was most cordially embraced. He offered his presents; they were not received, because they were too excessive: he yielded himself voluntarily a servant and vassal, and was content his whole posterity should be liable to the same bondage; this was not accepted of, because it seemed not equitable: he surrendered, by virtue of the decree of his great parliamentary council, his whole countries and kingdoms to him, offering the deed and conveyance, signed, sealed and ratified by all those that were concerned in it; this was altogether refused, and the parchments cast into the fire. In end, this free goodwill and simple meaning of the Canarians wrought such tenderness in my father's heart, that he could not abstain from shedding tears, and wept most profusely; then, by choice words, very congruously adapted, strove in what he could to diminish the estimation of the good offices which he had done them, saying, that any courtesy he had conferred upon them was not worth a rush, and what favour soever he had showed them he was bound to do it. But so much the more did Alpharbal augment the repute thereof. What was the issue? Whereas for his ransom, in the greatest extremity of rigour and most tyrannical dealing, could not have been exacted above twenty times a hundred thousand crowns, and his eldest sons detained as hostages till that sum had been paid, they made themselves perpetual tributaries, and obliged to give us every year two millions of gold at four and twenty carats fine. The first year we received the whole sum of two millions; the second year of their own accord they paid freely to us three and twenty hundred thousand crowns; the third year six and twenty hundred thousand; the fourth year, three millions, and do so increase it always out of their own goodwill that we shall be constrained to forbid them to bring us any more. This is the nature of gratitude and true thankfulness. For time, which gnaws and diminisheth all things else, augments and increaseth benefits; because a noble action of liberality, done to a man of reason, doth grow continually by his generous thinking of it and remembering it.

Being unwilling, therefore, any way to degenerate from the hereditary mildness and clemency of my parents, I do now forgive you, deliver you from all fines and imprisonments, fully release you, set you at liberty, and every way make you as frank and free as ever you were before. Moreover, at your going out of the gate, you shall have every one of you three months' pay to bring you home into your houses and families, and shall have a safe convoy of six hundred cuirassiers and eight thousand foot under the conduct of Alexander, esquire of my body, that the clubmen of the country may not do you any injury. God be with you. I am sorry from my heart that Picrochole is not here; for I would have given him to understand that this war was undertaken against my will and without any hope to increase either my goods or my renown. But seeing he is lost, and that no man can tell where nor how he went away, it is my will that his kingdom remain entire to his son; who, because he is too young, he not being yet full five years old, shall be brought up and instructed by the ancient princes and learned men of the kingdom. And because a realm thus desolate may easily come to ruin, if the covetousness and avarice of those who by their places are obliged to administer justice in it be not curbed and restrained, I ordain and will have it so, that Ponocrates be overseer and superintendent above all his governors, with whatever power and authority is requisite thereto, and that he be continually with the child until he find him able and capable to rule and govern by himself.

Now I must tell you, that you are to understand how a too feeble and dissolute facility in pardoning evildoers giveth them occasion to commit wickedness afterwards more readily, upon this pernicious confidence of receiving favour. I consider that Moses, the meekest man that was in his time upon the earth, did severely punish the mutinous and seditious people of Israel. I consider likewise that Julius Cæsar, who was so gracious an emperor that Cicero said of him that his fortune had nothing more excellent than that he could, and his virtue nothing better than that he would, always save and pardon every man, he, notwithstanding all this, did in certain places most rigorously punish the authors of rebellion. After the example of these good men, it is my will and pleasure that you deliver over unto me before you depart hence, first, that fine fellow Marquet, who was the prime cause, origin, and ground work of this war by his vain presumption and overweening; secondly, his fellow cake-bakers, who were neglective in checking and reprehending his idle hairbrained humour in the instant time; and lastly all the counsellors, captains, officers, and domestics of Picrochole, who had been incendiaries or fomenters of the war by provoking, praising, or counselling him to come out of his limits thus to trouble us.

CHAPTER 47

HOW THE VICTORIOUS GARGANTUISTS WERE RECOMPENSED AFTER THE BATTLE

WHEN Gargantua had finished his speech, the seditious men whom he required were delivered up unto him, except Swashbuckler, Dirt-tail, and Smalltrash, who ran away six hours before the battle—one of them as far as to Laineil-neck at one course, another to the valley of Vire, and the third even unto Logroine, without looking back or taking breath by the way—and two of the cake-bakers who were slain in the fight. Gargantua did them no other hurt but that he appointed them to pull at the presses of his printing-house which he had newly set up. Then those who died there he caused to be honourably buried in Black-soille valley and Burn-hag field, and gave order that the wounded should be dressed and had care of in his great hospital or nosocome. After this, considering the great prejudice done to the town and its inhabitants, he reimbursed their charges and repaired all the losses that by their confession upon oath could appear they had sustained; and, for their better defence and security in times coming against all sudden uproars and invasions, commanded a strong citadel to be built there with a competent garrison to maintain it. At his departure he did very graciously thank all the soldiers of the brigades that had been at this overthrow, and sent them back to their winter-quarters in their several stations and garrisons; the decumane legion only excepted, whom in the field on that day he saw do some great exploit, and their captains also, whom he brought along with himself unto Grangousier.

At the sight and coming of them the good man was so joyful, that it is not possible fully to describe it. He made them a feast the most magnificent, plentiful, and delicious

that ever was seen since the time of king Ahasuerus. At the
taking up of the table he distributed amongst them his whole
cupboard of plate, which weighed eight hundred thousand
and fourteen bezants* of gold, in great antique vessels, huge
pots, large basins, big tasses, cups, goblets, candlesticks,
comfit-boxes, and other such plate, all of pure massy gold,
besides the precious stones, enamelling, and workmanship,
which by all men's estimation was more worth than the
matter of the gold. Then unto every one of them out of his
coffers caused he to be given the sum of twelve hundred
thousand crowns ready money. And further, he gave to each
of them forever and in perpetuity, unless he should happen
to decease without heirs, such castles and neighbouring lands
of his as were most commodious for them. To Ponocrates he
gave the rock Clermond; to Gymnast, the Coudray; to Eudemon, Montpensier; Rivau, to Tolmere; to Ithibolle, Montsoreau; to Acamas, Cande; Varenes, to Chironacte; Gravot,
to Sebast; Quinquenais, to Alexander; Legre, to Sophrone,
and so of his other places.

CHAPTER 48

HOW GARGANTUA CAUSED TO BE BUILT FOR THE MONK THE ABBEY OF THELEME

THERE was left only the monk to provide for, whom
Gargantua would have made Abbot of Sevillé, but he refused it. He would have given him the Abbey of Bourgueil,
or of Sanct Florent which was better, or both, if it pleased
him; but the monk gave him a very peremptory answer, that
he would never take upon him the charge nor government of
monks. For how shall I be able, said he, to rule over others,
that have not full power and command over myself? If you

* Each bezant is worth five pounds English money.

think I have done you, or may hereafter do any acceptable
service, give me leave to found an abbey after my own mind
and fancy. The notion pleased Gargantua very well, who
thereupon offered him all the country of Theleme by the
river of Loire till within two leagues of the great forest of
Port-Huaulx. The monk then requested Gargantua to insti-
tute his religious order contrary to all others. First, then,
said Gargantua, you must not build a wall about your convent, for all other abbeys are strongly walled and mured
about. See, said the monk, and not without cause (seeing
wall and mur signify but one and the same thing); where
there is mur before and mur behind, there is store of murmur, envy, and mutual conspiracy. Moreover, seeing there
are certain convents in the world whereof the custom is, if
any woman come in, I mean chaste and honest women, they
immediately sweep the ground which they have trod upon;
therefore was it ordained, that if any man or woman entered
into religious orders should by chance come within this new
abbey, all the rooms should be thoroughly washed and
cleansed through which they had passed. And because in all
other monasteries and nunneries all is compassed, limited
and regulated by hours, it was decreed that in this new
structure there should be neither clock nor dial, but that
according to the opportunities and incident occasions, all
their hours should be disposed of; for, said Gargantua, the
greatest loss of time that I know is to count the hours. What
good comes of it? Nor can there be any greater dotage in
the world than for one to guide and direct his courses by the
sound of a bell, and not by his own judgment and discretion.

Item, Because at that time they put no women into nunneries but such as were either purblind, blinkards, lame,
crooked, ill-favoured, misshapen, fools, senseless, spoiled, or
corrupt; nor encloistered any men but those that were either

sickly, subject to defluxions, ill-bred louts, simple sots, or
peevish trouble-houses. But to the purpose, said the monk.
A woman that is neither fair nor good, to what use serves
she? To make a nun of, said Gargantua. Yea, said the monk,
and to make shirts and smocks. Therefore was it ordained
that into this religious order should be admitted no women
that were not fair, well-featured, and of a sweet disposition;
nor men that were not comely, personable, and well condi-
tioned.

Item, Because in the convents of women, men come not
but underhand, privily, and by stealth, it was therefore
enacted that in this house there shall be no women in case
there be not men, nor men in case there be not women.

Item, Because both men and women that are received
into religious orders after the expiring of their noviciate
or probation year were constrained and forced perpetually
to stay there all the days of their life, it was therefore
ordered that all whatever, men or women, admitted within
this abbey, should have full leave to depart with peace and
contentment whensoever it should seem good to them so to do.

Item, For that the religious men and women did ordinarily
make three vows, to. wit, those of chastity, poverty and obedience, it was therefore constituted and appointed that in
this convent they might be honourably married, that they
might be rich, and live at liberty. In regard of the legitimate
time of the persons to be initiated, and years under and above
which they were not capable of reception, the women were
to be admitted from ten till fifteen, and the men from twelve
till eighteen.

CHAPTER 49

For the fabric and furniture of the abbey Gargantua
caused to be delivered out in ready money seven and twenty
hundred thousand, eight hundred and one and thirty of those
golden rams of Berry which have a sheep stamped on the
one side and a flowered cross on the other; and for every
year, until the whole work were completed, he allotted three
score nine thousand crowns of the sun, and as many of the
seven stars, to be charged all upon the receipt of the custom.
For the foundation and maintenance thereof for ever, he
settled a perpetual free-farm-rent of three and twenty hundred, three score and nine thousand, five hundred and fourteen rose nobles, exempted from all homage, fealty, service,
or burden whatsoever, and payable every year at the gate of
the abbey; and of this by letters patent passed a very good
grant. The architecture was in a figure hexagonal, and in
such a fashion that in every one of the six corners there was
built a great round tower of threescore foot in diameter, and
were all of a like form and bigness. Upon the north side ran
along the river of Loire, on the bank whereof was situated
the tower called Arctic. Going towards the east, there was
another called Calaer,—the next following Anatole,—the
next Mesembrine,—the next Hesperia, and the last Criere.
Every tower was distant from other the space of three hundred and twelve paces. The whole edifice was everywhere
six storeys high, reckoning the cellars underground for one.
The second was arched after the fashion of a basket-handle;
the rest were ceiled with pure wainscot, flourished with
Flanders fretwork, in the form of the foot of a lamp, and
covered above with fine slates, with an endorsement of lead,

carrying the antique figures of little puppets and animals of all sorts, notably well suited to one another, and gilt, together with the gutters, which, jutting without the walls from betwixt the crossbars in a diagonal figure, painted with gold and azure, reached to the very ground, where they ended into great conduit-pipes, which carried all away into the river from under the house.

This same building was a hundred times more sumptuous and magnificent than ever was Bonnivet, Chambourg, or Chantilly; for there were in it nine thousand, three hundred and two and thirty chambers, every one whereof had a withdrawing room, a handsome closet, a wardrobe, an oratory, and neat passage, leading into a great and spacious hall. Between every tower in the midst of the said body of building there was a pair of winding, such as we now call lantern stairs, whereof the steps were part of porphyry, which is a dark red marble spotted with white, part of Numidian stone, which is a kind of yellowishly-streaked marble upon various colours and part of serpentine marble, with light spots on a dark green ground, each of those steps being two and twenty foot in length and three fingers thick, and the just number of twelve betwixt every rest, or, as we now term it, landing-place. In every resting-place were two fair antique arches where the light came in: and by those they went into a cabinet, made even with and of the breadth of the said winding, and the reascending above the roofs of the house ended conically in a pavilion. By that vise or winding they entered on every side into a great hall, and from the halls into the chambers. From the Arctic tower unto the Criere were the fair great libraries in Greek, Latin, Hebrew, French, Italian, and Spanish, respectively distributed in their several cantons, according to the diversity of these languages. In the midst there was a wonderful scalier or winding-stair, the entry whereof was without the house, in a vault or arch six fathom broad. It was made in such symmetry and largeness that six men-at-arms with their lances in their rests might together in a breast ride all up to the very top of all the palace. From the tower Anatole to the Mesembrine were fair spacious galleries, all coloured over and painted with the ancient prowesses, histories and descriptions of the world. In the midst thereof there was likewise such another ascent and gate as we said there was on the river-side. Upon that gate was written in great antique letters that which followeth.

CHAPTER 50

THE INSCRIPTION SET UPON THE GREAT GATE OF THELEME

HERE enter not vile bigots, hypocrites,
Externally devoted apes, base snites,
Puffed-up, wry-necked beasts, worse than the Huns,
Or Ostrogoths, forerunners of baboons:
Cursed snakes, dissembled varlets, seeming sancts,
Slipshod cafards, beggars pretending wants,
Fat chuffcats, smell-feast knockers, doltish gulls,
Out-strouting cluster-fists, contentious bulls,
Fomenters of divisions and debates,
Elsewhere, not here, make sale of your deceits.

Your filthy trumperies
Stuffed with pernicious lies
(Not worth a bubble),
Would do but trouble
Our earthly paradise,
Your filthy trumperies.

Here enter not attorneys, barristers,
Nor bridle-champing law practitioners:

Clerks, commissaries, scribes, nor pharisees,
Wilful disturbers of the people's ease:
Judges, destroyers, with an unjust breath,
Of honest men, like dogs, even unto death.
Your salary is at the gibbet-foot:
Go drink there! for we do not here fly out
On those excessive courses, which may draw
A waiting on your courts by suits in law.

> Lawsuits, debates, and wrangling
> Hence are exiled, and jangling.
>   Here we are very
>   Frolic and merry,
> And free from all entangling,
> Lawsuits, debates, and wrangling.

Here enter not base pinching usurers,
Pelf-lickers, everlasting gatherers,
Gold-graspers, coin-gripers, gulpers of mists,
Niggish deformed sots, who, though your chests
Vast sums of money should to you afford,
Would ne'ertheless add more unto that hoard,
And yet not be content,—you clunchfist dastards,
Insatiable fiends, and Pluto's bastards,
Greedy devourers, chichy sneakbill rogues,
Hell-mastiffs gnaw your bones, you ravenous dogs.

> You beastly-looking fellows,
> Reason doth plainly tell us
>   That we should not
>   To you allot
> Room here, but at the gallows,
> You beastly-looking fellows.

Here enter not fond makers of demurs
In love adventures, peevish, jealous curs,
Sad pensive dotards, raisers of garboils,
Hags, goblins, ghosts, firebrands of household broils,
Nor drunkards, liars, cowards, cheaters, clowns,
Thieves, cannibals, faces o'ercast with frowns,
Nor lazy slugs, envious, covetous,
Nor blockish, cruel, nor too credulous,—
Here mangy, pocky folks shall have no place,
No ugly lusks, nor persons of disgrace.

> Grace, honour, praise, delight,
> Here sojourn day and night.
>   Sound bodies lined
>   With a good mind,
> Do here pursue with might
> Grace, honour, praise, delight.

Here enter you and welcome from our hearts,
All noble sparks endowed with gallant parts.
This is the glorious place which bravely shall
Afford wherewith to entertain you all.
Were you a thousand, here you shall not want
For anything; for what you'll ask we'll grant.
Stay here you lively, jovial, handsome, brisk,
Gay, witty, frolic, cheerful, merry, frisk,
Spruce, jocund, courteous, furtherers of trades,
And in a word, all worthy, gentle blades.

> Blades of heroic breasts
> Shall taste here of the feasts,
>   Both privily
>   And civilly
> Of the celestial guests,
> Blades of heroic breasts.

Here enter you, pure, honest, faithful, true
Expounders of the Scriptures old and new.
Whose glosses do not blind our reason, but
Make it to see the clearer, and who shut
Its passages from hatred, avarice,
Pride, factions, covenants, and all sort of vice.
Come, settle here a charitable faith,
Which neighbourly affection nourisheth.
And whose light chaseth all corrupters hence,
Of the blest word, from the aforesaid sense.

> The holy sacred Word,
> May it always afford
> T' us all in common,
> Both man and woman,
> A spiritual shield and sword,
> The holy sacred Word.

Here enter you all ladies of high birth,
Delicious, stately, charming, full of mirth,
Ingenious, lovely, miniard, proper, fair,
Magnetic, graceful, splendid, pleasant, rare,
Obliging, sprightly, virtuous, young, solacious,
Kind, neat, quick, feat, bright, compt, ripe, choice, dear,
          precious
Alluring, courtly, comely, fine, complete,
Wise, personable, ravishing and sweet,
Come joys enjoy. The Lord celestial
Hath given enough wherewith to please us all.

> Gold give us, God forgive us,
> And from all woes relieve us;

That we the treasure
May reap of pleasure,
And shun whate'er is grievous,
Gold give us, God forgive us.

CHAPTER 51

WHAT MANNER OF DWELLING THE THELEMITES HAD

In the middle of the lower court there was a stately
fountain of fair alabaster. Upon the top thereof stood the
three graces, with their cornucopias, or horns of abundance,
and did jet out the water at their breasts, mouth, ears, eyes,
and other open passages of the body. The inside of the
buildings in this lower court stood upon great pillars of
chalcedony stone, and porphyry marble, made archways
after a goodly antique fashion. Within those were spacious
galleries, long and large, adorned with curious pictures, the
horns of bucks and unicorns: with rhinosceroses, water horses
called hippopotamus, the teeth and tusks of elephants, and
other things well worth the beholding. The lodging of the
ladies, for so we may call those gallant women, took up all
from the tower Arctic unto the gate Mesembrine. The men
possessed the rest. Before the said lodging of the ladies, that
they might have their recreation, between the first two
towers, on the outside, were placed the tilt-yard, the barriers
of lists for tournaments, the hippodrome or riding-court, the
theatre or public playhouse, and natatory or place to swim
in, with most admirable baths in three stages, situated above
one another, well furnished with all necessary accommodation, and store of myrtle-water. By the riverside was the fair
garden of pleasure, and in the midst of that the glorious
labyrinth. Between the two other towers were the courts for
the tennis and the baloon. Towards the tower Criere stood

the orchard, full of all fruit-trees, set and ranged in a quin-cuncial order. At the end of that was the great park, abounding with all sorts of venison. Betwixt the third couple of towers were the butts and marks for shooting with a snap-work gun, an ordinary bow for common archery, or with a crossbow. The office-houses were without the tower Hesperia, of one storey high. The stables were beyond the offices, and before them stood the falconry, managed by ostrich-keepers and falconers very expert in the art, and it was yearly supplied and furnished by the Candians, Venetians, Sarmates, now called Muscoviters, with all sorts of most excellent hawks, eagles, gerfalcons, goshawks, sacres, laniers, falcons, sparrowhawks, marlins, and all other kinds of them, so gentle and perfectly well manned, that, flying of themselves sometimes from the castle for their own disport, they would not fail to catch whatever they encountered. The venery, where the beagles and hounds were kept, was a little farther off, drawing towards the park.

All the halls, chambers and closets or cabinets were richly hung with tapestry and hangings of divers sorts, according to the variety of the seasons of the year. All the pavements and floors were covered with green cloth. The beds were all embroidered. In every back-chamber or withdrawing room there was a looking-glass of pure crystal set in a frame of fine gold, garnished all about with pearls, and was of such greatness that it would represent to the full the whole lineaments and proportion of the person that stood before it. At the going out of the halls which belong to the ladies' lodgings were the perfumers and trimmers through whose hands the gallants passed when they were to visit the ladies. Those sweet artificers did every morning furnish the ladies' chambers with the spirit of roses, orange-flower water, and angelica; and to each of them gave a little precious casket, vapouring forth the most odoriferous exhalations of the choicest aromatical scents.

CHAPTER 52

HOW THE MEN AND WOMEN OF THE RELIGIOUS ORDER OF THELEME WERE APPARELLED

THE ladies at the foundation of this order were apparelled after their own pleasure and liking; but, since that of their own accord and freewill they have reformed themselves, their accoutrements were in manner as followeth. They wore stockings of scarlet crimson, or ingrained purple dye, which reached just three inches above the knee, having a list beautified with exquisite embroideries and rare incisions of the cutter's art. The garters were of the colour of their bracelets, and circled the knee a little, both over and under. Their shoes, pumps and slippers, were either of red, violet, or crimson-velvet, pinked and jagged like lobster's wadles.

Next to their smock they put on the pretty kirtle or vasquin of pure silk camblet: above that went the taffety or tabby farthingale, of white, red, tawny, grey, or of any other colour. Above this taffety petticoat they had another of cloth of tissue or brocade, embroidered with fine gold and interlaced with needlework, or as they thought good, and according to the temperature and disposition of the weather, had their upper coats of satin, damask or velvet, and these either orange, tawny, green, ash-coloured, blue, yellow, bright-red, crimson or white, and so forth; or had them of cloth of gold, cloth of silver, or some other choice stuff, enriched with purple, or embroidered according to the dignity of the festival days and times wherein they wore them.

Their gowns, being still correspondent to the season, were either of cloth of gold frizzled with a silver raised work; of red satin covered with gold purple; of tabby, or taffety, white, blue, black, tawny, &c., of silk serge, silk camblet, velvet, cloth of silver, silver tissue, cloth of gold, gold wire, figured velvet, or figured satin, tinselled and overcast with golden threads, in divers variously purfled draughts.

In the summer, some days, instead of gowns, they wore light handsome mantles, made either of the stuff of the aforesaid attire, or like Moresco rugs, of violet velvet frizzled, with a raised work of gold upon silver purl, or with a knotted cord-work of gold embroidery, everywhere garnished with little Indian pearls. They always carried a fair pannache, or plume of feathers, of the colour of their muff, bravely adorned and tricked out with glistening spangles of gold. In the winter time they had their taffety gowns of all colours, as above-named, and those lined with the rich furrings of hind-wolves, or speckled-lynxes, black-spotted weasels, martlet skins of Calabria, sables and other costly furs of an inestimable value. Their beads, rings, bracelets, collars, carcanets, and neck-chains were all of precious stones, such as carbuncles, rubies, baleus, diamonds, sapphires, emeralds, turquoises, garnets, agates, beryls, and excellent margarites. Their head-dressing also varied with the season of the year, according to which they decked themselves. In winter, it was of the French fashion; in the spring, of the Spanish; in summer, of the fashion of Tuscany, except only upon the holy days and Sundays, at which times they were accoutred in the French mode, because they accounted it more honourable and better befitting the garb of a matronal pudicity.

The men were apparelled after their fashion. Their stockings were of tamine or of cloth serge, of white, black, scarlet, or some other ingrained colour. Their breeches were of velvet, of the same colour with their stockings, or very near,

embroidered and cut according to their fancy. Their doublet
was of cloth of gold, of cloth of silver, of velvet, satin, damask, taffeties, &c., of the same colours, cut, embroidered, and
suitably trimmed up in perfection. The points were of silk of
the same colours; the tags were of gold well enamelled. Their
coats and jerkins were of cloth of gold, cloth of silver, gold
tissue or velvet embroidered, as they thought fit. Their
gowns were every whit as costly as those of the ladies. Their
girdles were of silk, of the colour of their doublets. Every
one had a gallant sword by his side, the hilt and the handle
whereof were gilt, and the scabbard of velvet, of the colour
of his breeches, with a chape of gold, and pure goldsmith's
work. The dagger was of the same. Their caps or bonnets
were of black velvet, adorned with jewels and buttons of
gold. Upon that they wore a white plume, most prettily and
minion-like parted by so many rows of gold spangles, at the
end whereof hung dangling in a more sparkling resplendency,
fair rubies, emeralds, diamonds, &c., but there was such a
sympathy betwixt the gallants and the ladies, that every day
they were apparelled in the same livery. And that they might
not miss, there were certain gentlemen appointed to tell the
youths every morning what vestments the ladies would on
that day wear: for all was done according to the pleasure
of the ladies. In these so handsome clothes, and habiliments
so rich, think not that either one or other of either sex did
waste any time at all; for the masters of the wardrobes had
all their raiments and apparel so ready for every morning,
and the chamber-ladies so well skilled, that in a trice they
would be dressed, and completely in their clothes from head
to foot. And to have those accoutrements with the more
conveniency, there was about the wood of Theleme, a row
of houses of the extent of half a league, very neat and
cleanly, wherein dwelt the goldsmiths, lapidaries, jewellers,

embroiderers, tailors, gold-drawers, velvet-weavers, tapestry-makers and upholsterers, who wrought there every one in his own trade, and all for the aforesaid jolly friars and nuns of the new stamp. They were furnished with matter and stuff from the hands of the Lord Nausiclete, who every year brought them seven ships from the Perlas and Cannibal Islands, laden with ingots of gold, with raw silk, with pearls and precious stones. And if any margarites, called unions, began to grow old and lose somewhat of their natural whiteness and lustre, those with their art they did renew, by tendering them to eat to some pretty cocks, as they use to give casting unto hawks.

CHAPTER 53

HOW THE THELEMITES WERE GOVERNED, AND OF THEIR MANNER OF LIVING

ALL their life was spent not in laws, statutes, or rules, but according to their own free will and pleasure. They rose out of their beds when they thought good; they did eat, drink, labour, sleep, when they had a mind to it, and were disposed for it. None did awake them, none did offer to constrain them to eat, drink, nor to do any other thing; for so had Gargantua established it. In all their rule and strictest tie of their order there was but this one clause to be observed,

DO WHAT THOU WILT.

Because men that are free, well-born, well-bred, and conversant in honest companies, have naturally an instinct and spur that prompteth them unto virtuous actions, and withdraws them from vice, which is called honour. Those same men, when by base subjection and constraint, they are brought under and kept down, turn aside from that noble disposition by which they formerly were inclined to virtue, to shake off and break that bond of servitude wherein they are so tyrannously enslaved; for it is agreeable with the nature of man to long after things forbidden and to desire what is denied us.

By this liberty they entered into a very laudable emulation to do all of them what they saw did please one. If any of the gallants or ladies should say, Let us drink, they would all drink. If any one of them said, Let us play, they all played. If one said, Let us go a-walking into the fields, they went all. If it were to go a-hawking or a-hunting, the ladies mounted upon dainty well-paced nags, seated in a stately palfrey saddle, carried on their lovely fists, miniardly begloved every one of them, either a sparrowhawk or a laneret or a marlin, and the young gallants carried the other kinds of hawks. So nobly were they taught, that there was neither he nor she amongst them but could read, write, sing, play upon several musical instruments, speak five or six several languages, and compose in them all very quaintly, both in verse and prose. Never were seen so valiant knights, so noble and worthy, so dextrous and skilful both on foot and a-horseback, more brisk and lively, more nimble and quick, or better handling all manner of weapons than were there. Never were seen ladies so proper and handsome, so miniard and dainty, less forward or more ready with their hand and with their needle in every honest and free action belonging to that sex, than were there. For this reason, when the time came that any man of the said abbey, either at the request of his parents, or for some other cause, had a mind to go out of it, he carried along with him one of the ladies, namely, her whom he had before that chosen for his mistress, and [they] were married together. And if they had formerly in Theleme lived in good devotion and amity, and did continue therein and increase it to a greater height in their state of matrimony; and did entertain that mutual love till the very last day of their life, in no less vigour and fervency than at the very day of their wedding.

The Second Book of

RABELAIS

TREATING OF THE HEROIC DEEDS AND SAYINGS
OF THE GOOD PANTAGRUEL

CHAPTER 1

It will not be an idle nor unprofitable thing, seeing we are at leisure, to put you in mind of the fountain and original source whence is derived unto us the good Pantagruel. For I see that all good historiographers have thus handled their chronicles, not only the Arabians, Barbarians, and Latins, but also the gentle Greeks, who were eternal drinkers. You must therefore remark that at the beginning of the world—I speak of a long time; it is above forty quarantains, or forty times forty nights, according to the supputation of the ancient Druids—a little after that Abel was killed by his brother Cain, the earth, imbrued with the blood of the just, was one year so exceeding fertile in all those fruits which it usually produceth to us, and especially in medlars, that ever since throughout all ages it hath been called the year of the great medlars; for three of them did fill a bushel. In it the Kalends were found by the Grecian almanacks. There was that year nothing of the month of March in the time of Lent, and the middle of August was in May. In the month of October, as I take it, or at least September, that I may not err, for I will carefully take heed of that, was the week so famous in the annals, which they call the week of the three Thursdays; for it had three of them by means of their irregular leap-years, called Bissextiles, occasioned by the sun's having tripped and stumbled a little towards the left hand, like a debtor afraid of sergeants, coming right upon him to arrest him; and the moon varied from her course above five fathom; and there was manifestly seen the motion

of trepidation in the firmament of the fixed stars, called
Aplanes, so that the middle Pleiade, leaving her fellows, de-
clined towards the equinoctial, and the star named Spica left
the constellation of the Virgin to withdraw herself towards
the Balance, known by the name of Libra, which are cases
very terrible, and matters so hard and difficult that astrolo-
gians cannot set their teeth in them; and indeed their teeth
had been pretty long if they could have reached thither.

However, account you it for a truth, that everybody then
did most heartily eat of these medlars, for they were fair to
the eye and in taste delicious. But even as Noah, that holy
man, to whom we are so much beholding, bound, and
obliged, for that he planted to us the vine, from whence we
have that nectarian, delicious, precious, heavenly, joyful, and
deific liquor, which they call the piot or tiplage, was deceived
in the drinking of it, for he was ignorant of the great virtue
and power thereof; so likewise the men and women of that
time did delight much in eating of that fair great fruit, but
divers and very different accidents did ensue thereupon; for
there fell upon them all in their bodies a most terrible swell-
ing, but not upon all in the same place, for some were swollen
in the belly, and their belly strouted out big like a great tun,
of whom it is written, *Ventrem omnipotentem*, who were all
very honest men, and merry blades. And of this race came
St. Fatgulch and Shrove Tuesday.* Others did swell at the
shoulders, who in that place were so crump and knobby that
they were therefore called Montifers, which is as much to
say as Hill-carriers, of whom you see some yet in the world,
of divers sexes and degrees. Of this race came Æsop, some of
whose excellent words and deeds you have in writing. Others
grew in the legs, and to see them you would have said they
had been cranes, or the reddish-long-billed-storklike-scrank-

* Pansart, Mardigras.

legged sea-fowls called flamans, or else men walking upon stilts or scatches. The little grammar-school boys, known by the name of Grimos, called those leg-grown slangams Jambus, in allusion to the French word jambe, which signifieth a leg. In others, their nose did grow so, that it seemed to be the beak of a limbeck, in every part thereof most variously diapered with the twinkling sparkles of crimson blisters budding forth, and purpled with pimples all enamelled with thickest wheals of a sanguine colour, bordered with gules; and such have you seen the Canon or Prebend Panzoult, and Woodenfoot, the physician of Angiers. Of which race there were few that liked the ptisane, but all of them were perfect lovers of the pure Septembral juice. Naso and Ovid had their extraction from thence, and all those of whom it is written, *Ne reminiscaris*. Others grew in ears, which they had so big that out of one would have been stuff enough got to make a doublet, a pair of breeches, and a jacket, whilst with the other they might have covered themselves as with a Spanish cloak: and they say that in Bourbonnois this race remaineth yet. Others grew in length of body, and of these came the giants, and of them Pantagruel.

And the first was Chalbroth,
Who begat Sarabroth,
Who begat Faribroth,
Who begat Hurtali, that was a brave eater of pottage, and reigned in the time of the flood;
Who begat Nembroth,
Who begat Atlas, that with his shoulders he kept the sky from falling;
Who begat Goliah,
Who begat Erix, that invented the hocus pocus plays of legerdemain;

Who begat Titius,

Who begat Eryon,

Who begat Polyphemus,

Who begat Cacus,

Who begat Etion, the first man that ever had the pox, for not drinking fresh in summer, as Bartachin witnesseth;

Who begat Enceladus,

Who begat Ceus,

Who begat Tiphæus,

Who begat Alæus,

Who begat Othus,

Who begat Ægeon,

Who begat Briareus, that had a hundred hands;

Who begat Porphyrio,

Who begat Adamastor,

Who begat Antæus,

Who begat Agatho,

Who begat Porus, against whom fought Alexander the Great;

Who begat Aranthas,

Who begat Gabbara, that was the first inventor of the drinking of healths;

Who begat Goliah of Secondille,

Who begat Offot, that was terribly well nosed for drinking at the barrel-head;

Who begat Artachæus,

Who begat Oromedon,

Who begat Gemmagog, the first inventor of Poulan shoes, which are open on the foot and tied over the instep with a latchet,

Who begat Sisyphus,

Who begat the Titans, of whom Hercules was born;

Who begat Enay, the most skilful man that ever was, in mat-

ter of taking the little worms (called cirons) out of the
hands;

Who begat Fierabras, that was vanquished by Oliver, peer
of France and Rowland's comrade;

Who begat Morgan, the first in the world that played at
dice with spectacles;

Who begat Fracassus, of whom Merlin Coccaius hath written, and of him was born Ferragus,

Who begat Hapmouche, the first that ever invented the
drying of neat's tongues in the chimney; for, before that
people salted them as they do now gammons of bacon;

Who began Bolivorax,

Who begat Longis,

Who begat Gayoffo, whose ballocks were of poplar, and his
pendulum of the service or sorb-apple-tree;

Who begat Maschefain,

Who begat Bruslefer,

Who begat Angoulevent,

Who begat Galehaut, the inventor of flagons;

Who begat Mirelangaut,

Who begat Gallaffre,

Who begat Salourdin,

Who begat Roboast,

Who begat Sortibrant of Conimbres,

Who begat Brusbant of Mommiere,

Who begat Bruyer that was overcome by Ogier the Dane,
peer of France,

Who begat Mabrun,

Who begat Foutasnon,

Who begat Haquelebac,

Who begat Vitdegrain,

Who begat Grangousier,

Who begat Gargantua,
Who begat the noble Pantagruel, my master.

I know that, reading this passage, you will make a doubt within yourselves, and that grounded upon very good reason, which is this—how it is possible that this relation can be true, seeing at the time of the flood all the world was destroyed, except Noah and seven persons more with him in the ark, into whose number Hurtali is not admitted? Doubtless the demand is well made and very apparent, but the answer shall satisfy you, or my wit is not rightly caulked. And because I was not at that time to tell you anything of my own fancy, I will bring unto you the authority of the Massorets, good honest fellows, true ballockeering blades and exact Hebraical bagpipers, who affirm, that verily the said Hurtali was not within the ark of Noah, neither could he get in, for he was too big, but he sat astride upon it, with one leg on one side and another on the other, as little children use to do upon their wooden horses; or as the great bull of Berne, which was killed at Marinian, did ride for his hackney the great murdering piece called the cannon-pevier, a pretty beast of a fair and pleasant amble without all question.

In that posture, he, after God, saved the said ark from danger, for with his legs he gave it the brangle that was needful, and with his foot turned it whither he pleased, as a ship answereth her rudder. Those that were within sent him up victuals in abundance by a chimney, as people very thankfully acknowledging the good that he did them. And sometimes they did talk together as Icaromenippus did to Jupiter, according to the report of Lucian. Have you understood all this well? Drink then one good draught without water, for if you believe it not,—no truly do I not, quoth she.

CHAPTER 2

OF THE NATIVITY OF THE MOST DREAD AND REDOUBTED
PANTAGRUEL

GARGANTUA at the age of four hundred fourscore forty and four years, begat his son Pantagruel, upon his wife named Badebec, daughter to the king of the Amaurots in Utopia, who died in childbirth; for he was so wonderfully great and lumpish that he could not possibly come forth into the light of the world without thus suffocating his mother. But that we may fully understand the cause and reason of the name of Pantagruel which at his baptism was given him, you are to remark that in that year there was so great drought over all the country of Africa, that there passed thirty and six months, three weeks, four days, thirteen hours and a little more without rain, but with a heat so vehement that the whole earth was parched and withered by it. Neither was it more scorched and dried up with heat in the days of Elijah than it was at that time; for there was not a tree to be seen that had either leaf or bloom upon it. The grass was without verdure or greenness, the rivers were drained, the fountains dried up, the poor fishes abandoned and forsaken by their proper element, wandering and crying upon the ground most horribly. The birds did fall down from the air for want of moisture and dew wherewith to refresh them. The wolves, foxes, harts, wild boars, fallow deer, hares, coneys, weasels, brocks, badgers, and other such beasts, were found dead in the fields with their mouths open. In respect of men, there was the pity, you should have seen them lay out their tongues like hares that have been run six hours. Many did throw themselves into the wells. Others entered within a cow's belly to be in the shade; those Homer calls Alibants. All the country was idle, and could do no virtue. It was a most lamentable case to have seen the labour of mortals in defending themselves from the vehemency of this horrific drought; for they had work enough to do to save the holy water in the churches from being wasted; but there was such order taken by the counsel of my lords the cardinals and of our holy Father, that none did dare to take above one lick. Yet when anyone came into the church, you should have seen above twenty poor thirsty fellows hang upon him that was the distributor of the water, and that with a wide open throat, gaping for some little drop, like the rich glutton in Luke, that might fall by, lest anything should be lost. O, how happy was he in that year who had a cool cellar under ground, well plenished with fresh wine!

The philosopher reports, in moving the question, Wherefore it is that the sea-water is salt? that at the time when Phœbus gave the government of his resplendent chariot to his son Phæton, the said Phæton, unskilful in the art, and not knowing how to keep the ecliptic line betwixt the two tropics of the latitude of the sun's course, strayed out of his way, and came so near the earth that he dried up all the countries that were under it, burning a great part of the heavens which the philosophers call Vialactea, and the huff-snuffs St. James's way; although the most coped, lofty, and high-crested poets affirm that to be the place where Juno's milk fell when she gave suck to Hercules. The earth at that time was so excessively heated that it fell into an enormous sweat, yea, such a one as made it sweat out the sea, which is therefore salt, because all sweat is salt; and this you cannot but confess to be true if you will taste of your own, or of those that have the pox, when they are put into sweating, it is all one to me.

Just such another case fell out this same year: for on a certain Friday, when the whole people were bent upon their devotions, and had made goodly processions, with store of litanies, and fair preachings, and beseechings of God Almighty to look down with his eye of mercy upon their miserable and disconsolate condition, there was even then visibly seen issue out of the ground great drops of water, such as fall from a puff-bagged man in a top sweat, and the poor hoidens began to rejoice as if it had been a thing very profitable unto them; for some said that there was not one drop of moisture in the air whence they might have any rain, and that the earth did supply the default of that. Other learned men said that it was a shower of the antipodes, as Seneca saith in his fourth book *Quæstionum naturalium,* speaking of the source and spring of Nilus. But they were deceived, for, the procession being ended, when everyone went about to gather of this dew, and to drink of it with full bowls, they found that it was nothing but pickle and the very brine of salt, more brackish in taste than the saltest water of the sea. And because in that very day Pantagruel was born, his father gave him that name; for *Panta* in Greek is as much to say as all, and *Gruel* in the Hagarene language doth signify thirsty, inferring hereby that at his birth the whole world was a-dry and thirsty, as likewise foreseeing that he would be some day supreme lord and sovereign of the thirsty Ethrappels, which was shown to him at that very same hour by a more evident sign. For when his mother Badebec was in the bringing of him forth, and that the midwives did wait to receive him, there came first out of her belly three score and eight tregeneers, that is, salt-sellers, every one of them leading in a halter a mule heavy laden with salt; after whom issued forth nine dromedaries, with great loads of gammons of bacon and dried neat's tongues on their backs. Then followed seven camels loaded with links and chitterlings, hog's puddings, and sausages. After them came out five great wains, full of leeks, garlic, onions, and chibots, drawn with five-and-thirty strong cart-horses, which was six for every one, besides the thiller. At the sight hereof the said midwives were much amazed, yet some of them said, Lo, here is good provision, and indeed we need it; for we drink but lazily, as if our tongues walked on crutches, and not lustily like Lansman Dutches. Truly this is a good sign; there is nothing here but what is fit for us; these are the spurs of wine, that set it a-going. As they were tattling thus together after their own manner of chat, behold! out comes Pantagruel all hairy like a bear, whereupon one of them, inspired with a prophetical spirit, said, This will be a terrible fellow; he is born with all his hair; he is undoubtedly to do wonderful things, and if he live he shall have age.

CHAPTER 3

OF THE GRIEF WHEREWITH GARGANTUA WAS MOVED AT THE DECEASE OF HIS WIFE BADEBEC

WHEN Pantagruel was born, there was none more aston-ished and perplexed than was his father Gargantua; for of the one side seeing his wife Badebec dead, and on the other side his son Pantagruel born, so fair and so great, he knew not what to say nor what to do. And the doubt that troubled his brain was to know whether he should cry for the death of his wife or laugh for the joy of his son. He was *hinc inde* choked with sophistical arguments, for he framed them very well *in modo et figura*, but he could not resolve them, re-maining pestered and entangled by this means, like a mouse caught in a trap or kite snared in a gin. Shall I weep? said he. Yes, for why? My so good wife is dead, who was the most this, the most that, that ever was in the world. Never shall I see her, never shall I recover such another; it is unto me an

inestimable loss! O my good God, what had I done that thou
shouldst thus punish me? Why didst thou not take me away
before her, seeing for me to live without her is but to lan-
guish? Ah, Badebec, Badebec, my minion, my dear heart,
my sugar, my sweeting, my honey, my bob and hit, my slip-
shoe-lovey, never shall I see thee! Ah, poor Pantagruel, thou
hast lost thy good mother, thy sweet nurse, thy well-beloved
lady! O false death, how injurious and despiteful hast thou
been to me! How malicious and outrageous have I found thee
in taking her from me, my well-beloved wife, to whom im-
mortality did of right belong.

With these words he did cry like a cow, but on a sudden
fell a-laughing like a calf, when Pantagruel came into his
mind. Ha, my little son, said he, my childilolly, fedlifondy,
dandlichucky, my pallocky, my pretty rogue! O how jolly
thou art, and how much am I bound to my gracious God,
that hath been pleased to bestow on me a son so fair, so
spriteful, so lively, so smiling, so pleasant, and so gentle!
Ho, ho, ho, ho, how glad I am! Let us drink, ho, and put
away melancholy! Bring of the best, rinse the glasses, lay
the cloth, drive out these dogs, blow this fire, light candles,
shut that door there, cut this bread in sippets for brewis, send
away these poor folks in giving them what they ask, hold
my gown. I will strip myself into my doublet (*en cuerpo*), to
make the gossips merry and keep them company.

As he spake this, he heard the litanies and the mementos
of the priests that carried his wife to be buried, upon which
he left the good purpose he was in, and was suddenly ravished another way, saying, Lord God must I again contrist
myself? This grieves me. I am no longer young, I grow old,
the weather is dangerous; I may perhaps take an ague, then
shall I be foiled, if not quite undone. By the faith of a gentleman, it were better to cry less, and drink more. My wife is

dead, well, by G—! (*da jurandi*) I shall not raise her again
by my crying: she is well, she is in paradise at least, if she
be no higher: she prayeth to God for us, she is happy, she
is above the sense of our miseries, nor can our calamities
reach her. What though she be dead, must not we also die?
The same debt which she hath paid hangs over our heads:
nature will require it of us, and we must all of us some day
taste of the same sauce. Let her pass then, and the Lord
preserve the survivors; for I must now cast about how to
get another wife. But I will tell you what you shall do, said
he to the midwives, in France called wise women (where be
they, good folks? I cannot see them). Go you to my wife's
interment, and I will the while rock my son; for I find myself
somewhat altered and distempered, and should otherwise be
in danger of falling sick; but drink one good draught first,
you will be the better for it. And believe me, upon mine
honour, they at his request went to her burial and funeral
obsequies. In the meanwhile, poor Gargantua staying at
home, and willing to have somewhat in remembrance of her
to be engraven upon her tomb, made this epitaph in the manner as followeth:

> Dead is the noble Badebec,
> Who had a face like a rebeck;
> A Spanish body, and a belly
> Of Switzerland; she died, I tell ye,
> In childbirth. Pray to God, that her
> He pardon wherein she did err.
> Here lies her body, which did live
> Free from all vice, as I believe,
> > And did decease at my bedside
> > The year and day in which she died.

CHAPTER 4

OF THE INFANCY OF PANTAGRUEL

I FIND by the ancient historiographers and poets that divers have been born in this world after very strange manners, which would be too long to repeat; read therefore the seventh chapter of Pliny, if you have so much leisure. Yet have you never heard of any so wonderful as that of Pantagruel; for it is a very difficult matter to believe, how in the little time he was in his mother's belly he grew both in body and strength. That which Hercules did was nothing, when in his cradle he slew two serpents, for those serpents were but little and weak, but Pantagruel, being yet in the cradle, did far more admirable things, and more to be amazed at. I pass by here the relation of how at every one of his meals he supped of the milk of four thousand and six hundred cows, and how, to make him a skillet to boil his milk in, there were set a-work all the braziers of Somure in Anjou, of Villedieu in Normandy, and of Bramont in Lorrain. And they served in this whitepotmeat to him in a huge great bell, which is yet to be seen in the city of Bourges in Berry, near the palace, but his teeth were already so well grown, and so strengthened with vigour, that of the said bell he bit off a great morsel, as very plainly doth appear till this hour.

One day in the morning, when they would have made him suck one of his cows—for he never had any other nurse, as the history tells us—he got one of his arms loose from the swaddling bands wherewith he was kept fast in the cradle, laid hold on the said cow under the left foreham, and grasping her to him ate up her udder and half of her paunch, with the liver and the kidneys, and had devoured all up if she had not cried out most horribly, as if the wolves had held her by the legs, at which noise company came in and took away the said cow from Pantagruel. Yet could they not so well do it but that the quarter whereby he caught her was left in his hand, of which quarter he gulped up the flesh in a trice, even with as much ease as you would eat a sausage, and that so greedily with desire of more, that, when they would have taken away the bone from him, he swallowed it down whole, as a cormorant would do a little fish; and afterwards began fumblingly to say, Good, good, good—for he could not yet speak plain—giving them to understand thereby that he had found it very good, and that he did lack but so much more. Which when they saw that attended him, they bound him with great cable ropes, like those that are made at Tain for the carriage of salt to Lyons, or such as those are whereby the great French ship rides at anchor in the road of New-haven in Normandy. But, on a certain time, a great bear, which his father had bred, got loose, came towards him, began to lick his face, for his nurses had not thoroughly wiped his chaps, at which unexpected approach being on a sudden offended, he as lightly rid himself of those great cables as Samson did of the hawser ropes wherewith the Philistines had tied him, and, by your leave, takes me up my lord the bear, and tears him in pieces like a pullet, which served him for a gorgeful, or good warm bit for that meal.

Whereupon Gargantua, fearing lest his child should hurt himself, caused four great chains of iron to be made to bind him, and so many strong wooden arches unto his cradle, most firmly stocked and morticed in huge frames. Of those chains you have one at Rochelle, which they draw up at night be-twixt the two great towers of the haven. Another is at Lyons, —a third at Angiers,—and the fourth was carried away by the devils to bind Lucifer, who broke his chains in those days by reason of a colic that did extraordinarily torment him, taken with eating a sergeant's soul fried for his breakfast.

And therefore you may believe that which Nicholas de Lyra saith upon that place of the Psalter where it is written, *Et Og Regem Basan,* that the said Og, being yet little, was so strong and robustious, that they were fain to bind him with chains of iron in his cradle. Thus continued Pantagruel for a while very calm and quiet, for he was not able so easily to break those chains, especially having no room in the cradle to give a swing with his arms. But see what happened once upon a great holiday that his father Gargantua made a sumptuous banquet to all the princes of his court. I am apt to believe that the menial officers of the house were so embusied in waiting each on his proper service at the feast, that nobody took care of poor Pantagruel, who was left *a reculorum,* behindhand, all alone, and as forsaken. What did he? Hark what he did, good people. He strove and essayed to break the chains of the cradle with his arms, but could not, for they were too strong for him. Then did he keep with his feet such a stamping stir, and so long, that at last he beat out the lower end of his cradle, which notwithstanding was made of a great post five foot in square; and as soon as he had gotten out his feet, he slid down as well as he could till he had got his soles to the ground, and then with a mighty force he rose up, carrying his cradle upon his back, bound to him like a tortoise that crawls up against a wall; and to have seen him, you would have thought it had been a great carrick of five hundred tons upon one end. In this manner he entered into the great hall where they were banqueting, and that very boldly, which did much affright the company; yet, because his arms were tied in, he could not reach anything to eat, but with great pain stopped now and then a little to take with the whole flat of his tongue some lick, good bit, or morsel. Which when his father saw, he knew well enough that they had left him without giving him anything to eat, and therefore commanded that he should be loosed from the said chains, by the counsel of the princes and lords there present. Besides that also the physicians of Gargantua said that, if they did thus keep him in the cradle, he would be all his lifetime subject to the stone. When he was unchained, they made him to sit down, where, after he had fed very well, he took his cradle and broke it into more than five hundred thousand pieces with one blow of his fist that he struck in the midst of it, swearing that he would never come into it again.

CHAPTER 5

OF THE ACTS OF THE NOBLE PANTAGRUEL IN HIS YOUTHFUL AGE

THUS grew Pantagruel from day to day, and to everyone's eye waxed more and more in all his dimensions, which made his father to rejoice by a natural affection. Therefore caused he to be made for him, whilst he was yet little, a pretty crossbow wherewith to shoot at small birds, which now they call the great cross-bow at Chantelle. Then he sent him to the school to learn, and to spend his youth in virtue. In the prosecution of which design he came first to Poictiers, where, as he studied and profited very much, he saw that the scholars were oftentimes at leisure and knew not how to bestow their time, which moved him to take such compassion on them, that one day he took from a long ledge of rocks, called there Passelourdin, a huge great stone, of about twelve fathoms square and fourteen handfuls thick, and with great ease set it upon four pillars in the midst of a field, to no other end but that the said scholars, when they had nothing else to do, might pass their time in getting up on that stone, and feast it with store of gammons, pasties, and flagons, and carve their names upon it with a knife, in token of which deed till this hour the stone is called the lifted stone. And in remembrance hereof there is none entered into the register and matricular book of the said university, or accounted capable of taking any degree therein, till he have first drunk in the caballine fountain of Croustelles, passed at Passelourdin, and got up upon the lifted stone.

Afterwards, reading the delectable chronicles of his ancestors, he found that Geoffrey of Lusignan, called Geoffrey with the great tooth, grandfather to the cousin-in-law of the eldest sister of the aunt of the son-in-law of the uncle of the good daughter of his stepmother, was interred at Maillezais; therefore one day he took campos (which is a little vacation from study to play a while), that he might give him a visit as unto an honest man. And going from Poictiers with some of his companions, they passed by the Gugé [Legugé], visiting the noble Abbot Ardillon; then by Lusignan, by Sansay, by Celles, by Coolonges, by Fontenay-le-Comte, saluting the learned Tiraqueau, and from thence arrived at Maillezais, where he went to see the sepulchre of the said Geoffrey with the great tooth; which made him somewhat afraid, looking upon the picture, whose lively draughts did set him forth in the representation of a man in an extreme fury, drawing his great Malchus falchion half way out of his scabbard. When the reason hereof was demanded, the canons of the said place told him that there was no other cause of it but that *Pictoribus atque Poetis, &c.*, that is to say, that painters and poets have liberty to paint and devise what they list after their own fancy. But he was not satisfied with their answer, and said, He is not thus painted without a cause, and I suspect that at his death there was some wrong done him, whereof he requireth his kindred to take revenge. I will inquire further into it, and then do what shall be reasonable. Then he returned not to Poictiers, but would take a view of the other

universities of France. Therefore, going to Rochelle, he took
shipping and arrived at Bordeaux, where he found no great
exercise, only now and then he would see some mariners and
lightermen a-wrestling on the quay or strand by the river-
side. From thence he came to Toulouse, where he learned to
dance very well, and to play with the two-handed sword, as
the fashion of the scholars of the said university is to bestir
themselves in games whereof they may have their hands full;
but he stayed not long there when he saw that they did cause
burn their regents alive like red herring, saying, Now God
forbid that I should die this death! for I am by nature sufficiently dry already, without heating myself any further.

He went then to Montpellier, where he met with the good
wives of Mirevaux, and good jovial company withal, and
thought to have set himself to the study of physic; but he
considered that that calling was too troublesome and melancholic, and that physicians did smell of glisters like old devils.
Therefore he resolved he would study the laws; but seeing
that there were but three scald- and one bald-pated legist in
that place, he departed from thence, and in his way made the
bridge of Guard and the amphitheatre of Nîmes in less than
three hours, which, nevertheless, seems to be a more divine
than human work. After that he came to Avignon, where he
was not above three days before he fell in love. Which his
tutor and pedagogue Epistemon perceiving, he drew him
out of that place, and brought him to Valence in Dauphiny,
where he saw no great matter of recreation, only that the
lubbers of the town did beat the scholars, which so incensed
him with anger, that when, upon a certain very fair Sunday,
the people being at their public dancing in the streets, and
one of the scholars offering to put himself into the ring to
partake of that sport the foresaid lubberly fellows would not
permit him the admittance into their society, he, taking the

scholar's part, so belaboured them with blows, and laid such a load upon them, that he drove them all before him, even to the brink of the river Rhone, and would have there drowned them, but that they did squat to the ground, and there lay close a full half-league under the river. The hole is to be seen there yet.

After that he had departed from thence, and in three strides and one leap came to Angiers, where he found himself very well, and would have continued there some space, but that the plague drove them away. So from thence he came to Bourges where he studied a good long time, and profited very much in the faculty of the laws, and would sometimes say that the books of the civil law were like unto a wonderfully precious, royal, and triumphant robe of cloth of gold edged with dirt; for in the world are no goodlier books to be seen, more ornate, nor more eloquent than the texts of the Pandects, but the bordering of them, that is to say, the gloss of Accursius, is so scurvy, vile, base, and unsavoury, that it is nothing but filthiness and villainy.

Going from Bourges, he came to Orleans, where he found store of swaggering scholars that made him great entertainment at his coming, and with whom he learned to play at tennis so well that he was a master of that game. For the students of the said place make a prime exercise of it; and sometimes they carried him unto Cupid's houses of commerce (in that city termed islands, because of their being most ordinarily environed with other houses, and not contiguous to any), there to recreate his person at the sport of poussavant.

CHAPTER 6

HOW PANTAGRUEL CAME TO PARIS, AND OF THE CHOICE BOOKS
OF THE LIBRARY OF ST. VICTOR

AFTER that Pantagruel had studied very well at Orleans,
he resolved to see the great University at Paris, but, before
his departure, he was informed that there was a huge big bell
at St. Anian in the said town of Orleans, under the ground,
which had been there above two hundred and fourteen years,
for it was so great that they could not by any device get it
so much as above the ground, although they used all the
means that are found in Vitruvius *de Architectura,* Albertus
de Re Ædificatoria, Euclid, Theon, Archimedes, and Hero
de Ingeniis; for all that was to no purpose. Wherefore, condescending heartily to the humble request of the citizens and
inhabitants of the said town, he determined to remove it to
the tower that was erected for it. With that he came to the
place where it was, and lifted it out of the ground with his
little finger as easily as you would have done a hawk's bell
or bellwether's tingle-tangle; but, before he would carry it
to the foresaid tower or steeple appointed for it, he would
needs make some music with it about the town, and ring
it alongst all the streets as he carried it in his hand, wherewith all the people were very glad. But there happened one
great inconveniency, for with carrying it so, and ringing it
about the streets, all the good Orleans wine turned instantly,
waxed flat and was spoiled, which nobody there did perceive till the night following; for every man found himself
so altered and a-dry with drinking these flat wines, that they
did nothing but spit, and that as white as Malta cotton, saying, we have of the Pantagruel, and our very throats are
salted. This done, he came to Paris with his retinue. And at
his entry everyone came out to see him—as you know well

enough that the people of Paris is sottish by nature, by B flat
and B sharp—and beheld him with great astonishment, mixed
with no less fear that he would carry away the palace into
some other country, *a remotis,* and far from them, as his
father formerly had done the great peal of bells at Our Lady's
Church to tie about his mare's neck. Now after he had stayed
there a pretty space, and studied very well in all the seven
liberal arts, he said it was a good town to live in, but not to
die; for that the grave-digging rogues of St. Innocent used
in frosty nights to warm their bums with dead men's bones.
In his abode there he found the library of St. Victor a very
stately and magnific one, especially in some books which
were there, of which, followeth the Repertory and Catalogue, *Et primo,*

The for Godsake of Salvation.

The Codpiece of the Law.

The Slipshoe of the Decretals.

The Pomegranate of Vice.

The Clew-bottom of Theology.

The Duster or Foxtail-flap of Preachers, composed by Tur-
lupin.

The Henbane of the Bishops.

Marmotretus de baboonis et apis, cum Commento Dorbellis.

Decretum Universitatis Parisiensis super gorgiasitate mulier-
cularum ad placitum.

The Apparition of Sancte Geltrude to a Nun of Poissy, being
in travail at the bringing forth of a child.

Ars honeste fartandi in societate, per Marcum Corvinum
[Ortuinum].

The Mustard-pot of Penance.

The Gamashes, alias the Boots of Patience.

De brodiorum usu, et honestate quartandi, per Sylvestrem
Prioratem Jacobinum.

The Cosened or Gulled in Court.

The Frail of the Scriveners.

The Marriage-packet.

The Cruizy or Crucible of Contemplation.

The Flimflams of the Law.

The Prickle of Wine.

The Spur of Cheese.

Ruboffatorium [Decrotatorium] scholarium.

Tartaretus de modo cacandi.

The Bravades of Rome.

Bricot de Differentiis Browsarum.

The Cobbled Shoe of Humility.

The Trivet of good Thoughts.

The Kettle of Magnanimity.

The Cavilling Entanglements of Confessors.

The Snatchfare of the Curates.

Reverendi patris fratris Lubini, provincialis Bavardiæ, de
gulpendis lardslicionibus libri tres.

Pasquilli Doctoris Marmorei, de capreolis cum artichoketa
comedendis, tempore Papali ab Ecclesia interdicto.

The Invention of the Holy Cross, personated by six wily
Priests.

The Spectacles of Pilgrims bound for Rome.

Majoris de modo faciendi puddinos.

The Bagpipe of the Prelates.

Beda de optimitate triparum.

The Complaint of the Barristers upon the Reformation of
Comfits.

The Furred Cat of the Solicitors and Attorneys.

Of Peas and Bacon, *cum Commento*.

The Small Vales or Drinking Money of the Indulgences.

Præclarissimi juris utriusque Doctoris Maistre Pilloti, &c., Scrapfarthingi de botchandis glossæ Accursianæ Triflis repetitio enucidiluculidissima.

Stratagemata Francharchiæri de Baniolet.

Carlbumpkinus de Re Militari cum Figuris Tevoti.

De usu et utilitate flayandi equos et equas, authore Magistro nostro de Quebecu.

The Sauciness of Country-Stewards.

M. N. Rostocostojambedanesse de mustarda post prandium servienda, libri quatuordecim, apostillati per M. Vaurillonis.

The Covillage or Wench-tribute of Promoters.

[Jabolenus de Cosmographia Purgatorii.]

Quæstio subtilissima, utrum Chimæra in vacuo bombinans, possit comedere secundas intentiones; et fuit debatuta per decem hebdomadas in Consilio Contantiensi.

The Bridle-champer of the Advocates.

Smutchudlamenta Scoti.

The Rasping and Hard-scraping of the Cardinals.

De calcaribus removendis, Decades undecim, per M. Albericum de Rosata.

Ejusdem de castramentandis criminibus libri tres.

The Entrance of Anthony de Leve into the Territories of Brazil.

[Marforii, bacalarii cubantis Romæ] de peelandis aut unskinnanndis blurrandisque Cardinalium mulis.

The said Author's Apology against those who allege that the Pope's mule doth eat but at set times.

Prognosticatio quæ incipit, Silvii Triquebille, balata per M. N., the deep-dreaming gull Sion.

Boudarini Episcopi de emulgentiarum profectibus Æneades novem, cum privilegio Papali ad triennium et postea non.

The Cowl or Capouch of the Monks.

The Mumbling Devotion of the Celestine Friars.

The Passage-toll of Beggarliness.

The Teeth-chatter or Gum-didder of Lubberly Lusks.

The Paring-shovel of the Theologues.

The Drench-horn of the Masters of Arts.

The Scullions of Olcam, the uninitiated Clerk.

Magistri N. Lickdishetis, de garbellisiftationibus horarum canonicarum, libri quadriginta.

Arsiversitatorium confratriarum, incerto authore.

The Glusgoatony or Rasher of Cormorants and Ravenous Feeders.

The Rammishness of the Spaniards supergivuregondigaded by Friar Inigo.

The Muttering of Pitiful Wretches.

Dastardismus rerum Italicarum, authore Magistro Burnegad.

R. Lullius de Batisfolagiis Principum.

Calibistratorium caffardiæ, authore M. Jecobo Hocstraten hereticometra.

The Crackarades of Balists or stone-throwing Engines, Contrepate Clerks, Scriveners, Brief-writers, Rapporters, and Papal Bull-despatchers lately compiled by Regis.

A perpetual Almanack for those that have the gout and the pox.

Manera sweepandi fornacellos per Mag. Eccium.

The Shable or Scimetar of Merchants.

The Pleasures of Monachal Life.

The Hotchpot of Hypocrites.

The History of the Hobgoblins.

The Ragamuffinism of the pensionary maimed Soldiers.

The Gulling Fibs and Counterfeit Shows of Commissaries.

The Litter of Treasurers.

The Juglingatorium of Sophisters.

Antipericatametanaparbeugedamphicribrationes Toordicantium.

The Periwinkle of Ballad-makers.

The Push-forward of the Alchemists.

The Niddy-noddy of the Satchel-loaded Seekers, by Friar Bindfastatis.

The Shackles of Religion.

The Racket of Swag-waggers.

The Leaning-stock of old Age.

The Muzzle of Nobility.

The Ape's Paternoster.

The Crickets and Hawk's-bells of Devotion.

The Pot of the Ember-weeks.

The Mortar of Politic Life.

The Flap of the Hermits.

The Riding-hood or Monterg of the Penitentiaries.

The Trictrac of the Knocking Friars.

Blockheadodus, de vita et honestate bragadochiorum.

Lyrippii Sorbonici Moralisationes, per M. Lupoldum.

The Carrier-horse-bells of Travelles.

The Bibbings of the tippling Bishops.

Dolloporediones Doctorum Coloniensium adversus Reuclin.

The Cymbals of Ladies.

The Dunger's Martingale.

Whirlingfriskorum Chasemarkerorum per Fratrem Crackwoodloguetis.

The Clouted Patches of a Stout Heart.

The Mummery of the Racket-keeping Robin-goodfellows.

Gerson, de auferibilitate Papæ ap Ecclesia.

The Catalogue of the Nominated and Graduated Persons.

Jo. Dytebrodii, de terribilitate excommunicationis libellus acephalos.

Ingeniositas invocandi diabolos et diabolas, per M. Guin-
golphum.

The Hotchpotch or Gallimaufry of the perpetually begging
Friars.

The Morris-dance of the Heretics.

The Whinings of Cajetan.

Muddisnout Doctoris Cherubici, de origine Roughfooted-
arum, at Wryneckedorum ritibus, libri septem.

Sixty-nine fat Breviaries.

The Nightmare of the five Orders of Beggars.

The Skinnery of the New Start-ups extracted out of the
fallow-butt, incornifistibulated and plodded upon in the
angelic sun.

The Raver and idle Talker in cases of Conscience.

The Fat Belly of the Presidents.

The Baffling Flouter of the Abbots.

Sutoris adversus eum qui vocaverat eum Slabsauceatorem et
quod Slabsauceatores non sunt damnati ab Ecclesia.

Cacatorium medicorum.

The Chimney-sweeper of Astrology.

Campi clysteriorum per paragraph C.

The Bumsquibcracker of Apothecaries.

The Kissbreech of Chirurgery.

Justinianus de Whiteleperotis tollendis.

Antidotarium animæ.

Merlinus Coccaius, de patria diabolorum.

The Practice of Iniquity, by Cleuraunes Sadden.

The Mirror of Baseness, by Radnecu Waldenses.

The Engrained Rogue, by Dwarsencas Eldenu.

The Merciless Cormorant, by Hoxinidno the Jew.

Of which library some books are already printed, and the
rest are now at the press in this noble city of Tubingen.

CHAPTER 7

HOW PANTAGRUEL FOUND PANURGE, WHOM HE LOVED ALL HIS LIFETIME

ONE day, as Pantagruel was taking a walk without the city, towards St. Anthony's abbey, discoursing and philosophating with his own servants and some other scholars, [he] met with a young man of very comely stature, and surpassing handsome in all the lineaments of his body, but in several parts thereof most pitifully wounded; in such bad equipage in matter of his apparel, which was but tatters and rags, and every way so far out of order that he seemed to have been a-fighting with mastiff-dogs, from whose fury he had made an escape; or, to say better, he looked, in the condition wherein he then was, like an apple-gatherer of the country of Perche.

As far off as Pantagruel saw him, he said to those that stood by, Do you see that man there, who is a-coming hither upon the road from Charenton bridge? By my faith, he is only poor in fortune; for I may assure you that by his physiognomy it appeareth that nature hath extracted him from some rich and noble race, and that too much curiosity hath thrown him upon adventures which possibly have reduced him to this indigence, want, and penury. Now as he was just amongst them, Pantagruel said unto him, Let me entreat you, friend, that you may be pleased to stop here a little and answer me to that which I shall ask you, and I am confident you will not think your time ill bestowed; for I have an extreme desire, according to my ability, to give you some supply in this distress wherein I see you are; because I do very much commiserate your case, which truly moves me to great pity. Therefore, my friend, tell me who you are; whence you come: whither you go; what you desire; and what your name is. The companion answered him in the German * tongue, thus:

"Junker, Gott geb euch glück und heil. Furwahr, lieber Junker, ich lasz euch wissen, das da ihr mich von fragt, ist ein arm und erbärmlich Ding, und wer viel darvon zu sagen, welches euch verdrüssig zu hören, und mir zu erzelen wer, wiewol die Poeten und Oratorn vorzeiten haben gesagt in ihren Sprüchen und Sentenzen, dasz die gedechtniss des Elends und Armuth vorlängst erlitten ist eine grosse Lust."
My friend, said Pantagruel, I have no skill in that gibberish of yours; therefore, if you would have us to understand you, speak to us in some other language. Then did the droll answer him thus:

"Albarildim gotfano dechmin brin alabo dordio falbroth ringuam albaras. Nin portzadikin almucatin milko prin alelmin en thoth dalheben ensouim; kuthim al dum alkatim nim broth dechoth porth min michais im endoth, pruch dalmaisoulum hol moth danfrihim lupaldas in voldemoth. Nin hur diavosth mnarbotim dalgousch palfrapin duch in scoth pruch galeth dal chinon, min foulchrich al conin brutathen doth dal prin."

Well, my friend, said Pantagruel, but cannot you speak French? That I can do, sir, very well, said the companion, God be thanked. It is my natural language and mother tongue, for I was born and bred in my younger years in the garden of France, to-wit, Touraine. Then, said Pantagruel, tell us what is your name, and from whence you are come; for, by my faith, I have already stamped in my mind such a deep impression of love towards you, that, if you will condescend unto my will, you shall not depart out of my company, and you and I shall make up another couple of friends such as Æneas and Achates were. Sir, said the companion,

---

* The first edition reads "Dutch."

my true and proper Christian name is Panurge, and now I come out of Turkey, to which country I was carried away prisoner at that time when they went to Metelin with a mischief. And willingly would I relate unto you my fortunes, which are more wonderful than those of Ulysses were; but, seeing that it pleaseth you to retain me with you, I most heartily accept of the offer, protesting never to leave you should you go to all the devils in hell. We shall have therefore more leisure at another time, and a fitter opportunity wherein to report them; for at this present I am in a very urgent necessity to feed; my teeth are sharp, my belly empty, my throat dry, and my stomach fierce and burning, all is ready. If you will but set me to work, it will be as good as a balsamum for sore eyes to see me gulch and raven it. For God's sake, give order for it. Then Pantagruel commanded that they should carry him home and provide him good store of victuals; which being done, he ate very well that evening, and, capon like, went early to bed; then slept until dinner-time the next day, so that he made but three steps and one leap from the bed to the board.

CHAPTER 8

OF THE QUALITIES AND CONDITIONS OF PANURGE

PANURGE was of a middle stature, not too high nor too low, and had somewhat an aquiline nose, made like the handle of a razor. He was at that time five and thirty years old or thereabouts, fine to gild like a leaden dagger—for he was a notable cheater and coneycatcher—he was a very gallant and proper man of his person, only that he was a little lecherous, and naturally subject to a kind of disease which at that time they called lack of money—it is an incomparable grief, yet, nothwithstanding, he had three score and three tricks to come by it at his need, of which the most honourable and most ordinary was in manner of thieving, secret purloining and filching, for he was a wicked lewd rogue, a cozener, drinker, roister, rover, and a very dissolute and debauched fellow, if there were any in Paris; otherwise, and in all matters else, the best and most virtuous man in the world; and he was still contriving some plot, and devising mischief against the sergeants and the watch.

At one time he assembled three or four especial good hacksters and roaring boys, made them in the evening drink like Templars, afterwards led them till they came under St. Geneviève, or about the college of Navarre, and, at the hour that the watch was coming up that way—which he knew by putting his sword upon the pavement, and his ear by it, and, when he heard his sword shake, it was an infallible sign that the watch was near at that instant—then he and his companions took a tumbrel or dung cart, and gave it the brangle, hurling it with all their force down the hill, and so overthrew all the poor watchmen like pigs, and then ran away upon the other side; for in less than two days he knew all the streets, lanes, and turnings in Paris as well as his *Deus det*.

He commonly carried a whip under his gown, wherewith he whipped without remission the pages whom he found carrying wine to their masters, to make them mend their pace. In his coat he had above six and twenty little fobs and pockets always full; one with some lead-water, and a little knife as sharp as a glover's needle, wherewith he used to cut purses; another with some kind of bitter stuff, which he threw into the eyes of those he met; another with clot-burrs, penned with little geese or capon's feathers, which he cast upon the gowns and caps of honest people, and often made them fair horns, which they wore about all the city, sometimes all their life. In another, he had a great many little horns full of fleas and lice, which he borrowed from the beggars of St. Innocent, and cast them with small canes or quills to write with into the necks of the daintiest gentlewomen that he could find, yea, even in the church, for he never seated himself above in the choir, but always sat in the body of the church amongst the women, both at mass, at vespers, and at sermon. In another, he used to have good store of hooks and buckles, wherewith he would couple men and women together that sat in company close to one another, but especially those that wore gowns of crimson taffeties, that, when they were about to go away, they might rend all their gowns. In another, he had a squib furnished with tinder, matches, stones to strike fire, and all other tackling necessary for it. In another, two or three burning glasses, wherewith he made both men and women sometimes mad, and in the church put them quite out of countenance, for he said that there was but an antistrophe, or little more difference than of a literal inversion, between a woman *folle a la messe* and *molle a la fesse*.

Item, he had another pocket full of itching powder, called stone-alum, whereof he would cast some into the backs of those women whom he judged to be most beautiful and stately, which did so ticklishly gall them, that some would strip themselves in the open view of the world, and there dance like a cock upon hot embers, or a drumstick on a tabor. Others, again, ran about the streets, and he would run after them. To such as were in the stripping vein he would very civilly come to offer his attendance, and cover them with his cloak, like a courteous and very gracious man.

Item, in another he had a little leather bottle full of old oil, wherewith, when he saw any man or woman in a rich new handsome suit, he would grease, smutch, and spoil all the best parts of it under colour and pretense of touching them, saying, This is good cloth; this is good satin; good taffeties! Madam, God give you all that your noble heart desireth! You have a new suit, pretty sir;—and you a new gown, sweet mistress;—God give you joy of it, and maintain you in all prosperity! And with this would lay his hand upon their shoulder, at which touch such a villainous spot was left behind, so enormously engraven to perpetuity in the very soul, body, and reputation, that the devil himself could never have taken it away. Then, upon his departing, he would say, Madam, take heed you do not fall, for there is a filthy great hole before you, whereinto if you put your foot, you will quite spoil yourself.

CHAPTER 9

HOW PANTAGRUEL DEPARTED FROM PARIS, HEARING NEWS
THAT THE DIPSODES HAD INVADED THE LAND OF THE
AMAUROTS; AND THE CAUSE WHEREFORE THE LEAGUES
ARE SO SHORT IN FRANCE

A LITTLE while after Pantagruel heard news that his father Gargantua had been translated into the land of the fairies by Morgue, as heretofore were Ogier and Arthur; as also,* that the report of his translation being spread abroad, the Dipsodes, had issued out beyond their borders, with inroads had wasted a great part of Utopia, and at that very time had besieged the great city of the Amaurots. Whereupon departing from Paris without bidding any man farewell, for the business required diligence, he came to Rouen.

Now Pantagruel in his journey seeing that the leagues of that little territory about Paris called France were very short in regard of those of other countries, demanded the cause

* In the original edition it stands "together, and that,"—M.

and reason of it from Panurge, who told him a story which
Marotus of the Lac, monachus, set down in the Acts of the
Kings of Canarre, saying that in old times countries were
not distinguished into leagues, miles, furlongs, nor parasangs,
until that King Pharamond divided them, which was done
in manner as followeth. The said king chose at Paris a hundred fair, gallant, lusty, brisk young men, all resolute and
bold adventurers in Cupid's duels, together with a hundred
comely, pretty, handsome, lovely and well-complexioned
wenches of Picardy, all which he caused to be well entertained and highly fed for the space of eight days. Then having called for them, he delivered to every one of the young
men his wench, with store of money to defray their charges,
and this injunction besides, to go unto diver places here and
there. And wheresoever they should biscot and thrum their
wenches, that, they setting a stone there, it should be
accounted for a league. Thus went away those brave fellows
and sprightly blades most merrily, and because they were
fresh and had been at rest, they very often jummed and
fanfreluched almost at every field's end, and this is the
cause why the leagues about Paris are so short. But when
they had gone a great way, and were now as weary as poor
devils, all the oil in their lamps being almost spent, they
did not chink and duffle so often, but contented themselves
(I mean for the men's part) with one scurvy paltry bout
in a day, and this is that which makes the leagues in Brittany, Delanes, Germany, and other more remote countries
so long. Other men give other reasons for it, but this seems
to me of all other the best. To which Pantagruel willingly
adhered. Parting from Rouen, they arrived at Honfleur,
where they took shipping, Pantagruel, Panurge, Epistemon,
Eusthenes, and Carpalin.

In which place, waiting for a favourable wind, and caulk-

ing their ship, he received from a lady of Paris, which I [he]
had formerly kept and entertained a good long time, a letter
directed on the outside thus;—To the best beloved of
the fair women, and least loyal of the valiant men.—
P.N.T.G.R.L.

CHAPTER 10

A LETTER WHICH A MESSENGER BROUGHT TO PANTAGRUEL FROM A LADY OF PARIS, TOGETHER WITH THE EXPOSITION OF A POSY WRITTEN IN A GOLD RING

WHEN Pantagruel had read the superscription he was
much amazed, and therefore demanded of the said messenger
the name of her that had sent it. Then opened he the letter,
and found nothing written in it, nor otherwise enclosed, but
only a gold ring, with a square table diamond. Wondering at
this, he called Panurge to him, and showed him the case.
Whereupon Panurge told him that the leaf of paper was
written upon, but with such cunning and artifice that no
man could see the writing at the first sight. Therefore, to
find it out, he set it by the fire to see if it was made with
sal ammoniac soaked in water. Then put he it into the water,
to see if the letter was written with the juice of tithymalle.
After that he held it up against the candle, to see if it was
written with the juice of white onions.

Then he rubbed one part of it with oil of nuts, to see if
it were not written with the lee of a fig-tree, and another
part of it with the milk of a woman giving suck to her eldest
daughter, to see if it was written with the blood of red toads
or green earth-frogs. Afterwards he rubbed one corner with
the ashes of a swallow's nest, to see if it were not written
with the dew that is found within the herb alcakengy, called
the winter-cherry. He rubbed, after that, one end with ear-

wax, to see if it were not written with the gall of a raven. Then did he dip it into vinegar, to try if it was not written with the juice of the garden spurge. After that he greased it with the fat of a bat or flittermouse, to see if it was not written with the sperm of a whale, which some call ambergris. Then he put it very fairly into a basinful of fresh water, and forthwith took it out, to see whether it were written with stone-alum. But after all experiments, when he perceived that he could find out nothing, he called the messenger and asked him, Good fellow, the lady that sent thee hither, did she not give thee a staff to bring with thee? thinking that it had been according to the conceit whereof Aulus Gellius maketh mention. And the messenger answered him, No, sir. Then Panurge would have caused his head to be shaven, to see whether the lady had written upon his bald pate, with the hard lye whereof soap is made, that which she meant; but, perceiving that his hair was very long, he forebore, considering that it could not have grown to so great a length in so short a time.

Then he said to Pantagruel, Master, by the virtue of G—, I cannot tell what to do nor say in it. For, to know whether there be anything written upon this or no, I have made use of a good part of that which Master Francisco di Nianto, the Tuscan, sets down, who hath written the manner of reading letters that do not appear; that which Zoroastes published, *Peri grammaton acriton;* and Calphurnius Bassus, *De literis illegibilibus.* But I can see nothing, nor do I believe that there is anything else in it than the ring. Let us, therefore, look upon it. Which when they had done, they found this in Hebrew written within, *Lamach saba[ch]thani;* whereupon they called Epistemon, and asked him what that meant. To which he answered that they were Hebrew words, signifying, Wherefore hast thou forsaken me? Upon that Panurge suddenly replied, I know the mystery. Do you see this diamond? It is a false one. This, then, is the exposition of that which the lady means, *Diamant faux*, that is, false lover, why hast thou forsaken me? Which interpretation Pantagruel presently understood and withal remembering that at his departure he had not bid the lady farewell, he was very sorry, and would fain have returned to Paris to make his peace with her. But Epistemon put him in mind of Æneas's departure from Dido, and the saying of Heraclitus of Tarentum, That the ship being at anchor, when need requireth we must cut the cable rather than lose time about untying of it,—and that he should lay aside all other thoughts to succour the city of his nativity, which was then in danger. And, indeed, within an hour after that the wind arose at the north-north-west, wherewith they hoist sail, and put out, even into the main sea, so that within few days, passing by Porto Sancto and by the Madeiras, they went ashore in the Canary Islands. Parting from thence, they passed by Capobianco, by Senege, by Capoverde, by Gambre, by Sagres, by Melli, by the Cap di Buona Speranza, and set ashore again in the kingdom of Melinda. Parting from thence, they sailed away, with a tramontane or northerly wind, passing by Meden, by Uti, by Uden, by Gelasim, by the Isles of the Fairies, and alongst the kingdom of Achorie, till at last they arrived at the port of Utopia, distant from the city of the Amaurots three leagues and somewhat more.

When they were ashore, and pretty well refreshed, Pantagruel said, Gentlemen, the city is not far from hence; therefore, were it not amiss, before we set forward, to advise well what is to be done, that we be not like the Athenians, who never took counsel until after the fact? Are you resolved to live and die with me? Yes, sir, said they all, and be as confident of us as of your own fingers. Well, said he,

there is but one thing that keeps my mind in great doubt
and suspense, which is this, that I know not in what order
nor of what number the enemy is that layeth siege to the
city; for, if I were certain of that, I should go forward and
set on with the better assurance. Let us therefore consult
together, and bethink ourselves by what means we may come
to this intelligence. Whereunto they all said, Let us go
thither and see, and stay you here for us; for this very day,
without further respite, do we make account to bring you a
certain report thereof.

Myself, said Panurge, will undertake to enter into their
camp, within the very midst of their guards, unespied by
their watch, and merrily feast and lecher it at their cost,
without being known of any, to see the artillery and the
tents of all the captains, and thrust myself in with a grave
and magnific carriage amongst all their troops and companies, without being discovered. The devil would not be
able to peck me out with all his circumventions, for I am of
the race of Zopyaus.

And I, said Epistemon, know all the plots and stratagems
of the valiant captains and warlike champions of former
ages, together with all the tricks and subtleties of the art
of war. I will go, and, though I be detected and revealed, I
will escape by making them believe of you whatever I please,
for I am of the race of Sinon.

I, said Eusthenes, will enter and set upon them in their
trenches, in spite of their sentries and all their guards; for
I will tread upon their bellies and break their legs and arms,
yea, though they were every whit as strong as the devil himself, for I am of the race of Hercules.

And I, said Carpalin, will get in there if the birds can
enter, for I am so nimble of body, and light withal, that I
shall have leaped over their trenches, and ran clean through

all their camp, before they perceive me; neither do I fear shot, nor arrow, nor horse, how swift soever, were ye the Pegasus of Perseus or Pacolet, being assured that I shall be able to make a safe and sound escape before them all without any hurt. I will undertake to walk upon the ears of corn or grass in the meadows, without making either of them do so much as bow under me, for I am of the race of Camilla the Amazon.

CHAPTER 11

HOW PANURGE, CARPALIN, EUSTHENES, AND EPISTEMON, THE GENTLEMEN ATTENDANTS OF PANTAGRUEL, VANQUISHED AND DISCOMFITED SIX HUNDRED AND THREESCORE HORSEMEN VERY CUNNINGLY

As he was speaking this, they perceived six hundred and threescore light horsemen, gallantly mounted, who made an outroad thither to see what ship it was that was newly arrived in the harbour, and came in a full gallop to take them if they had been able. Then said Pantagruel, My lads, retire yourselves unto the ship; here are some of our enemies coming apace, but I will kill them here before you like beasts, although they were ten times so many; in the meantime, withdraw yourselves, and take your sport at it. Then answered Panurge, No, sir; there is no reason that you should do so, but, on the contrary, retire you unto the ship, both you and the rest, for I alone will here discomfit them; but we must not linger; come, set forward. Whereunto the others said, It is well advised, sir; withdraw yourself, and we will help Panurge here; so shall you know what we are able to do. Then said Pantagruel, Well, I am content; but, if that you be too weak, I will not fail to come to your assistance. With this Panurge took two great cables of the ship and tied them to the kemstock or capstan which was on the deck towards the hatches, and fastened them in the ground, making a long circuit, the one further off, the other within that. Then said he to Epistemon, Go aboard the ship, and, when I give you a call, turn about the capstan upon the orlop diligently, drawing unto you the two cable-ropes; and said to Eusthenes and to Carpalin, My bullies, stay you here, and offer yourselves freely to your enemies. Do as they bid you, and make as if you would yield unto them, but take heed you come not within the compass of the ropes—be sure to keep yourselves free of them. And presently he went aboard the ship, and took a bundle of straw and a barrel of gunpowder, strewed it round about the compass of the cords, and stood by with a brand of fire or match lighted in his hand. Presently came the horsemen with great fury, and the foremost ran almost home to the ship, and, by reason of the slipperiness of the bank, they fell, they and their horses, to the number of four and forty; which the rest seeing, came on, thinking that resistance had been made them at their arrival. But Panurge said unto them, My masters, I believe that you have hurt yourselves; I pray you pardon us, for it is not our fault, but the slipperiness of the sea-water that is always flowing; we submit ourselves to your good pleasure. So said likewise his two other fellows, and Epistemon that was upon the deck. In the meantime Panurge withdrew himself, and seeing that they were all within the compass of the cables, and that his two companions were retired, making room for all those horses which came in a crowd, thronging upon the neck of one another to see the ship and such as were in it, cried out on a sudden to Epistemon, Draw, draw! Then began Epistemon to wind about the capstan, by doing whereof the two cables so entangled and empestered the legs of the horses, that they were all of them thrown down to the ground easily, together with their riders. But they, seeing that, drew their swords, and would have cut them; whereupon Panurge set fire to the train, and there burnt them all up like damned souls, both men and horses, not one escaping save one alone, who being mounted on a fleet Turkey courser, by mere speed in flight got himself out of the circle of the ropes. But when Carpalin perceived him, he ran after him with such nimbleness and celerity that he overtook him in less than a hundred paces; then, leaping close behind him upon the crupper of his horse, clasped him in his arms, and brought him back to the ship.

This exploit being ended, Pantagruel was very jovial, and wondrously commended the industry of these gentlemen, whom he called his fellow-soldiers, and made them refresh themselves and feed well and merrily upon the seashore, and drink heartily with their bellies upon the ground, and their prisoner with them, whom they admitted to that familiarity; only that the poor devil was somewhat afraid that Pantagruel would have eaten him up whole, which, considering the wideness of his mouth and capacity of his throat was no great matter for him to have done; for he could have done it as easily as you would eat a small comfit, he showing no more in his throat than would a grain of millet-seed in the mouth of an ass.

CHAPTER 12

HOW PANTAGRUEL AND HIS COMPANY WERE WEARY IN EAT-ING STILL SALT MEATS; AND HOW CARPALIN WENT A-HUNTING TO HAVE SOME VENISON

THUS as they talked and chatted together, Carpalin said, And, by the belly of St. Quenet, shall we never eat any venison? This salt meat makes me horribly dry. I will go fetch you a quarter of one of those horses which we have burnt; it is well roasted already. As he was rising up to go about it, he perceived under the side of a wood a fair great roebuck, which was come out of his fort, as I conceive, at the sight of Panurge's fire. Him did he pursue and run after with as much vigour and swiftness as if it had been a bolt out of a crossbow, and caught him in a moment; and whilst he was in his course he with his hands took in the air four great bustards, seven bitterns, six and twenty grey partridges, two and thirty red-legged ones, sixteen pheasants, nine woodcocks, nineteen herons, two and thirty cushats and ringdoves; and with his feet killed ten or twelve hares and rabbits, which were then at relief and pretty big withal, eighteen rails in a knot together, with fifteen young wild-boars, two little beavers, and three great foxes. So, striking the kid with his falchion athwart the head, he killed him, and, bearing him on his back, he in his return took up his hares, rails, and young wild-boars, and, as far off as he could be heard, cried out and said, Panurge, my friend, vinegar, vinegar! Then the good Pantagruel, thinking he had fainted, commanded them to provide him some vinegar; but Panurge knew well that there was some good prey in hands, and forthwith showed unto noble Pantagruel how he was bearing upon his back a fair roebuck, and all his girdle bordered with hares. Then immediately did Epistemon make, in the name of the nine Muses, nine antique wooden spits. Eusthenes did help to flay, and Panurge placed two great cuirassier saddles in such sort that they served for andirons, and making their prisoner to be their cook they roasted their venison by the fire wherein the horsemen were burnt; and making great cheer with a good deal of vinegar, the devil a one of them did forbear from his victuals—it was a triumphant and incomparable spectacle to see how they ravened and devoured.

Then said Pantagruel, Would to God every one of you had
two pairs of little anthem or sacring bells, hanging at your
chin, and that I had at mine the great clocks of Rennes, of
Poictiers, of Tours, and of Cambray, to see what a peal they
would ring with the wagging of our chaps. But, said Panurge,
it were better we thought a little upon our business, and by
what means we might get the upper hand of our enemies.
That is well remembered, said Pantagruel. Therefore spoke
he thus to the prisoner, My friend, tell us here the truth, and
do not lie to us at all, if thou wouldst not be flayed alive,
for it is I, that eat the little children. Relate unto us at
full the order, the number, and the strength of the army.
To which the prisoner answered, Sir, know for a truth that
in the army there are three hundred giants, all armed with
armour of proof, and wonderful great. Nevertheless, not fully
so great as you, except one that is their head, named Loupgarou, who is armed from head to foot with cyclopical anvils.
Furthermore, one hundred three score and three thousand
foot, all armed with the skins of hobgoblins, strong and
valiant men; eleven thousand four hundred men-at-arms or
cuirassiers; three thousand six hundred double cannons, and
arquebusiers without number; four score and fourteen thousand pioneers; one hundred and fifty thousand whores, fair
like goddesses—(That is for me, said Panurge)—whereof
some are Amazons, some Lionnoises, others Parisiennes,
Taurangelles, Angevines, Poictevines, Normandes, and High
Dutch—there are of them of all countries and all languages.

Yea but, said Pantagruel, is the king there? Yes, sir, said
the prisoner; he is there in person, and we call him Anarchus,
king of the Dipsodes, which is as much to say as thirsty
people, for you never saw men more thirsty, nor more willing to drink, and his tent is guarded by the giants. It is
enough, said Pantagruel. Come, brave boys, are you resolved

to go with me? To which Panurge answered, God confound him that leaves you! I have already bethought myself how I will kill them all like pigs, and so the devil one leg of them shall escape. But I am somewhat troubled about one thing. And what is that? said Pantagruel. It is, said Panurge, how I shall be able to set forward to the justling, and brag-mardizing of all the whores that be there this afternoon, in such sort that there escape not one unbumped by me, breasted and jummed after the ordinary fashion of man and women in the Venetian conflict. Ha, ha, ha, ha, said Pantagruel.

And Carpalin said: The devil take these sink-holes, if, by G—, I do not bumbaste some one of them. Then said Eusthenes: What! shall not I have any, whose paces, since we came from Rouen, were never so well winded up as that my needle could mount to ten or eleven o'clock, till now that I have it hard, stiff, and strong, like a hundred devils? Truly, said Panurge, thou shalt have of the fattest, and of those that are most plump and in the best case.

How now! said Epistemon; everyone shall ride, and I must lead the ass? The devil take him that will do so. We will make use of the right of war, *Qui potest capere, capiat.* No, no, said Panurge, but tie thine ass to a crook, and ride as the world doth. And the good Pantagruel laughed at all this, and said unto them, You reckon without your host. I am much afraid that, before it be night, I shall see you in such taking that you will have no great stomach to ride, but more like to be rode upon with sound blows of pike and lance. Baste, said Epistemon, enough of that! I will not fail to bring them to you, either to roast or boil, to fry or to put in paste. They are not so many in number as were in the army of Xerxes, for he had thirty hundred thousand fighting-men, if you will believe Herodotus and Trogus

Pompeius, and yet Themistocles with a few men overthrew them all. For God's sake, take you no care for that. Up then, my lads, said Pantagruel, and let us march along.

CHAPTER 13

HOW PANTAGRUEL GOT THE VICTORY VERY STRANGELY OVER THE DIPSODES AND THE GIANTS

AFTER all this talk, Pantagruel took the prisoner to him and sent him away, saying, Go thou unto thy king in his camp, and tell him tidings of what thou hast seen, and let him resolve to feast me to-morrow about noon; for, as soon as my galleys shall come, which will be to-morrow at furthest, I will prove unto him by eighteen hundred thousand fighting-men and seven thousand giants, all of them greater than I am, that he hath done foolishly and against reason thus to invade my country. Wherein Pantagruel feigned that he had an army at sea. But the prisoner answered that he would yield himself to be his slave, and that he was content never to return to his own people, but rather with Pantagruel to fight against them, and for God's sake besought him that he might be permitted so to do. Whereunto Pantagruel would not give consent, but commanded him to depart thence speedily and begone as he had told him, and to that effect gave him a boxful of eupherbium, together with some grains of the black chameleon thistle, steeped into aqua vitæ, and made up into the condiment of a wet sucket, commanding him to carry it to his king, and to say unto him, that if he were able to eat one ounce of that without drinking after it he might then be able to resist him without any fear or apprehension of danger.

The prisoner then besought him with joined hands that in the hour of the battle he would have compassion upon him. Whereat Pantagruel said unto him, After that thou hast delivered all unto the king, put thy whole confidence in God, and he will not forsake thee; because, although for my part I be mighty, as thou mayst see, and have an infinite number of men in arms, I do nevertheless trust neither in my force nor in mine industry, but all my confidence is in God my protector, who doth never forsake those that in him do put their trust and confidence. This done, the prisoner requested him that he would afford him some reasonable composition for his ransom. To which Pantagruel answered, that his end was not to rob nor ransom men, but to enrich them and reduce them to total liberty. Go thy way, said he, in the peace of the living God, and never follow evil company, lest some mischief befall thee. The prisoner being gone, Pantagruel said to his men, Gentlemen, I have made this prisoner believe that we have an army at sea; as also that we will not assault them till to-morrow at noon, to the end that they, doubting of the great arrival of our men, may spend this night in providing and strengthening themselves, but in the meantime my intention is that we charge them about the hour of the first sleep.

Let us leave Pantagruel here with his apostles, and speak of King Anarchus and his army. When the prisoner was come, he went unto the king and told him how there was a great giant come, called Pantagruel, who had overthrown and made to be cruelly roasted all the six hundred and nine and fifty horsemen, and he alone escaped to bring the news. Besides that, he was charged by the said giant to tell him that the next day, about noon, he must make a dinner ready for him, for at that hour he was resolved to set upon him. Then did he give him that box wherein were those confitures. But as soon as he had swallowed down one spoonful of them, he was taken with such a heat in the throat, together with an ulceration in the flap of the top of the windpipe, that his tongue peeled with it in such sort that, for all they could do unto him, he found no ease at all but by drinking only without cessation; for as soon as ever he took the goblet from his head, his tongue was on a fire, and therefore they did nothing but still pour in wine into his throat with a funnel. Which when his captains, bashaws, and guard of his body did see, they tasted of the same drugs to try whether they were so thirst-procuring and alterative or no. But it so befell them as it had done their king, and they plied the flagon so well that the noise ran throughout all the camp, how the prisoner was returned; that the next day they were to have an assault; that the king and his captains did already prepare themselves for it, together with his guards, and that with carousing lustily and quaffing as hard as they could. Every man, therefore, in the army began to tipple, ply the pot, swill and guzzle it as fast as they could. In sum, they drunk so much, and so long, that they fell asleep like pigs, all out of order throughout the whole camp.

Let us now return to the good Pantagruel, and relate how he carried himself in this business. Departing from the place of the trophies, he took the mast of their ship in his hand like a pilgrim's staff, and put within the top of it two hundred and seven and thirty puncheons of white wine of Anjou, the rest was of Rouen, and tied up to his girdle the bark all full of salt, as easily as the lansquenets carry their little panniers, and so set onward on his way with his fellow-soldiers. When he was come near to the enemy's camp, Panurge said unto him, Sir, if you would do well, let down this white wine of Anjou from the scuttle of the mast of the ship, that we may all drink thereof, like Bretons.

Hereunto Pantagruel very willingly consented, and they

drank so neat that there was not so much as one poor drop left of two hundred and seven and thirty puncheons, except one boracho or leathern bottle of Tours which Panurge filled for himself, for he called that his vademecum, and some scurvy lees of wine in the bottom, which served him instead of vinegar. After they had whittled and curried the can pretty handsomely, Panurge gave Pantagruel to eat some devilish drugs compounded of lithotripton, which is a stone-dissolving ingredient, nephrocatarticon, that purgeth the reins, the marmalade of quinces, called codiniac, a confection of cantharides, which are green flies breeding on the tops of olive-trees, and other kinds of diuretic or piss-procuring simples. This done, Pantagruel said to Carpalin, Go into the city, scrambling like a cat up against the wall, as you can well do, and tell them that now presently they come out and charge their enemies as rudely as they can and having said so, come down, taking a lighted torch with you, wherewith you shall set on fire all the tents and pavilions in the camp; then cry as loud as you are able with your great voice, and then come away from thence. Yea but, said Carpalin, were it not good to cloy all their ordnance? No, no, said Pantagruel, only blow up all their powder. Carpalin, obeying him, departed suddenly and did as he was appointed by Pantagruel, and all the combatants came forth that were in the city, and when he had set fire in the tents and pavilions, he passed so lightly through them, and so highly and profoundly did they snort and sleep, that they never perceived him. He came to the place where their artillery was, and set their munition on fire. But here was the danger. The fire was so sudden that poor Carpalin had almost been burnt. And had it not been for his wonderful agility he had been fried like a roasting pig. But he departed away so speedily that a bolt

or arrow out of a crossbow could not have had a swifter
motion. When he was clear of their trenches, he shouted
aloud, and cried out so dreadfully, and with such amazement to the hearers, that it seemed all the devils of hell had
been let loose. At which noise the enemies awaked, but can
you tell how? Even no less astonished than are monks at
the ringing of the first peal to matins.

In the meantime Pantagruel began to sow the salt that
he had in his bark, and because they slept with an open
gaping mouth, he filled all their throats with it, so that those
poor wretches were made by it to cough like foxes. Ha,
Pantagruel, how thou addest greater heat to the firebrand
that is in us!

The enemies, after that they were awaked, seeing on one
side the fire in the camp, and on the other the inundation
of the urinal deluge, could not tell what to say nor what to
think. Some said that it was the end of the world and the
final judgment, which ought to be by fire. Others again
thought that the sea-gods, Neptune, Proteus, Triton, and
the rest of them, did persecute them, for that indeed they
found it to be like sea-water and salt.

O who were able now condignly to relate how Pantagruel
did demean himself against the three hundred giants! O
my Muse, my Calliope, my Thalia, inspire me at this time,
restore unto me my spirits; for this is the logical bridge
of asses! Here is the pitfall, here is the difficulty, to have
ability enough to express the horrible battle that was fought!
Ah, would to God that I had now a bottle of the best wine
that ever those drank who shall read this so veridical history!

CHAPTER 14

HOW PANTAGRUEL DISCOMFITED THE THREE HUNDRED GIANTS ARMED WITH FREESTONE, AND LOUPGAROU THEIR CAPTAIN

THE giants, seeing all their camp drowned, carried away their king Anarchus upon their backs as well as they could out of the fort, as Æneas did to his father Anchises, in the time of the conflagration of Troy. When Panurge perceived them, he said to Pantagruel, Sir, yonder are the giants coming forth against you; lay on them with your mast gallantly, like an old fencer; for now is the time that you must show yourself a brave man and an honest. And for our part we will not fail you. I myself will kill to you a good many boldly enough; for why, David killed Goliath very easily; and then this great lecher, Eusthenes, who is stronger than four oxen, will not spare himself. Be of good courage, therefore, and valiant, charge amongst them with point and edge, and by all manner of means. Well, said Pantagruel, of courage I have more than for fifty francs, but let us be wise, for Hercules first never undertook against two. That is well cracked, well scummered, said Panurge; do you compare yourself with Hercules? You have, by G—, more strength in your teeth, and more scent in your bum, than ever Hercules had in all his body and soul. So much is a man worth as he esteems himself. Whilst they spake those words, behold! Loupgarou was come with all his giants, who, seeing Pantagruel in a manner alone, was carried away with temerity and presumption, for hopes that he had to kill the good man. Whereupon he said to his companions the giants, You wenchers of the low country, by Mahoom! if any of you undertake to fight against these men here, I will put you cruelly to death. It is my will that you let me fight single. In the meantime you shall have good sport to look upon us.

Then all the other giants retired with their king to the place where the flagons stood, and Panurge and his comrade with them, who counterfeited those that have had the pox, for he wreathed about his mouth, shrunk up his fingers, and with a harsh and hoarse voice said unto them, I forsake—od, fellow-soldiers, if I would have it to be believed that we make any war at all. Give us somewhat to eat with you whilest our masters fight against one another. To this the king and giants jointly condescended, and accordingly made them to banquet with them. In the meantime Panurge told them the follies of Turpin, the examples of St. Nicholas, and the tale of a tub. Loupgarou then set forward towards Pantagruel, with a mace all of steel, and that of the best sort, weighing nine thousand seven hundred quintals and two quarterons, at the end whereof were thirteen pointed diamonds, the least whereof was as big as the greatest bell of Our Lady's Church at Paris—there might want perhaps the thickness of a nail, or at most, that I may not lie, of the back of those knives which they call cutlugs or earcutters, but for a little off or on, more or less, it is no matter—and it was enchanted in such sort that it could never break, but contrarily, all that it did touch did break immediately. Thus then, as he approached with great fierceness and pride of heart, Pantagruel, casting up his eyes to heaven, recommended himself to God with all his soul, making such a vow as followeth.

O thou Lord God, who hast always been my protector and my saviour! thou seest the distress wherein I am at this time. Nothing brings me hither but a natural zeal, which thou hast permitted unto mortals, to keep and defend themselves, their wives and children, country and family, in case thy own proper cause were not in question, which is the faith; for in such a business thou wilt have no coadjutors,

nly a catholic confession and service of thy word, and hast
orbidden us all àrming and defence. For thou art the
Almighty, who in thine own cause, and where thine own
business is taken to heart, canst defend it far beyond all
hat we can conceive, thou who hast thousand thousands of
hundreds of millions of legions of angels, the least of which
s able to kill all mortal men, and turn about the heavens
nd earth at his pleasure, as heretofore it very plainly appeared in the army of Sennacherib. If it may please thee,
herefore, at this time to assist me, as my whole trust and
onfidence is in thee alone, I vow unto thee, that in all coun-
ries whatsoever wherein I shall have any power or authority,
vhether in this of Utopia or elsewhere, I will cause thy holy
ospel to be purely, simply, and entirely preached, so that
he abuses of a rabble of hypocrites and false prophets, who
y human constitutions and depraved inventions have em-
oisoned all the world, shall be quite exterminated from
bout me.

This vow was no sooner made, but there was heard a
oice from heaven saying, *Hoc fac et vinces;* that is to say,
Do this, and thou shalt overcome. Then Pantagruel, seeing
hat Loupgarou with his mouth wide open was drawing near
o him, went against him boldly, and cried out as loud as he
vas able, Thou diest, villain, thou diest! purposing by his
orrible cry to make him afraid, according to the discipline
f the Lacedæmonians. Withal, he immediately cast at him
ut of his bark, which he wore at his girdle, eighteen cags
nd four bushels of salt, wherewith he filled both his mouth,
hroat, nose, and eyes. At this Loupgarou was so highly in-
ensed that, most fiercely setting upon him, he thought even
hen with a blow of his mace to have beat out his brains. But
Pantagruel was very nimble, and had always a quick foot
nd a quick eye, and therefore with his left foot did he

step back one pace, yet not so nimbly but that the blow falling upon the bark, broke it in four thousand fourscore and six pieces, and threw all the rest of the salt about the ground. Pantagruel, seeing that, most gallantly displayed the vigour of his arms, and, according to the art of the axe gave him with the great end of his mast a homethrust little above the breast; then, bringing along the blow to the left side, with a slash struck him between the neck and shoulders. After that, advancing his right foot, he gave him a push upon the couillons with the upper end of his said mast, wherewith breaking the scuttle on the top thereof he split three or four puncheons of wine that were left therein

Upon that Loupgarou thought that he had pierced his bladder. Pantagruel, being not content with this, would have doubled it by a side-blow; but Loupgarou, lifting up his mace, advanced one step upon him, and with all his force would have dashed it upon Pantagruel, wherein, to speak the truth, he so sprightfully carried himself, that, God had not succoured the good Pantagruel, he had been cloven from the top of his head to the bottom of his milt But the blow glanced to the right side by the brisk nimbleness of Pantagruel, and his mace sank into the ground above threescore and thirteen foot, through a huge rock, out of which the fire did issue greater than nine thousand and six tons. Pantagruel, seeing him busy about plucking out his mace, which stuck in the ground between the rocks, ran upon him, and would have clean cut off his head, if by mischance his mast had not touched a little against the stock of Loupgarou's mace, which was enchanted, as we have said before. By this means his mast broke off about three handfuls above his hand, whereat he stood amazed like a bell-founder, and cried out, Ah, Panurge, where art thou? Panurge, seeing that, said to the king and the giants, B

G—, they will hurt one another if they be not parted. But the giants were as merry as if they had been at a wedding. Then Pantagruel, thus destitute of a staff, took up the end of his mast, striking athwart and alongst upon the giant, but he did him no more hurt than you would do with a fillip upon a smith's anvil. In the [mean] time Loupgarou was drawing his mace out of the ground, and, having already plucked it out, was ready therewith to have struck Pantagruel, who, being very quick in turning, avoided all his blows in taking only the defensive part in hand, until on a sudden he saw that Loupgarou did threaten him with these words, saying, Now, villain, will not I fail to chop thee as small as minced meat, and keep thee henceforth from ever making any more poor men athirst! For then, without any more ado, Pantagruel struck him such a blow with his foot against the belly that he made him fall backwards, his heels over his head, and dragged him thus along at flay-buttock above a flight-shot. Then Loupgarou cried out, bleeding at the throat, Mahoom, Mahoom, Mahoom! at which noise all the giants arose to succour him. But Panurge said unto them, Gentlemen, do not go, if you will believe me, for our master is mad, and strikes athwart and alongst, he cares not where; he will do you a mischief. But the giants made no account of it, seeing that Pantagruel had never a staff.

And when Pantagruel saw those giants approach very near unto him, he took Loupgarou by the two feet, and lift up his body like a pike in the air, wherewith, it being harnessed with anvils, he laid such heavy load amongst those giants armed with freestone, that, striking them down as a mason doth little knobs of stones, there was not one of them that stood before him whom he threw not flat to the ground. And by the breaking of this stony armour there was made such a horrible rumble as put me in mind of the fall of the butter-tower of St. Stephen's at Bourges when it melted before the sun. Panurge with Carpalin and Eusthenes, did cut in the meantime the throats of those that were struck down, in such sort that there escaped not one. Pantagruel to any man's sight was like a mower, who with his scythe, which was Loupgarou, cut down the meadow grass, to-wit, the giants; but with this fencing of Pantagruel's Loupgarou lost his head, which happened when Pantagruel struck down one whose name was Riflandouille, or Pudding-plunderer, who was armed cap-à-pie with Grison stones, one chip whereof splintering abroad cut off Epistemon's neck clean and fair. For otherwise the most part of them were but lightly armed with a kind of sandy brittle stone, and the rest with slates. At last, when he saw that they were all dead, he threw the body of Loupgarou as hard as he could against the city, where falling like a frog upon his belly in the great Piazza thereof, he with the said fall killed a singed he-cat, a wet she-cat, a farting duck, and a bridled goose.

CHAPTER 15

HOW EPISTEMON, WHO HAD HIS HEAD CUT OFF, WAS FINELY HEALED BY PANURGE, AND OF THE NEWS WHICH HE BROUGHT FROM THE DEVILS, AND OF THE DAMNED PEOPLE IN HELL

THIS gigantal victory being ended, Pantagruel withdrew himself to the place of the flagons, and called for Panurge and the rest, who came unto him safe and sound, except Eusthenes, whom one of the giants had scratched a little in the face whilst he was about the cutting of his throat, and Epistemon, who appeared not at all. Whereat Pantagruel was so aggrieved that he would have killed himself. But Panurge said unto him, Nay, sir, stay a while, and we will search for him amongst the dead, and find out the truth of all. Thus as they went seeking after him, they found him stark dead, with his head between his arms all bloody. Then Eusthenes cried out, Ah, cruel death! hast thou taken from me the perfectest amongst men? At which words Pantagruel rose up with the greatest grief that ever any man did see, and said to Panurge, Ha, my friend! the prophecy of our two glasses and the javelin staff was a great deal too deceitful. But Panurge answered, My dear bullies all, weep not one drop more, for, he being yet all hot, I will make him as sound as ever he was. In saying this, he took the head and held it warm foregainst his codpiece, that the wind might not enter into it. Eusthenes and Carpalin carried the body to the place where they had banqueted, not out of any hope that ever he would recover, but that Pantagruel might see it.

Nevertheless Panurge gave him very good comfort, saying, If I do not heal him, I will be content to lose my head, which is a fool's wager. Leave off, therefore, crying, and help me. Then cleansed he his neck very well with pure white wine and, after that, took his head, and into it synapised some powder of diamerdis, which he always carried about him in one of his bags. Afterwards he anointed it with I know not what ointment, and set it on very just, vein against vein, sinew against sinew, and spondyle against spondyle, that he might not be wry-necked—for such people he mortally hated. This done, he gave it round about some fifteen or sixteen stitches with a needle that it might not fall off again; then, on all sides and everywhere, he put a little ointment on it, which he called resuscitative.

Suddenly Epistemon began to breathe, then opened his eyes, yawned, sneezed, and afterwards let a great household fart. Whereupon Panurge said, Now, certainly, he is healed,

—and therefore gave him to drink a large full glass of
strong white wine, with a sugared toast. In this fashion was
Epistemon finely healed, only that he was somewhat hoarse
for above three weeks together, and had a dry cough of
which he could not be rid but by the force of continual drinking. And now he began to speak, and said that he had seen
the devil, had spoken with Lucifer familiarly, and had been
very merry in hell and in the Elysian fields, affirming very
seriously before them all that the devils were boon companions and merry fellows. But, in respect of the damned
he said he was very sorry that Panurge had so soon called
him back into this world again; for, said he, I took wonderful delight to see them. How so? said Pantagruel. Because
they do not use them there, said Epistemon, so badly as you
think they do. Their estate and condition of living is but
only changed after a very strange manner; for I saw Alexander the Great there, amending and patching on clouts
upon old breeches and stockings, whereby he got but a very
poor living.

Xerxes was a crier of mustard.
Romulus, a salter and patcher of patterns.
Numa, a nailsmith.
Tarquin, a porter.
Piso, a clownish swain.
Sylla, a ferryman.
Cyrus, a cowherd.
Themistocles, a glass-maker.
Epaminondas, a maker of mirrors or looking-glasses.
Brutus and Cassius, surveyors or measurers of land.
Demosthenes, a vine-dresser.
Cicero, a fire-kindler.
Fabius, a threader of beads.

Artaxerxes, a rope-maker.

Æneas, a miller.

Achilles was a scaldpated maker of hay-bundles.

Agamemnon, a lick-box.

Ulysses, a hay-mower.

Nestor, a deer-keeper or forester.

Darius, a gold-finder or jakes-farmer.

Ancus Martius, a ship-trimmer.

Camillus, a foot-post.

Marcellus, a sheller of beans.

Drusus, a taker of money at the doors of playhouses.

Scipio Africanus, a crier of lee in a wooden slipper.

Asdrubal, a lantern-maker.

Hannibal, a kettlemaker and seller of eggshells.

Priamus, a seller of old clouts.

Lancelot of the Lake was a flayer of dead horses.

All the Knights of the Round Table were poor day-
bourers, employed to row over the rivers of Cocytus,
Phlegeton, Styx, Acheron, and Lethe, when my lords the
devils had a mind to recreate themselves upon the water,
as in the like occasion are hired the boatmen at Lyons, the
gondoliers of Venice, and oars at London. But with this
difference, that these poor knights have only for their fare
a bob or flirt on the nose, and in the evening a morsel of
coarse mouldy bread.

Trajan was a fisher of frogs.

Antoninus, a lackey.

Commodus, a jet-maker.

Pertinax, a peeler of walnuts.

Lucullus, a maker of rattles and hawks'-bells.

Justinian, a pedlar.

Hector, a snap-sauce scullion.

Paris was a poor beggar.

Cambyses, a mule-driver.

Nero, a base blind fiddler, or player on that instrument which is called a windbroach. Fierabras was his serving-man who did him a thousand mischievous tricks, and would make him eat of the brown bread and drink of the turned wine when himself did both eat and drink of the best.

Julius Cæsar and Pompey were boat-wrights and tighter of ships.

Valentine and Orson did serve in the stoves of hell, and were sweat-rubbers in hot houses.

Giglan and Govian [Gauvin] were poor swineherds.

Geoffrey with the great tooth was a tinder-maker and seller of matches.

Godfrey de Bouillon, a hood-maker.

Jason was a bracelet-maker.

Don Pietro de Castille, a carrier of indulgences.

Morgan, a beer-brewer.

Huon of Bordeaux, a hooper of barrels.

Pyrrhus, a kitchen-scullion.

Antiochus, a chimney-sweeper.

Octavian, a scraper of parchment.

Nerva, a mariner.

Pope Julius was a crier of pudding-pies, but he left off wearing there his great buggerly beard.

John of Paris was a greaser of boots.

Arthur of Britain, an ungreaser of caps.

Perce-Forest, a carrier of faggots.

Pope Boniface the Eighth, a scummer of pots.

Pope Nicholas the Third, a maker of paper.

Pope Alexander, a ratcatcher.

Pope Sixtus, an anointer of those that have the pox.

What, said Pantagruel, have they the pox there too? Surely, said Epistemon, I never saw so many; there are here, I think, about a hundred millions; for believe, that those who have not had the pox in this world must have it in the other.

Cotsbody, said Panurge, then I am free; for I have been as far as the hole of Gibraltar, reached unto the outmost bounds of Hercules, and gathered of the ripest.

Ogier the Dane was a furbisher of armour.

The King Tigranes, a mender of thatched houses.

Galien Restored, a taker of moldwarps.

The four sons of Aymon were all toothdrawers.

Pope Calixtus was a barber of a woman's *sine qua non*.

Pope Urban, a bacon-picker.

Melusina was a kitchen drudge-wench.

Matabrune, a laundress.

Cleopatra, a crier of onions.

Helen, a broker of chambermaids.

Semiramis, the beggars' lice-killer.

Dido did sell mushrooms.

Penthesilea sold cresses.

Lucretia was an alehouse-keeper.

Hortensia, a spinstress.

Livia, a grater of verdigris.

After this manner, those that had been great lords and ladies here, got but a poor scurvy wretched living there below. And, on the contrary, the philosophers and others, who in this world had been altogether indigent and wanting, were great lords there in their turn. I saw Diogenes there strut it out most pompously, and in great magnificence, with a rich purple gown on him, and a golden sceptre in his right hand. And, which is more, he would now and then make Alexander the Great mad, so enormously would be abuse him when he had not well patched his breeches; for he used to pay his skin with sound bastinadoes. I saw Epictetus there most gallantly apparalled after the French fashion, sitting under a pleasant arbour, with store of handsome gentle women, frolicking, drinking, dancing, and making good cheer, with abundance of crowns of the sun. Above the lattice were written these verses for his device:

> To leap and dance, to sport and play,
>   And drink good wine both white and brown,
> Or nothing else do all the day
>   But tell bags full of many a crown.

When he saw me, he invited me to drink with him very courteously, and I being willing to be entreated, we tippled and chopined together most theologically. In the meantime came Cyrus to beg one farthing of him for the honour of Mercury, therewith to buy a few onions for his supper. No, no, said Epictetus, I do not use in my almsgiving to bestow farthings. Hold, thou varlet, there's a crown for thee; be an honest man. Cyrus was exceeding glad to have met with such a booty; but the other poor rogues, the kings that are there below, as Alexander, Darius, and others, stole it away from him by night. I saw Pathelin, the treasurer of Rhadamanthus, who, in cheapening the pudding-pies that Pope Julius cried, asked him how much a dozen. Three blanks, said the Pope. Nay, said Pathelin, three blows with a cudgel. Lay them down here, you rascal, and go fetch more. The poor Pope went away weeping, who, when he came to his master the pie-maker, told him that they had taken away his pudding-pies. Whereupon his master gave him such a sound lash with an eelskin, that his own would have been worth nothing to make bag-pipe bags of. I saw Master John Le Maire there personate the Pope in such

ashion that he made all the poor kings and popes of this
world kiss his feet, and, taking great state upon him, gave
them his benediction, saying, Get the pardons, rogues, get
the pardons; they are good cheap. I absolve you of bread
and pottage, and dispense with you to be never good for
anything. Then, calling Caillet and Triboulet to him, he
spoke these words, My lords the cardinals, despatch their
bulls, to wit, to each of them a blow with a cudgel upon
the reins. Which accordingly was forthwith performed. I
heard Master Francis Villon ask Xerxes, How much the
mess of mustard? A farthing, said Xerxes. To which the said
Villon answered, The pox take thee for a villain! As much
of square-eared wheat is not worth half that price, and now
thou offerest to enhance the price of victuals.

Well, said Pantagruel, reserve all these fair stories for
another time, only tell us how the usurers are there handled.

I saw them, said Epistemon, all very busily employed in
seeking of rusty pins and old nails in the kennels of the
streets, as you see poor wretched rogues do in this world.
But the quintal, or hundredweight, of this old ironware is
there valued but at the price of a cantle of bread, and yet
they have but a very bad despatch and riddance in the sale
of it. Thus the poor misers are sometimes three whole weeks
without eating one morsel or crumb of bread, and yet
work both day and night, looking for the fair to come.
Nevertheless, of all this labour, toil, and misery, they reckon
nothing, so cursedly active they are in the prosecution of
that their base calling, in hopes, at the end of the year, to
earn some scurvy penny by it.

Come, said Pantagruel, let us now make ourselves merry
one bout, and drink, my lads, I beseech you, for it is very
good drinking all this month. Then did they uncase their
flagons by heaps and dozens, and with their leaguer-provision

made excellent good cheer. But the poor King Anarchus
could not all this while settle himself towards any fit of
mirth; whereupon Panurge said, Of what trade shall we make
my lord the king here, that he may be skilful in the art when
he goes thither to sojourn amongst all the devils of hell?
Indeed, said Pantagruel, that was well advised of thee. Do
with him what thou wilt, I give him to thee. Gramercy, said
Panurge, the present is not to be refused, and I love it
from you.

CHAPTER 16

HOW PANTAGRUEL ENTERED INTO THE CITY OF THE AMAU-
ROTS, AND HOW PANURGE MARRIED KING ANARCHUS TO
AN OLD LANTERN-CARRYING HAG, AND MADE HIM A
CRIER OF GREEN SAUCE

AFTER this wonderful victory, Pantagruel sent Carpalim
unto the city of the Amaurots to declare and signify unto
them how the King Anarchus was taken prisoner and all
the enemies of the city overthrown. Which news when they
heard all the inhabitants of the city came forth to meet him
in good order, and with great triumphant pomp, conducting
him with a heavenly joy into the city, where innumerable
bonfires were set on through all the parts thereof, and fair
round tables, which were furnished with store of good
victuals, set out in the middle of the streets. This was a
renewing of the golden age in the time of Saturn, so good
was the cheer which then they made.

But Pantagruel, having assembled the whole senate and
common councilmen of the town, said, My masters, we must
now strike the iron whilst it is hot. It is therefore my will
that, before we frolic it any longer, we advise how to assault
and take the whole kingdom of the Dipsodes. To which

effect let those that will go with me provide themselves
against to-morrow after drinking, for then will I begin to
march. Not that I need any more men than I have to help
me to conquer it, for I could make it as sure that way as if
I had it already; but I see this city is so full of inhabitants
that they scarce can turn in the streets. I will, therefore,
carry them as a colony into Dipsody, and will give them all
that country, which is fair, wealthy, fruitful, and pleasant,
above all other countries in the world, as many of you can
tell who have been there heretofore. Every one of you, therefore, that will go along, let him provide himself as I have
said. This counsel and resolution being published in the city,
the next morning there assembled in the piazza before the
palace to the number of eighteen hundred fifty-six thousand
and eleven, besides women and little children. Thus began
they to march straight into Dipsody, in such good order as
did the people of Israel when they departed out of Egypt
to pass over the Red Sea.

But before we proceed any further in this purpose, I will
tell you how Panurge handled his prisoner the King Anarchus; for having remembered that which Epistemon had
related, how the kings and rich men in this world were used
in the Elysian fields, and how they got their living there by
base and ignoble trades, he, therefore, one day apparelled
his king in a pretty little canvas doublet, all jagged and
pinked like the tippet of a light horseman's cap, together
with a pair of large mariner's breeches, and stockings without shoes,—For, said he, they would but spoil his sight,—
and a little peach-coloured bonnet with a great capon's
feather in it—I lie, for I think he had two—and a very
handsome girdle of a sky-colour and green (in French called
pers et vert), saying that such a livery did become him well,
for that he had always been perverse, and in this plight

bringing him before Pantagruel, said unto him, Do you know this roister? No, indeed, said Pantagruel. It is, said Panurge, my lord the king of the three batches, or threadbare sovereign. I intend to make him an honest man. These devilish kings which we have here are but as so many calves; they know nothing and are good for nothing but to do a thousand mischiefs to their poor subjects, and to trouble all the world with war for their unjust and detestable pleasure. I will put him to a trade, and make him a crier of green sauce. Go to, begin and cry, Do you lack any green sauce? and the poor devil cried. That is too low, said Panurge; then took him by the ear, saying, Sing higher in Ge, sol, re, ut. So, so, poor devil, thou hast a good throat; thou wert never so happy as to be no longer king. And Pantagruel made himself merry with all this; for I dare boldly say that he was the best little gaffer that was to be seen between this and the end of a staff. Thus was Anarchus made a good crier of green sauce. Two days thereafter Panurge married him with an old lantern-carrying hag, and he himself made the wedding with fine sheep's heads, brave haslets with mustard, gallant salligots with garlic, of which he sent five horseloads unto Pantagruel, which he ate up all, he found them so appetizing. And for their drink they had a kind of small well-watered wine, and some sorbapple-cider. And, to make them dance, he hired a blind man that made music to them with a windbroach.

After dinner he led them to the palace and showed them to Pantagruel, and said, pointing to the married woman, You need not fear that she will crack. Why? said Pantagruel. Because, said Panurge, she is well slit and broke up already. What do you mean by that? said Pantagruel. Do not you see, said Panurge, that the chestnuts which are roasted in the fire, if they be whole they crack as if they were mad,

and, to keep them from cracking, they make an incision in
them and slit them? So this new bride is in her lower parts
well slit before, and therefore will not crack behind.

Pantagruel gave them a little lodge near the lower street
and a mortar of stone wherein to bray and pound their
sauce, and in this manner did they do their little business,
he being as pretty a crier of green sauce as ever was seen
in the country of Utopia. But I have been told since that his
wife doth beat him like plaister, and the poor sot dare not
defend himself, he is so simple.

CHAPTER 17

HOW PANTAGRUEL WITH HIS TONGUE COVERED A WHOLE ARMY, AND WHAT THE AUTHOR SAW IN HIS MOUTH

Thus, as Pantagruel with all his army had entered into
the country of the Dipsodes, everyone was glad of it, and
incontinently rendered themselves unto him, bringing him
out of their own good wills the keys of all the cities where
he went, the Almirods only excepted, who, being resolved to
hold out against him, made answer to his heralds that they
would not yield but upon very honourable and good conditions.

What! said Pantagruel, do they ask any better terms than
the hand at the pot and the glass in their fist? Come, let us
go sack them, and put them all to the sword. Then did they
put themselves in good order, as being fully determined to
give an assault, but by the way, passing through a large
field, they were overtaken with a great shower of rain,
whereat they began to shiver and tremble, to crowd, press,
and thrust close to one another. When Pantagruel saw that,
he made their captains tell them that it was nothing, and
that he saw well above the clouds that it would be nothing

but a little dew; but, howsoever, that they should put themselves in order, and he would cover them. Then did they put
themselves in a close order, and stood as near to [each]
other as they could, and Pantagruel drew out his tongue
only halfway and covered them all, as a hen doth her
chickens. In the meantime, I, who relate to you these so
veritable stories, hid myself under a burdock-leaf, which was
not much less in largeness than the arch of the bridge of
Montrible, but when I saw them thus covered, I went towards them to shelter myself likewise; which I could not
do, for that they were so, as the saying is, *At the yard's end
there is no cloth left*. Then, as well as I could, I got upon it,
and went along full two leagues upon his tongue, and so
long marched that at last I came into his mouth. But, O gods
and goddesses! what did I see there? Jupiter confound me
with his trisulk lightning if I lie! I walked there as they do
in Sophia [at] Constantinople, and saw there great rocks,
like the mountains in Denmark—I believe that those were
his teeth. I saw also fair meadows, large forests, great and
strong cities not a jot less than Lyons or Poictiers. The first
man I met with there was a good honest fellow planting
coleworts, whereat being very much amazed, I asked him,
My friend, what dost thou make here? I plant coleworts,
said he. But how, and wherewith? said I. Ha, sir, said he,
everyone cannot have his ballocks as heavy as a mortar,
neither can we be all rich. Thus do I get my poor living, and
carry them to the market to sell in the city which is here
behind. Jesus! said I, is there here a new world? Sure, said
he, it is never a jot new, but it is commonly reported that,
without this, there is an earth, whereof the inhabitants enjoy
the light of a sun and a moon, and that it is full of and replenished with very good commodities; but yet this is more
ancient than that. Yea but, said I, my friend, what is the

name of that city whither thou carriest thy coleworts to sell? It is called Aspharage, said he, and all the indwellers are Christians, very honest men, and will make you good cheer. To be brief, I resolved to go thither. Now, in my way, I met with a fellow that was lying in wait to catch pigeons, of whom I asked, My friend, from whence come these pigeons? Sir, said he, they come from the other world. Then I thought that when Pantagruel yawned, the pigeons went into his mouth in whole flocks, thinking that it had been a pigeon-house.

Then I went into the city, which I found fair, very strong, and seated in a good air; but at my entry the guard demanded of me my pass or ticket. Whereat I was much astonished, and asked them, My masters, is there any danger of the plague here? O Lord! said they, they die hard by here so fast that the cart runs about the streets. Good God! said I, and where? Whereunto they answered that it was in Larynx and Pharynx, which are two great cities such as Rouen and Nantes, rich and of great trading. And the cause of the plague was by a stinking and infectious exhalation which lately vapoured out of the abysms, whereof there have died above two and twenty hundred and threescore thousand and sixteen persons within this sevennight. Then I considered, calculated, and found that it was a rank and unsavoury breathing which came out of Pantagruel's stomach when he did eat so much garlic, as we have aforesaid.

Parting from thence, I passed amongst the rocks, which were his teeth, and never left walking till I got up on one of them; and there I found the pleasantest places in the world, great large tennis-courts, fair galleries, sweet meadows, store of vines, and an infinite number of banqueting summer outhouses in the fields, after the Italian fashion, full of pleasure and delight, where I stayed full four months,

and never made better cheer in my life as then. After that
I went down by the hinder teeth to come to the chaps. But
in the way I was robbed by thieves in a great forest that
is in the territory towards the ears. Then, after a little
further travelling, I fell upon a pretty petty village—truly
I have forgot the name of it—where I was yet merrier than
ever, and got some certain money to live by. Can you tell
how? By sleeping. For there they hire men by the day to
sleep, and they get by it sixpence a day, but they that can
snort hard, get at least ninepence. How I had been robbed
in the valley I informed the senators, who told me that, in
very truth, the people of that side were bad livers and naturally thievish, whereby I perceived well that, as we have
with us the countries Cisalpine and Transalpine, that is,
behither and beyond the mountains, so have they there the
countries Cidentine and Tradentine, that is, behither and
beyond the teeth. But it is far better living on this side,
and the air is purer. There I began to think that it is very
true which is commonly said, that the one half of the world
knoweth not how the other half liveth; seeing none before
myself had ever written of that country, wherein are above
five-and-twenty kingdoms inhabited, besides deserts, and a
great arm of the sea. Concerning which purpose I have composed a great book, entitled, The History of the Throttias,
because they dwell in the throat of my master Pantagruel.

At last I was willing to return, and, passing by his beard,
I cast myself upon his shoulders, and from thence slid down
to the ground, and fell before him. As soon as I was perceived by him, he asked me, Whence comest thou, Alcofribas? I answered him, Out of your mouth, my lord. And
how long hast thou been there? said he. Since the time,
said I, that you went against the Almirods. That is about
six months ago, said he. And wherewith didst thou live?

What didst thou drink? I answered, My lord, of the same
that you did, and of the daintiest morsels that passed through
your throat I took toll.

CHAPTER 18

HOW PANURGE ASKETH COUNSEL OF PANTAGRUEL WHETHER HE SHOULD MARRY, YEA, OR NO

To this Pantagruel replying nothing, Panurge prosecuted
the discourse he had already broached, and therewithal
fetching, as from the bottom of his heart, a very deep sigh,
said, My lord and master, you have heard the design I am
upon, which is to marry. I humbly beseech you, for the
affection which of a long time you have borne me, to give
me your best advice therein. Then, answered Pantagruel,
seeing you have so decreed, and taken deliberation thereon,
and that the matter is fully determined, what need is there
of any further talk thereof, resolved. Yea, but, quoth Panurge, I would be loth to act but forthwith to put into
execution what you have anything therein without your
counsel had thereto. It is my judgment also, quoth Pantagruel, and I advise you to it. Nevertheless, quoth Panurge,
if I understood aright that it were much better for me to
remain a bachelor as I am, than to run headlong upon new
hairbrained undertakings of conjugal adventure, I would
rather choose not to marry. Quoth Pantagruel, Then do not
marry. Yea but, quoth Panurge, would you have me so
solitarily drive out the whole course of my life, without
the comfort of a matrimonial consort? You know it is
written *Ve soli!* and a single person is never seen to reap the
joy and solace that is found with married folks. Then marry,
in the name of God, quoth Pantagruel. But if, quoth Panurge, my wife should make me a cuckold—as it is not un-

known unto you, how this hath been a very plentiful year
in the production of that kind of cattle—I would fly out,
and grow impatient beyond all measure and mean. I love
cuckolds with my heart, for they seem unto me to be of a
right honest conversation, and truly do very willingly frequent their company; but should I die for it, I would not
be one of their number. That is a point for me of a too
sore prickling point. Then do not marry, quoth Pantagruel,
for without all controversy this sentence of Seneca is in-
fallibly true, What thou to others shalt have done, others
will do the like to thee. Do you, quoth Panurge, aver that
without all exception? Yes, truly, quoth Pantagruel, without all exception. Ho, ho, says Panurge, by the wrath of a
little devil, his meaning is, either in this world or in the
other which is to come. Yet seeing I can no more do without
a wife than a blind man his staff—[for] the funnel must be
in agitation, without which manner of occupation I cannot
live—were it not a great deal better for me to apply and
associate myself to some one honest, lovely, and virtuous
woman, than as I do, by a new change of females every day,
run a hazard of being bastinadoed, or, which is worse, of the
great pox, if not of both together. For never—be it spoken
by their husbands' leave and favour—had I enjoyment yet
of an honest woman. Marry then, in God's name, quoth
Pantagruel. But if, quoth Panurge, it were the will of God,
and that my destiny did unluckily lead me to marry an
honest woman who should beat me, I should be stored with
more than two third parts of the patience of Job, if I were
not stark mad by it, and quite distracted with such rugged
dealings. For it hath been told me that those exceeding
honest women have ordinarily very wicked head-pieces,
therefore is it that their family lacketh not for good vinegar.
    Do not marry then, answered Pantagruel. Yea but, quoth

Panurge, considering the condition wherein I now am, out
of debt and unmarried; mark what I say, free from all debt,
in an ill hour, for, were I deeply on the score, my creditors
would be but too careful of my paternity, but being quit,
and not married, nobody will be so regardful of me, or carry
towards me a love like that which is said to be in a conjugal
affection. And if by some mishap I should fall sick, I would
be looked to very waywardly. The wise man saith, Where
there is no woman—I mean the mother of a family and wife
in the union of lawful wedlock—the crazy and diseased are
in danger of being ill used and of having much brabbling
and strife about them; as by clear experience hath been
made apparent in the persons of popes, legates, cardinals,
bishops, abbots, priors, priests, and monks; but there, assure
yourself, you shall not find me. Marry then, in the name of
God, answered Pantagruel. But if, quoth Panurge, being ill
at ease and possibly through that distemper made unable
to discharge the matrimonial duty that is incumbent to an
active husband, my wife, impatient of that drooping sickness and faint-fits of a pining languishment, should abandon
and prostitute herself to the embraces of another man, and
not only then not help and assist me in my extremity and
need, but withal flout at and make sport of that my grievous
distress and calamity; or peradventure, which is worse, em-
bezzle my goods and steal from me, as I have seen it oftentimes befall unto the lot of many other men, it were enough
to undo me utterly, to fill brimful the cup of my misfortune,
and make me play the mad-pate reeks of Bedlam. Do not
marry then, quoth Pantagruel. Yea but, said Panurge, I
shall never by any other means come to have lawful sons
and daughters, in whom I may harbour some hope of per-
petuating my name and arms, and to whom also I may
leave and bequeath my inheritances and purchased goods

(of which latter sort you need not doubt but that in some
one or other of these mornings I will make a fair and
goodly show), that so I may cheer up and make merry
when otherwise I should be plunged into a peevish sullen
mood of pensive sullenness, as I do perceive daily by the
gentle and loving carriage of your kind and gracious father
towards you; as all honest folks use to do at their homes
and private dwelling-houses. For being free from debt, and
yet not married, if casually I should fret and be angry,
although the cause of my grief and displeasure were never
so just, I am afraid, instead of consolation, that I should
meet with nothing else but scoffs, frumps, gibes, and mocks
at my disastrous fortune. Marry then, in the name of God,
quoth Pantagruel.

CHAPTER 19

HOW PANTAGRUEL REPRESENTETH UNTO PANURGE THE DIF-
    FICULTY OF GIVING ADVICE IN THE MATTER OF MAR-
    RIAGE; AND TO THAT PURPOSE MENTIONETH SOMEWHAT
    OF THE HOMERIC AND VIRGILIAN LOTTERIES

YOUR counsel, quoth Panurge, under your correction and
favour, seemeth unto me not unlike to the song of the
Gammer Yea-by-nay. It is full of sarcasms, mockeries, bitter
taunts, nipping bobs, derisive quips, biting jerks, and con-
tradictory iterations, the one part destroying the other. I
know not, quoth Pantagruel, which of all my answers to lay
hold on; for your proposals are so full of ifs and buts, that
I can ground nothing on them, nor pitch upon any solid and
positive determination satisfactory to what is demanded by
them. Are not you assured within yourself of what you have
a mind to do? The chief and main point of the whole matter

lieth there. All the rest is merely casual, and totally de-
pendeth upon the fatal disposition of the heavens.

We see some so happy in the fortune of this nuptial encounter, that their family shineth as it were with the radiant
effulgency of an idea, model, or representation of the joys
of paradise: and perceive others again, to be so unluckily
matched in the conjugal yoke, that those very basest of
devils, which tempt the hermits that inhabit the deserts of
Thebais and Montserrat are not more miserable than they.
It is therefore expedient, seeing you are resolved for once
to take a trial of the state of marriage, that, with shut eyes,
bowing your head, and kissing the ground, you put the business to a venture, and give it a fair hazard, in recommend-
ing the success of the residue to the disposure of Almighty
God. It lieth not in my power to give you any other manner
of assurance, or otherwise to certify you of what shall ensue
on this your undertaking. Nevertheless, if it please you, this
you may do. Bring hither Virgil's poems, that after having
opened the book, and with our fingers severed the leaves
thereof three several times, we may, according to the number
agreed upon betwixt ourselves, explore the future hap of your
intended marriage. For frequently by a Homeric lottery
have many hit upon their destinies; as is testified in the
person of Socrates, who, whilst he was in prison, hearing the
recitation of this verse of Homer, said of Achilles in the
Ninth of the Iliads—

We, the third day, to fertile Pthia came—

thereby foresaw that on the third subsequent day he was
to die. Of the truth whereof he assured Æschines; as Plato,
in Critone, Cicero, *in Primo, de Divinatione,* Diogenes, Laertius, and others, have to the full recorded in their works.

The like is also witnessed by Opilius Macrinus, to whom, being desirous to know if he should be the Roman emperor, befell, by chance of lot, this sentence in the Eighth of the Iliads—

Dotard, new warriors urge thee to be gone.
Thy life decays, and old age weighs thee down.

In fact, he, being then somewhat ancient, had hardly enjoyed the sovereignty of the empire for the space of fourteen months, when by Heliogabalus, then both young and strong, he was dispossessed thereof, thrust out of all and killed. Brutus doth also bear witness of another experiment of this nature, who willing, through his exploratory way by lot, to learn what the event and issue should be of the Pharsalian battle wherein he perished, he casually encountered on this verse, said of Patroclus in the Sixteenth of the Iliads—

Fate, and Latona's son have shot me dead.

And accordingly Apollo was the field-word in the dreadful day of that fight. Divers notable things of old have likewise been foretold and known by casting of Virgilian lots; yea, in matters of no less importance than the obtaining of the Roman empire, as it happened to Alexander Severus, who, trying his fortune at the said kind of lottery, did hit upon this verse written in the Sixth of the Æneids—

Tu regere imperio populos, Romane, memento.

Know, Roman, that thy business is to reign.

He, within very few years thereafter, was effectually and in good earnest created and installed Roman emperor. A semblable story thereto is related of Adrian, who, being hugely perplexed within himself out of a longing humour to know in what account he was with the Emperor Trajan, and how large the measure of that affection was which he did bear unto him, had recourse, after the manner above specified, to the Maronian lottery, which by haphazard tendered him these lines out of the Sixth of the Æneids—

Quis procul ille autem, ramis insignis olivæ
Sacra ferens? Nosco crines incanaque menta
Regis Romani.

But who is he, conspicuous from afar,
With olive boughs, that doth his offerings bear?
By the white hair and beard I know him plain,
The Roman king.

Shortly thereafter was he adopted by Trajan, and succeeded him in the empire. Moreover, to the lot of the praiseworthy Emperor Claudius befell this line of Virgil, written in the Sixth of his Æneids—

Tertia dum Latio regnamtem viderit æstas.

Whilst the third summer saw him reign a king
In Latium.

And in effect he did not reign above two years. To the said Claudius also, inquiring concerning his brother Quintilius, whom he proposed as a colleague with himself in the empire, happened the response following in the Sixth of the Æneids—

Ostendent terris hunc tantum fata.

Whom Fate let us see,
And would no longer suffer him to be.

And it so fell out; for he was killed on the seventeenth day after he had attained unto the management of the imperial charge. The very same lot, also, with the like misluck, did betide the Emperor Gordian the younger. To Claudius Albinus, being very solicitous to understand somewhat of his future adventures, did occur this saying, which is written in the Sixth of the Æneids—

> *Hic rem Romanam magno turbante tumultu*
> *Sistet Eques, &c.*

> *The Romans, boiling with tumultuous rage,*
> *This warrior shall the dangerous storm assuage.*
> *With victories he the Carthaginian mauls,*
> *And with strong hand shall crush the rebel Gauls.*

Likewise, when the Emperor D. Claudius, Aurelian's predecessor, did with great eagerness research after the fate to come of his posterity, his hap was to alight on this verse in the First of the Æneids—

> *Hic ego nec metas rerum, nec tempora pono.*

> *No bounds are to be set, no limits here.*

Which was fulfilled by the goodly genealogical row of his race. When Mr. Peter Amy did in like manner explore and make trial if he should escape the ambush of the hobgoblins who lay in wait all-to-bemaul him, he fell upon this verse in the Third of the Æneids—

> *Heu! fuge crudeles terres, fuge littus avarum!*

> *Oh, tec the bloody land, the wicked shore!*

Which counsel he obeying, safe and sound forthwith avoided all these ambuscades.

Were it not to shun prolixity, I could enumerate a thousand such like adventures, which, conform to the dictate and verdict of the verse, have by that manner of lot-casting encounter befallen to the curious researchers of them. Do not you nevertheless imagine, lest you should be deluded, that I would upon this kind of fortune-flinging proof infer an uncontrollable and not to be gainsaid infallibility of truth.

CHAPTER 20

HOW PANTAGRUEL SHOWETH THE TRIAL OF ONE'S FORTUNE BY THE THROWING OF DICE TO BE UNLAWFUL

IT would be sooner done, quoth Panurge, and more expeditely, if we should try the matter at the chance of three fair dice. Quoth Pantagruel, That sort of lottery is deceitful, abusive, illicitous, and exceedingly scandalous. Never trust it. The accursed book of the Recreation of Dice was a great while ago excogitated in Achaia, near Bourre, by that ancient enemy of mankind, the infernal calumniator, who, before the statue or massive image of the Bourraic Hercules, did of old, and doth in several places of the world yet, make many simple souls to err and fall into his snares. You know how my father Gargantua hath forbidden it over all his kingdoms and dominions; how he hath caused to burn the moulds and draughts thereof, and altogether suppressed, abolished, driven forth, and cast it out of the land, as a most dangerous plague and infection to any well-polished state or commonwealth. What I have told you of dice, I say the same of play at cockall. It is a lottery of the like guile and deceitfulness; and therefore do not, for convincing of me, allege in opposition to this my opinion, or bring in the example of the fortunate cast of Tiberius, within the fountain of Aponus, at the oracle of Gerion. These are the baited hooks by which the devil attracts and draweth unto him the foolish souls of silly people into eternal perdition.

Nevertheless, to satisfy your humour in some measure, I am content to throw three dice upon this table, that, according to the number of the blots which shall happen to be cast up, we may hit upon a verse of that page which in the setting open of the book you shall have pitched upon.

Have you any dice in your pocket? A whole bagful, answered Panurge. That is provision against the devil, as is expounded by Merlin Coccaius, *Lib.* 2. *De Patria Diabolorum*. The devil would be sure to take me napping, and very much unawares, if he should find me without dice. With this, the three dice being taken out, produced, and thrown, they fell so pat upon the lower points that the cast was five, six and five. These are, quoth Panurge, sixteen in all. Let us take up the sixteenth line of the page. The number pleaseth me very well; I hope we shall have a prosperous and happy chance. May I be thrown amidst all the devils of hell, even as a great bowl cast athwart at a set of nine-pins, or cannon-ball shot among a battalion of foot, in case so many times I do not boult my future wife the first night of our marriage. Of that, forsooth, I make no doubt at all, quoth Pantagruel. You needed not to have rapped forth such a horrid imprecation, the sooner to procure credit for the performance of so small a business, seeing possibly the first bout will be amiss, and that you know is usually at tennis called fifteen. At the next justling turn you may readily amend that fault, and so complete your reckoning of sixteen. Is it so, quoth Panurge, that you understand the matter? And must my words be thus interpreted? Nay, believe me never yet was any solecism committed by that valiant

:hampion who often hath for me in Bellydale stood sentry
it the hypogastrian cranny. Did you ever hitherto find me
n the confraternity of the faulty? Never, I trow; never,
nor ever shall, for ever and a day. I do the feat like a goodly
friar or father confessor, without default. And therein am
I willing to be judged by the players. He had no sooner spoke
these words than the works of Virgil were brought in. But
before the book was laid open, Panurge said to Pantagruel,
My heart, like the furch of a hart in a rut, doth beat within
my breast. Be pleased to feel and grope my pulse a little on
this artery of my left arm. At its frequent rise and fall you
would say that they swinge and belabour me after the manner of a probationer, posed and put to a peremptory trial in
the examination of his sufficiency, for the discharge of the
learned duty of a graduate in some eminent degree in the
college of the Sorbonists.

But would not you hold it expedient, before we proceed
any further, that we should invocate Hercules and the Tene-
tian goddesses who in the chamber of lots are said to rule,
sit in judgment, and bear a presidential sway? Neither of
them, answered Pantagruel; only open up the leaves of the
book with your fingers, and set your nails awork.

CHAPTER 21

HOW PANTAGRUEL DOTH EXPLORE BY THE VIRGILIAN LOTTERY WHAT FORTUNE PANURGE SHALL HAVE IN HIS MARRIAGE

THEN at the opening of the book in the sixteenth row of
the lines of the disclosed page did Panurge encounter upon
this following verse:

Nec Deus hunc mensa, Dea nec dignata cubili est.

The god him from his table banished,
Nor would the goddess have him in her bed.

This response, quoth Pantagruel, maketh not very much
for your benefit or advantage; for it plainly signifies and
denoteth that your wife shall be a strumpet, and yourself
by consequence a cuckold. The goddess, whom you shall no
find propitious nor favourable unto you is Minerva, a most
redoubtable and dreadful virgin, a powerful and fulminating
goddess, an enemy to cuckolds and effeminate youngsters, to
cuckold-makers and adulterers. The god is Jupiter, a terrible
and thunder-striking god from heaven. And withal it is to
be remarked, that, conform to the doctrine of the ancient
Etrurians, the manubes, for so did they call the darling
hurls or slinging casts of the Vulcanian thunderbolts, did
only appertain to her and to Jupiter her father capital. This
was verified in the conflagration of the ships of Ajax Oileus,
nor doth this fulminating power belong to any other of the
Olympic gods. Men, therefore, stand not in such fear of them.
Moreover, I will tell you, and you may take it as extracted
out of the profoundest mysteries of mythology, that, when
the giants had enterprised the waging of a war against the
power of the celestial orbs, the gods at first did laugh at
those attempts, and scorned such despicable enemies, who
were, in their conceit, not strong enough to cope in feats
of warfare with their pages; but when they saw by the gigantic labour, the high hill Pelion set on lofty Ossa, and that
the mount Olympus was made to shake to be erected on the
top of both, then did they all stand aghast. Then was it that
Jupiter held a parliament, or general convention, wherein it
was unanimously resolved upon and condescended to by all
the gods, that they should worthily and valiantly stand to
their defence. And because they had often seen battles lost

by the cumbersome lets and disturbing encumbrances of
women, confusedly huddled in amongst armies, it was at
that time decreed and enacted that they should expel and
drive them out of heaven into Egypt and the confines of the
Nile, that whole crew of goddesses, disguised in the shapes
of weasels, polecats, bats, shrew-mice, ferrets, fulmarts,
and other such like odd transformations; only Minerva was
reserved to participate with Jupiter in the horrific fulminating power, as being the goddess both of war and learning,
of arts and arms, of counsel and despatch—a goddess armed
from her birth, a goddess dreaded in heaven, in the air, by
sea and land. By the belly of Saint Buff, quoth Panurge,
should I be Vulcan, whom the poet blazons? Nay, I am
neither a cripple, coiner of false money, nor smith, as he was.
My wife possibly will be as comely and handsome as ever
was his Venus, but not a whore like her, nor I a cuckold like
him. The crook-legged slovenly slave made himself to be
declared a cuckold by a definite sentence and judgment, in
the open view of all the gods. For this cause ought you to
interpret the afore-mentioned verse quite contrary to what
you have said. This lot importeth that my wife will be
honest, virtuous, chaste, loyal, and faithful; not armed, surly,
wayward, cross, giddy, humorous, heady, hairbrained
or extracted out of the brains as was the goddess Pallas;
nor shall this fair jolly Jupiter be my co-rival. He shall never
dip his bread in my broth, though we should sit together at
one table.

Consider his exploits and gallant actions. He was the manifest ruffian, wencher, and most infamous cuckold-maker that
ever breathed. He did always lecher it like a boar, and no
wonder, for he was fostered by a sow in the Isle of Candia,
if Agathocles the Babylonian be not a liar, and more ram-
mishly lascivious than a buck; whence it is that he is said

by others to have been suckled and fed with the milk of the Amalthæan goat. By the virtue of Acheron, he justled, bulled, and lastauriated in one day the third part of the world, beasts and people, floods and mountains; that was Europa. For this grand subagitatory achievement the Ammonians caused draw, delineate, and paint him in the figure and shape of a ram ramming, and horned ram. But I know well enough how to shield and preserve myself from that horned champion. He will not, trust me, have to deal in my person with a sottish, dunsical Amphytrion, nor with a silly witless Argus, for all his hundred spectacles, nor yet with the cowardly meacock Acrisius, the simple goosecap Lycus of Thebes, the doting blockhead Agenor, the phlegmatic peagoose Æsop, rough-footed Lycaon, the luskish misshapen Corytus of Tuscany, nor with the large-backed and strong-reined Atlas. Let him alter, change, transform, and metamorphose himself into a hundred various shapes and figures, into a swan, a bull, a satyr, a shower of gold, or into a cuckoo, as he did when he unmaidened his sister Juno; into an eagle, ram, or dove, as when he was enamoured of the virgin Phthia, who then dwelt in the Ægean territory; into fire, a serpent, yea, even into a flea; into Epicurean and Democratical atoms, or, more Magistronostrally, into those sly intentions of the mind, which in the schools are called second notions,—I'll catch him in the nick and take him napping. And would you know what I would do unto him? Even that which Saturn did to his father Cœlum—Seneca foretold it of me, and Lactantius hath confirmed it—what the goddess Rhea did to Athis. I would make him two stone lighter, rid him of his Cyprian cymbals, and cut so close and neatly by the breech, that there should not remain thereof so much as one ——, so cleanly would I shave him, and disable him forever from being Pope, for *Testiculos non*

habet. Hold there, said Pantagruel; hoc, soft and fair, my
lad! Enough of that,—cast up, turn over the leaves, and
try your fortune for the second time. Then did he fall upon
this ensuing verse;

> *Membra quatit, gelidusque coit fofmidine sanguis.*
>
> *His joints and members quake, he becomes pale,*
> *And sudden fear doth his cold blood congeal.*

This importeth, quoth Pantagruel, that she will soundly
bang your back and belly. Clean and quite contrary, answered Panurge; it is of me that he prognosticates, in saying
that I will beat her like a tiger if she vex me. Sir Martin
Wagstaff will perform that office, and in default of a cudgel,
the devil gulp me, if I should not eat her up quick, as
Candaul the Lydian king did his wife, whom he ravened
and devoured.

You are very stout, says Pantagruel, and courageous;
Hercules himself durst hardly adventure to scuffle with you
in this your raging fury. Nor is it strange; for the Jan is
worth two, and two in fight against Hercules are too strong.
Am I a Jan? quoth Panurge. No, no, answered Pantagruel.
My mind was only running upon lurch and tricktrack. Thereafter did he hit, at the third opening of the book, upon this
verse:

> *Fœmineo prœdœ, et spoliorum ardebat amore.*
>
> *After the spoil and pillage, as in a fire,*
> *He burnt with a strong feminine desire.*

This portendeth, quoth Pantagruel, that she will steal your
goods, and rob you. Hence this, according to these drawn
lots, will be your future destiny, I clearly see it,—you will

be a cuckold, you will be beaten, and you will be robbed
Nay, it is quite otherwise, quoth Panurge; for it is certain
that this verse presageth that she will love me with a perfect
liking. Nor did the satyr-writing poet lie in proof hereof
when he affirmed that a woman, burning with extreme affec
tion, takes sometimes pleasure to steal from her sweetheart
And what, I pray you? A glove, a point, or some such triflin;
top of no importance, to make him keep a gentle kind o
stirring in research and quest thereof. In like manner, these
small scolding debates and pretty brabbling contentions
which frequently we see spring up and for a certain space
boil very hot betwixt a couple of high-spirited lovers, are
nothing else but recreative diversions for their refreshment
spurs to and incentives of a more fervent amity than ever
As, for example, we do sometimes see cutlers with hammer
maul their finest whetstones, therewith to sharpen their iron
tools the better. And therefore do I think that these three
lots make much for my advantage; which, if not, I from
their sentence totally appeal. There is no appealing, quoth
Pantagruel, from the decrees of fate and destiny, of lot o
chance; as is recorded by our ancient lawyers, witness
Baldus, *Lib. ult. Cap. de Leg.* The reason hereof is, Fortune
doth not acknowledge a superior, to whom an appeal may be
made from her or any of her substitutes. And in this case
the pupil cannot be restored to his right in full, as openly by
the said author is alleged in *L. Ait Prætor, paragr. ult. ff. d.
minor.*

CHAPTER 22

HOW PANTAGRUEL ADVISETH PANURGE TO TRY THE FUTURE
GOOD OR BAD LUCK OF HIS MARRIAGE BY DREAMS

Now, seeing we cannot agree together in the manner o
expounding or interpreting the sense of the Virgilian lots

et us bend our course another way, and try a new sort of
divination. Of what kind? asked Panurge. Of a good ancient
nd authentic fashion, answered Pantagruel; it is by dreams.
'or in dreaming, such circumstances and conditions being
hereto adhibited, are clearly enough described by Hippoc-
ates, in Lib. περι των ευυνυιων, by Plato, Plotin, Iamblicus,
inesius, Aristotle, Xenophon, Galen, Plutarch, Artemidorus,
Daldianus, Herophilus, Q. Calaber, Theocritus, Pliny,
Athenæus, and others, the soul doth oftentimes foresee what
s to come. How true this is, you may conceive by a very
ulgar and familiar example; as when you see that at such a
ime as suckling babes, well nourished fed, and fostered with
good milk, sleep soundly and profoundly, the nurses in the
nterim get leave to sport themselves, and are licentiated to
ecreate their fancies at what range to them shall seem most
itting and expedient, their presence, sedulity, and attendance on the cradle being, during all that space, held unneces-
ary. Even just so, when our body is at rest, that the con-
oction is everywhere accomplished, and that, till it awake,
t lacks for nothing, our soul delighteth to disport itself and
s well pleased in that frolic to take a review of its native
country, which is the heavens, where it receiveth a most
notable participation of its first beginning with an imbue-
ment from its divine source, and in contemplation of that
infinite and intellectual sphere, whereof the centre is everywhere, and the circumference in no place of the universal
world, to wit, God, according to the doctrine of Hermes
Trismegistus, to whom no new thing happeneth, whom nothing that is past escapeth, and unto whom all things are alike
present, remarketh not only what is preterit and gone in the
inferior course and agitation of sublunary matters, but withal
taketh notice what is to come; then bringing a relation of
those future events unto the body, by the outward senses and

exterior organs, it is divulged abroad unto the hearing of others. Whereupon the owner of that soul deserveth to be termed a vaticinator, or prophet. Nevertheless, the truth is, that the soul is seldom able to report those things in such sincerity as it hath seen them; by reason of the imperfection and frailty of the corporeal senses, which obstruct the effectuating of that office; even, as the moon doth not communicate unto this earth of ours, that light which she receiveth from the sun with so much splendour, heat, vigour, purity, and liveliness as it was given her. Hence it is requisite for the better reading, explaining, and unfolding of these somniatory vaticinations and predictions of that nature, that a dexterous, learned, skilful, wise, industrious, expert, rational, and peremptory expounder or interpreter be pitched upon, such a one as by the Greeks is called onirocritic, or oniropolist. For this cause Heraclitus was wont to say, that nothing is by dreams revealed to us, that nothing is by dreams concealed from us, and that only we thereby have a mystical signification and secret evidence of things to come either for our own prosperous or unlucky fortune, or for the favourable or disastrous success of another. The sacred Scriptures testify no less, and profane histories assure us of it, in both which are exposed to our view a thousand several kinds of strange adventures, which have befallen pat according to the nature of the dream, and that as well to the party dreamer as to others. The Atlantic people, and those that inhabit the [is]land of Thasos, one of the Cyclades, are of this grand commodity deprived; for in their countries none yet ever dreamed. Of this sort were Cleon of Daulia, Thrasymedes, and in our days the learned Frenchman Villanovanus, neither of all which knew what dreaming was.

Fail not therefore to-morrow, when the jolly and fair

Aurora with her rosy fingers draweth aside the curtains of the night, to drive away the sable shades of darkness, to send your spirits wholly to the task of sleeping sound, and thereto apply yourself. In the meantime you must denude your mind of every human passion or affection, such as are love and hatred, fear and hope, for as of old the great vaticinator, most famous and renowned prophet Proteus, was not able in his disguise or transformation into fire, water, a tiger, a dragon, and other such like uncouth shapes and visors, to presage anything that was to come till he was restored to his own first natural and kindly form; just so doth man; for, at his reception of the art of divination and faculty of prognosticating future things, that part in him which is the most divine, to wit, the Nous, or Mens, must be calm, peaceable, untroubled, quiet, still, hushed, and not imbusied or distracted with foreign, soul-disturbing perturbations. I am content, quoth Panurge. But, I pray you, sir, must I this evening, ere I go to bed, eat much or little? I do not ask this without cause. For if I sup not well, large, round, and amply, my sleeping is not worth a forked turnip. All the night long I then but doze and rave, and in my slumbering fits talk idle nonsense, my thoughts being in a dull brown study, and as deep in their dumps as is my belly hollow.

Not a sup, answered Pantagruel, were best for you, considering the state of your complexion and healthy constitution of your body. A certain very ancient prophet, named Amphiaraus, wished such as had a mind by dreams to be imbued with any oracle, for four-and-twenty hours to taste no victuals, and to abstain from wine three days together. Yet shall not you be put to such a sharp, hard, rigorous, and extreme sparing diet. I am truly right apt to believe that a man whose stomach is replete with various cheer, and in a manner surfeited with drinking, is hardly able to conceive aright of spiritual things; yet am not I of the opinion of those who, after long and pertinacious fasting, think by such means to enter more profoundly into the speculation of celestial mysteries. You may very well remember how my father Gargantua (whom here for honour sake I name) hath often told us, that the writings of abstinent, abstemious, and long-fasting hermits were every whit as saltless, dry, jejune and insipid as were their bodies when they did compose them. It is a most difficult thing for the spirits to be in good plight, serene and lively, when there is nothing in the body but a kind of voidness and inanity, seeing the philosophers with the physicians jointly affirm that the spirits which are styled animal spring from, and have their constant practice in and through the arterial blood, refined and purified to the life within the admirable net, which wonderfully framed, lieth under the ventricles and tunnels of the brain. He gave us also the example of the philosopher who, when he thought most seriously to have withdrawn himself unto solitary privacy, far from the rustling clutterments of the tumultuous and confused world, the better to improve his theory, to contrive, comment, and ratiocinate, was, notwithstanding his uttermost endeavours to free himself from all untoward noises, surrounded and environed about so with the barking of curs, bawling of mastiffs, bleating of sheep, prating of parrots, tattling of jackdaws, grunting of swine, yelping of foxes, girning of boars, mewing of cats, cheeping of mice, squeaking of weasels, croaking of frogs, crowing of cocks, cackling of hens, calling of partridges, chanting of swans, chattering of jays, peeping of chickens, singing of larks, creaking of geese, chirping of swallows, clucking of moorfowls, cucking of cuckoos, bumbling of bees, rummage of hawks, chirming of linnets, croaking of ravens, creeching of owls, whicking of pigs, gushing of hogs, curing of pigeons, grumbling of cushat-doves, howling of panthers, curkling of quails, chirping of sparrows, crackling of crows, nuzzling of camels; wheening of whelps, buzzing of dromedaries, mumbling of rabbits, cricking of ferrets, humming of wasps, moiling of tigers, bruzzing of bears, sussing of kitlings, clamouring of scarfs, whimpering of fulmarts, cooing of buffaloes, warbling of nightingales, quavering of mavises, drintling of turkeys, coniating of storks, frantling of peacocks, clattering of magpies, murmuring of stock-doves, routing of cormorants, cigling of locusts, charming of eagles, guarring of puppies, snarling of messens, rantling of rats, guerieting of apes, snuttering of monkeys, pioling of pelicans, quacking of ducks, yelling of wolves, roaring of lions, neighing of horses, barring of elephants, hissing of serpents, and wailing of turtles, that he was much more troubled than if he had been in the middle of the crowd at the fair of Fontenay or Niort. Just so is it with those who are tormented with the grievous pangs of hunger. The stomach begins to gnaw, and bark, as it were, the eyes to look dim, and the veins, by greedily sucking some refection to themselves from the proper substance of all the members of a fleshy consistence, violently pull down and draw back that vagrant, roaming spirit, careless and neglecting of his nurse and natural host, which is the body; as when a hawk upon the fist, willing to take her flight by soaring aloft in the open spacious air, is on a sudden drawn back by a leash tied to her feet.

To this purpose also did he allege unto us the authority of Homer, the father of all philosophy, who said that the Grecians did not put an end to their mournful mood for the death of Patroclus, the most intimate friend of Achilles, till hunger in a rage declared herself, and their bellies pro-

tested to furnish no more tears unto their grief. For from
bodies emptied and macerated by long fasting there could
not be such a supply of moisture and brackish drops as
might be proper on that occasion.

Mediocrity at all times is commendable; nor in this case
are you to abandon it. You may take a little supper, but
thereat must you not eat of a hare, nor of any other flesh.
You are likewise to abstain from beans, from the preak, by
some called the polyp, as also from coleworts, cabbage, and
all other such like windy victuals, which may endanger the
troubling of your brains and the dimming or casting a kind
of mist over your animal spirits. For, as a looking-glass cannot exhibit the semblance or representation of the object
set before it, and exposed to have its image to the life
expressed, if that the polished sleekness thereof be darkened
by gross breathings, dampish vapours, and foggy, thick, infectious exhalations, even so the fancy cannot well receive
the impression of the likeness of those things which divination doth afford by dreams, if any way the body be annoyed or troubled with the fumish steam of meat which it
had taken in a while before; because betwixt these two
there still hath been a mutual sympathy and fellow-feeling of
an indissolubly knit affection. You shall eat good Eusebian
and Bergamot pears, one apple of the short-shank pippin
kind, a parcel of the little plums of Tours, and some few
cherries of the growth of my orchard. Nor shall you need
to fear that thereupon will ensue doubtful dreams, fallacious,
uncertain, and not to be trusted to, as by some peripatetic
philosophers hath been related; for that, say they, men do
more copiously in the season of harvest feed on fruitages
than at any other time. The same is mystically taught us by
the ancient prophets and poets, who allege that all vain and
deceitful dreams lie hid and in covert under the leaves which

re spread on the ground,—by reason that the leaves fall
rom the trees in the autumnal quarter. For the natural
ervour which, abounding in ripe, fresh, recent fruits cometh
y the quickness of its ebullition to be with ease evaporated
ato the animal parts of the dreaming person—the experi-
nent is obvious in most—is a pretty while before it be
xpired, dissolved, and evanished. As for your drink, you
re to have it of the fair, pure water of my fountain.

The condition, quoth Panurge, is somewhat hard. Never-
heless, cost what price it will, or whatsoever come of it,
heartily condescend thereto; protesting that I shall to-
aorrow break my fast betimes, after my somniatory exer-
itations. Furthermore, I recommend myself to Homer's
wo gates, to Morpheus, to Iselon, to Phantasus, and unto
'hobetor. If they in this my great need succour me and
rant me that assistance which is fitting, I will in honour of
hem all, erect a jolly, genteel altar, composed of the softest
own. If I were now in Laconia, in the temple of Juno, be-
wixt Œtile and Thalamis, she suddenly would disentangle
ay perplexity, resolve me of my doubts, and cheer me up
vith fair and jovial dreams in a deep sleep.

Then did he say thus unto Pantagruel: Sir, were it not
xpedient for my purpose to put a branch or two of curious
aurel betwixt the quilt and bolster of my bed, under the
illow on which my head must lean? There is no need at all
f that, quoth Pantagruel; for besides that it is a thing very
uperstitious, the cheat thereof hath been at large discovered
nto us, in the writings of Serapion, Ascalonites, Antiphon,
'hilochorus, Artemon, and Fulgentius Planciades. I could
ay as much to you of the left shoulder of a crocodile, as
lso of a chameleon, without prejudice be it spoken to the
redit which is due to the opinion of old Democritus; and
ikewise of the stone of the Bactrians, called Eumetrides,

and of the Ammonian horn; for so by the Æthiopians
termed a certain precious stone, coloured like gold, and
the fashion, shape, form, and proportion of a ram's horn,
the horn of Jupiter Ammon is reported to have been: th
over and above assuredly affirming that the dreams of tho
who carry it about them are no less veritable and infallib
than the truth of the divine oracles. Nor is this much unli
to what Homer and Virgil wrote of these two gates of slee
to which you have been pleased to recommend the manag
ment of what you have in hand. The one is of ivory, whic
letteth in confused, doubtful and uncertain dreams; f
through ivory, how small and slender soever it be, we can s
nothing, the density, opacity, and close compactedness
its material parts hindering the penetration of the visu
rays and the reception of the species of such things as a
visible. The other is of horn, at which an entry is made
sure and certain dreams, even as through horn, by reas
of the diaphanous splendour and bright transparency there
the species of all objects of the sight distinctly pass, and
without confusion appear, that they are clearly seen. Yo
meaning is, and you would thereby infer, quoth Friar Joh
that the dreams of all horned cuckolds, of which numb
Panurge, by the help of God and his future wife, is witho
controversy to be one, are always true and infallible.

CHAPTER 23

PANURGE'S DREAM, WITH THE INTERPRETATION THEREOF

At seven o'clock of the next following morning Panur
did not fail to present himself before Pantagruel, in who
chamber were at that time Epistemon, Friar John of t
Funnels, Ponocrates, Eudemon, Carpalin, and others,
whom, at the entry of Panurge, Pantagruel said, Lo! he

meth our dreamer. That word, quoth Epistemon, in an-
ent times cost very much, and was dearly sold to the chil-
en of Jacob. Then, said Panurge, I have been plunged into
y dumps so deeply, as if I had been lodged with Gaffer
oddy-cap. Dreamed indeed I have, and that right lustily;
it I could take along with me no more thereof that I did
odly understand save only that I in my vision had a pretty,
ir, young, gallant, handsome woman, who no less lovingly
id kindly treated and entertained me, hugged, cherished,
ckered, dandled, and made much of me, as if I had been
other neat dilly-darling minion, like Adonis. Never was
an more glad than I was then; my joy at that time was
comparable. She flattered me, tickled me, stroked me,
oped me, frizzled me, curled me, kissed me, embraced me,
id her hands about my neck, and now and then made jest-
gly pretty little horns above my forehead. I told her in
ie like disport, as I did play the fool with her, that she
ould rather place and fix them in a little below mine eyes,
at I might see the better what I should stick at with them;
r, being so situated, Momus then would find no fault there-
ith, as he did once with the position of the horns of bulls.
he wanton, toying girl, notwithstanding any remonstrance
mine to the contrary, did always drive and thrust them
rther in; yet thereby, which to me seemed wonderful, she
d not do me any hurt at all. A little after, though I know
ot how, I thought I was transformed into a tabor, and she
to a chough.

My sleeping there being interrupted, I awaked in a start,
igry, displeased, perplexed, chafing, and very wroth. There
ive you a large platterful of dreams, make thereupon good
ieer, and, if you please, spare not to interpret them accord-
ig to the understanding which you may have in them. Come,
arpalin, let us to breakfast. To my sense and meaning,

quoth Pantagruel, if I have skill or knowledge in the ar
of divination by dreams, your wife will not really, and t
the outward appearance of the world, plant or set horn:
and stick them fast in your forehead, after a visible manner
as satyrs use to wear and carry them; but she will be so fa
from preserving herself loyal in the discharge and observanc
of a conjugal duty, that, on the contrary, she will violate he
plighted faith, break her marriage-oath, infringe all matr
monial ties, prostitute her body to the dalliance of othe
men, and so make you a cuckold. This point is clearly an
manifestly explained and expounded by Artemidorus ju:
as I have related it. Nor will there be any metamorphos'
or transmutation made of you into a drum or tabor, bu
you will surely be as soundly beaten as ever was tabor a
a merry wedding. Nor yet will she be changed into a choug!
but will steal from you, chiefly in the night, as is the natu:
of that thievish bird. Hereby may you perceive your dream
to be in every jot conform and agreeable to the Virgilia
lots. A cuckold you will be, beaten and robbed. Then cri
out Father John with a loud voice, He tells the truth; upc
my conscience thou wilt be a cuckold—an honest one, I
warrant thee. O the brave horns that will be borne by the
Ha, ha, ha! Our good Master de Cornibus. God save the
and shield thee! Wilt thou be pleased to preach but tw
words of a sermon to us, and I will go through the paris
church to gather up alms for the poor.

You are, quoth Panurge, very far mistaken in your i:
terpretation; for the matter is quite contrary to your sen
thereof. My dream presageth that I shall by marriage I
stored with plenty of all manner of goods—the hornifyi:
of me showing that I will possess a cornucopia, that Ama
thæan horn which is called the horn of abundance, where
the fruition did still portend the wealth of the enjoyer. Y

possibly will say that they are rather to be like satyr's horns;
for you of these did make some mention. *Amen, Amen, Fiat,
fiatur, ad differentiam papæ.* Thus shall I have my touch-
her-home still ready. My staff of love, sempiternally in a
good case, will, satyr-like, be never toiled out—a thing
which all men wish for, and send up their prayers to that
purpose, but such a thing as nevertheless is granted but to
a few. Hence doth it follow by a consequence as clear as the
sunbeams that I will never be in the danger of being made
a cuckold, for the defect hereof is *Causa sine qua non;* yea,
the sole cause, as many think, of making husbands cuckolds.
What makes poor scoundrel rogues to beg, I pray you? Is
it not because they have not enough at home wherewith to
fill their bellies and their pokes? What is it makes the wolves
to leave the woods? Is it not the want of flesh meat? What
maketh women whores? You understand me well enough.
And herein may I very well submit my opinion to the judgment of learned lawyers, presidents, counsellors, advocates,
procurers, attorneys, and other glossers and commentators
on the venerable rubric, *De frigidis et maleficiatis.* You are,
in truth, sir, as it seems to me, (excuse my boldness if I have
transgressed), in a most palpable and absurd error to attribute my horns to cuckoldry. Diana wears them on her
head after the manner of a crescent. Is she a cucquean for
that? How the devil can she be cuckolded who never yet
was married? Speak somewhat more correctly, I beseech
you, lest she, being offended, furnish you with a pair of
horns shapen by the pattern of those which she made for
Actæon. The goodly Bacchus also carries horns,—Pan, Jupiter Ammon, with a great many others. Are they all cuckolds?
If Jove be a cuckold, Juno is a whore. This follows by the
figure metalepsis: as to call a child, in the presence of his
father and mother, a bastard, or whore's son, is tacitly and

underboard no less than if he had said openly the father is a cuckold and his wife a punk. Let our discourse come nearer to the purpose. The horns that my wife did make me are horns of abundance, planted and grafted in my head for the increase and shooting up of all good things. This will I affirm for truth, upon my word, and pawn my faith and credit both upon it. As for the rest, I will be no less joyful, frolic, glad, cheerful, merry, jolly, and gamesome, than a well-bended tabor in the hands of a good drummer at a nuptial feast, still making a noise, still rolling, still buzzing and cracking. Believe me, sir, in that consisteth none of my least good fortunes. And my wife will be jocund, feat, compt, neat, quaint, dainty, trim, tricked up, brisk, smirk, and smug, even as a pretty little Cornish chough. Who will not believe this, let hell or the gallows be the burden of his Christmas carol.

I remark, quoth Pantagruel, the last point or particle which you did speak of, and, having seriously conferred it with the first, find that at the beginning you were delighted with the sweetness of your dream; but in the end and final closure of it you startingly awaked, and on a sudden were forthwith vexed in choler and annoyed. Yea, quoth Panurge, the reason of that was because I had fasted too long. Flatter not yourself, quoth Pantagruel; all will go to ruin. Know for a certain truth, that every sleep that endeth with a starting, and leaves the person irksome, grieved, and fretting, doth either signify a present evil, or otherwise presageth and portendeth a future imminent mishap. To signify an evil, that is to say, to show some sickness hardly curable, a kind of pestilentious or malignant boil, botch, or sore, lying and lurking hid, occult, and latent within the very centre of the body, which many times doth by the means of sleep, whose nature is to reinforce and strengthen the faculty and virtue of concoction, begin according to the theorems of physic to declare itself, and moves toward the outward superficies. At this sad stirring is the sleeper's rest and ease disturbed and broken, whereof the first feeling and stinging smart admonisheth that he must patiently endure great pain and trouble, and thereunto provide some remedy; as when we say proverbially, to incense hornets, to move a stinking puddle, and to awake a sleeping lion, instead of these more usual expressions, and of a more familiar and plain meaning, to provoke angry persons, to make a thing worse by meddling with it, and to irritate a testy choleric man when he is at quiet. On the other part, to presage or foretell an evil, especially in what concerneth the exploits of the soul in matter of somnial divinations, is as much to say as that it giveth us to understand that some dismal fortune or mischance is destinated and prepared for us, which shortly will not fail to come to pass. A clear and evident example hereof is to be found in the dream and dreadful awaking of Hecuba, as likewise in that of Eurydice, the wife of Orpheus, neither of which was [no] sooner finished, saith Ennius, but that incontinently thereafter they awaked in a start, and were affrighted horribly. Thereupon these accidents ensued: Hecuba had her husband Priamus, together with her children, slain before her eyes, and saw then the destruction of her country; and Eurydice died speedily thereafter in a most miserable manner. Æneas, dreaming that he spoke to Hector a little after his decease, did on a sudden in a great start awake, and was afraid. Now hereupon did follow this event: Troy that same night was spoiled, sacked, and burnt. At another time the same Æneas dreaming that he saw his familiar geniuses and penates, in a ghastly fright and astonishment awaked, of which terror and amazement the issue was, that the very next day subse-

quent, by a most horrible tempest on the sea, he was like
to have perished and been cast away. Moreover, Turnus
being prompted, instigated, and stirred up by the fantastic
vision of an infernal fury to enter into a bloody war against
Æneas, awaked in a start much troubled and disquieted in
spirit; in sequel whereof, after many notable and famous
routs, defeats, and discomfitures in open field, he came at
last to be killed in a single combat by the said Æneas. A
thousand other instances I could afford, if it were needful,
of this matter. Whilst I relate these stories of Æneas, remark
the saying of Fabius Pictor, who faithfully averred that
nothing had at any time befallen unto, was done, or enterprised by him, whereof he preallably had not notice, and
beforehand foreseen it to the full, by sure predictions altogether founded on the oracles of somnial divination. To
this there is no want of pregnant reasons, no more than of
examples. For if repose and rest in sleeping be a special
gift and favour of the gods, as is maintained by the philosophers, and by the poet attested in these lines,

> *Then sleep, that heavenly gift, came to refresh*
> *Of human labourers the wearied flesh;*

such a gift or benefit can never finish or terminate in wrath
and indignation without portending some unlucky fate and
most disastrous fortune to ensue. Otherwise it were a molesta-
tion, and not an ease; a scourge, and not a gift; at least,
[not] proceeding from the gods above, but from the infernal
devils our enemies, according to the common vulgar saying.

Suppose the lord, father, or master of a family, sitting at
a very sumptuous dinner, furnished with all manner of good
cheer, and having at his entry to the table his appetite sharp
set upon his victuals, whereof there was great plenty, should

be seen rise in a start, and on a sudden fling out of his chair, abandoning his meat, frighted, appalled, and in a horrid terror, who should not know the cause hereof would wonder, and be astonished exceedingly. But what? he heard his male servants cry, Fire, fire, fire, fire! his serving-maids and women yell, Stop thief, stop thief! and all his children shout as loud as ever they could, Murder, O murder, murder! Then was it not high time for him to leave his banqueting, for application of a remedy in haste, and to give speedy order for succouring of his distressed household? Truly I remember that the Cabalists and Massorets, interpreters of the sacred Scriptures, in treating how with verity one might judge of evangelical apparitions (because oftentimes the angel of Satan is disguised and transfigured into an angel of light), said that the difference of these two mainly did consist in this: the favourable and comforting angel useth in his appearing unto man at first to terrify and hugely affright him, but in the end he bringeth consolation, leaveth the person who hath seen him joyful, well-pleased, fully content and satisfied; on the other side, the angel of perdition, that wicked, devilish, and malignant spirit, at his appearance unto any person in the beginning cheereth up the heart of his beholder, but at last forsakes him, and leaves him troubled, angry, and perplexed.

CHAPTER 24

HOW PANURGE SPOKE TO THE SIBYL OF PANZOUST

THEIR voyage was three days journeying. On the third whereof was shown unto them the house of the vaticinatress standing on the knap or top of a hill, under a large and spacious walnut-tree. Without great difficulty they entered into that straw-thatched cottage, scurvily built, naughtily movabled, and all besmoked. It matters not, quoth Epistemon; Heraclitus, the grand Scotist and tenebrous darksome philosopher, was nothing astonished at his introit into such a coarse and paltry habitation; for he did usually show forth unto his spectators and disciples that the gods made as cheerfully their residence in these mean, homely mansions as in sumptuous magnific palaces, replenished with all manner of delight, pomp, and pleasure. I withal do really believe that the dwelling place of the so famous and renowned Hecate was just such another petty cell as this is, when she made a feast therein to the valiant Theseus; and that of no other better structure was the cot or cabin of Hyreus, or Œnopion wherein Jupiter, Neptune, and Mercury were not ashamed, all three together, to harbour and sojourn a whole night, and there take a full and hearty repast; for the payment of the shot they thankfully pissed Orion. They finding the ancient woman at a corner of her own chimney, Epistemon said, She is indeed a true sibyl, and the lively portrait of one represented by the *Gxei chaminoi* of Homer. The old hag was in a pitiful bad plight and condition in matter of the outward state and complexion of her body, the ragged and tattered equipage of her person in the point of accoutrement, and beggarly poor provision of fare for her diet and entertainment; for she was ill apparelled, worse nourished, toothless, blear-eyed, crook-shouldered, snotty, her nose still dropping, and herself still drooping, faint, and pithless; whilst in this woefully wretched case she was making ready for her dinner porridge of wrinkled green coleworts, with a bit skin of yellow bacon, mixed with a twice-before-cooked sort of waterish, unsavoury broth, extracted out of bare and hollow bones. Epistemon said, By the cross of a groat, we are to blame, nor shall we get from her any response at all, for we have not brought along with us the branch of gold. I have, quoth Panurge, provided pretty well for that, for here I have it within my bag, in the substance of a gold ring, accompanied with some fair pieces of small money. No sooner were these words spoken, when Panurge coming up towards her, after the ceremonial performance of a profound and humble salutation, presented her with six neats' tongues dried in the smoke, a great butter-pot full of fresh cheese, a borachio furnished with good beverage, and a ram's cod stored with single pence, newly coined. At last he, with a low courtesy, put on her medical finger a pretty handsome golden ring, whereinto was right artificially enchased a precious toadstone of Beausse. This done, in few words and very succinctly did he set open and expose unto her the motive reason of his coming, most civilly and courteously entreating her that she might be pleased to vouchsafe to give him an ample and plenary intelligence concerning the future good luck of his intended marriage.

The old trot for a while remained silent, pensive and grinning like a dog; then, after she had set her withered breech upon the bottom of a bushel, she took into her hands three old spindles, which when she had turned and whirled betwixt her fingers very diversely and after several fashions, she pried more narrowly into, by the trial of their points, the sharpest whereof she retained in her hand, and threw the other two under a stone trough. After this she took a pair of yarn windles, which she nine times unintermittingly veered and frisked about; then at the ninth revolution or turn, without touching them any more, maturely perpending the manner of their motion, she very demurely waited on their repose and cessation from any further stirring. In sequel whereof she pulled off one of her wooden pattens, put her apron over her head, as a priest uses to do his amice when he is going to sing mass, and with a kind of antique, gaudy, party-coloured string knit it under her neck. Being thus covered and muffled, she whiffed off a lusty good draught out of the borachio, took three several pence forth of the ramcod fob, put them into so many walnut-shells, which she set down upon the bottom of a feather-pot, and then, after she had given them three whisks of a broom besom athwart the chimney, casting into the fire half a bavin of long heather, together with a branch of dry laurel, she observed with a very hush and coy silence in what form they did burn, and saw that, although they were in flame, they made no kind of noise or crackling din. Hereupon she gave a most hideous and horribly dreadful shout, muttering betwixt her teeth some few barbarous words of a strange termination.

This so terrified Panurge that he forthwith said to Epistemon, The devil mince me into gallimaufry if I do not tremble for fear! I do not think but that I am now enchanted; for she uttereth not her voice in the terms of any Christian language. O look, I pray you, how she seemeth unto me to be by three full spans higher than she was when she began to hood herself with her apron. What meaneth this restless wagging of her slouchy chaps? What can be the signification of the uneven shrugging of her hulchy shoulders? To what end doth she quaver with her lips, like a monkey in the dismembering of a lobster? My ears through horror glow; ah! how they tingle! I think I hear the shrieking of Proserpina; the devils are breaking loose to be all here. O the foul, ugly, and deformed beasts! Let us run away! By the hook of God, I am like to die for fear! I do not love the devils; they vex me and are unpleasant fellows. Now let us fly, and betake us to our heels. Farewell, gammer; thanks and gramercy for your goods! I will not marry; no, believe me, I will not. I fairly quit my interest therein, and totally abandon and renounce it from this time forward, even as much as at present. With this, as he endeavoured to make an escape out of the room, the old crone did anticipate his flight and make him stop. The way how she prevented him was this: whilst in her hand she held the spindle, she flung out to a back-yard close by her lodge, where, after she had peeled off the barks of an old sycamore three several times, she very summarily, upon eight leaves which dropped from thence, wrote with the spindle-point some curt and briefly-couched verses, which she threw into the air, then said unto them, Search after them if you will; find them if you can; the fatal destinies of your marriage are written in them.

No sooner had she done thus speaking than she did withdraw herself unto her lurking-hole, where on the upper seat of the porch she tucked up her gown, her coats, and smock, as high as her arm-pits and gave them a full inspection of the nockandroe; which being perceived by Panurge, he said to Epistemon, God's bodikins, I see the sibyl's hole! She suddenly then bolted the gate behind her, and was never seen since any more. They jointly ran in haste after the fallen and dispersed leaves, and gathered them at last, though not without great labour and toil, for the wind had scattered them amongst the thorn-bushes of the valley. When they had ranged them each after the other in their due places, they found out their sentence, as it is metrified in this octastich.

Thy fame upheld,*
Even so, so:
And she with child
Of thee: No.

* Properly, as corrected by Ozell:
Thy fame will be shell'd
By her, I trow.

> Thy good end
> Suck she shall
> And flay thee, friend,
> But not all.

CHAPTER 25

HOW PANTAGRUEL AND PANURGE DID DIVERSELY EXPOUND THE VERSES OF THE SIBYL OF PANZOUST

THE leaves being thus collected and orderly disposed, Epistemon and Panurge returned to Pantagruel's court, partly well pleased and other part discontented; glad for their being come back, and vexed for the trouble they had sustained by the way, which they found to be craggy, rugged, stony, rough, and ill-adjusted. They made an ample and full relation of their voyage unto Pantagruel, as likewise of the estate and condition of the sibyl. Then, having presented to him the leaves of the sycamore, they show him the short and twattle verses that were written in them. Pantagruel, having read and considered the whole sum and substance of the matter, fetched from his heart a deep, heavy sigh; then said to Panurge, You are now, forsooth, in a good taking, and have brought your hogs to a fine market. The prophecy of the sibyl doth explain and lay out before us the same very predictions which have been denoted, foretold, and presaged to us by the decree of the Virgilian lots and the verdict of your own proper dreams, to wit, that you shall be very much disgraced, shamed, and discredited by your wife; for that she will make you a cuckold in prostituting herself to others, being big with child by another than you,—will steal from you a great deal of your goods, and will beat you, scratch and bruise you, even to plucking the skin in a part from off you,—will leave the print of her blows in some member of your

body. You understand as much, answered Panurge, in the
veritable interpretation and expounding of recent prophecies
as a sow in the matter of spicery. Be not offended, sir, I beseech you, that I speak thus boldly; for I find myself a little
in choler, and that not without cause, seeing it is the contrary
that is true. Take heed, and give attentive ear unto my words.
The old wife said that, as the bean is not seen till first it be
unhusked, and that its swad or hull be shelled and peeled
from off it, so is it that my virtue and transcendent worth
will never come by the mouth of fame to be blazed abroad
proportionable to the height, extent, and measure of the excellency thereof, until preallably I get a wife and make the
full half of a married couple. How many times have I heard
you say that the function of a magistrate, or office of dignity,
discovereth the merits, parts and endowments of the person
so advanced and promoted, and what is in him. That is to
say, we are then best able to judge aright of the deservings of
a man when he is called to the management of affairs; for
when before he lived in a private condition, we could have no
more certain knowledge of him than of a bean within his
husk. And thus stands the first article explained; otherwise,
could you imagine that the good fame, repute, and estimation
of an honest man should depend upon the tale of a whore?

Now to the meaning of the second article! My wife will
be with child,—here lies the prime felicity of marriage,—but
not of me. Copsody, that I do believe indeed! It will be of a
pretty little infant. O how heartily I shall love it! I do already dote upon it; for it will be my dainty feedle-darling,
my genteel dilly-minion. From thenceforth no vexation, care,
or grief shall take such deep impression in my heart, how
hugely great or vehement soever it otherwise appear, but that
it shall evanish forthwith at the sight of that my future babe,
and at the hearing of the chat and prating of its childish

gibberish. And blessed be the old wife. By my truly, I have a
mind to settle some good revenue or pension upon her out of
the readiest increase of the lands of my Salmigondinois; not
an inconstant and uncertain rent-seek, like that of witless,
giddy-headed bachelors, but sure and fixed, of the nature of
the well-paid incomes of regenting doctors. If this interpretation doth not please you, think you my wife will bear me in
her flanks, conceive with me, and be of me delivered, as
women use in child-bed to bring forth their young ones; so
as that it may be said, Panurge is a second Bacchus, he hath
been twice born; he is re-born, as was Hippolytus,—as was
Proteus, one time of Thetis, and secondly, of the mother of
the philosopher Apollonius,—as were the two Palici, near the
flood Simæthos in Sicily. His wife was big of child with him.
In him is renewed and begun again the palintocy of the
Megarians and the palingenesy of Democritus. Fie upon such
errors! To hear stuff of that nature rends mine ears.

You expound this passage allegorically, and interpret it to
theft and larceny. I love the exposition, and the allegory
pleaseth me; but not according to the sense whereto you
stretch it. It may be that the sincerity of your affection which
you bear me moveth you to harbour in your breast those
refractory thoughts concerning me, with a suspicion of my
adversity to come. We have this saying from the learned,
That a marvellously fearful thing is love, and that true love
is never without fear. But, sir, according to my judgment,
you do understand both of and by yourself that here stealth
signifieth nothing else, no more than in a thousand other places
of Greek and Latin, old and modern writings, but the sweet
fruits of amorous dalliance, which Venus liketh best when
reaped in secret, and culled by fervent lovers filchingly. Why
so, I prithee tell? Because when the feat of the loose-coat
skirmish happeneth to be done underhand and privily, be-

tween two well-disposed, athwart the steps of a pair of stairs
lurkingly, and in covert behind a suit of hangings, or close
hid and trussed upon an unbound faggot, it is more pleasing
to the Cyprian goddess, and to me also—I speak this without
prejudice to any better or more sound opinion—than to perform that cullbusting art after the Cynic manner, in the view
of the clear sunshine, or in a rich tent, under a precious stately
canopy, within a glorious and sublime pavilion, or yet on a
soft couch betwixt rich curtains of cloth of gold, without
affrightment, at long intermediate respites, enjoying of pleasures and delights a bellyful, at all great ease, with a huge
fly-flap fan of crimson satin and a bunch of feathers of some
East-Indian ostrich serving to give chase unto the flies all
round about; whilst, in the interim, the female picks her teeth
with a stiff straw picked even then from out of the bottom of
the bed she lies on. If you be not content with this my exposition, are you of the mind that my wife will suck and sup me
up as people use to gulp and swallow oysters out of the shell?
or as the Cilician women, according to the testimony of
Dioscorides, were wont to do the grain of alkermes? Assuredly
that is an error. Who seizeth on it, doth neither gulch up nor
swill down, but takes away what hath been packed up,
catcheth, snatcheth, and plies the play of hey-pass, repass.

The fourth article doth imply that my wife will flay me,
but not all. O the fine word! You interpret this to beating
strokes and blows. Speak wisely. Will you eat a pudding? Sir,
I beseech you to raise up your spirits above the low-sized
pitch of earthly thoughts unto that height of sublime contemplation which reacheth to the apprehension of the mysteries and wonders of Dame Nature. And here be pleased to
condemn yourself, by a renouncing of those errors which you
have committed very grossly and somewhat perversely in expounding the prophetic sayings of the holy sibyl. Yet put the

case (albeit I yield not to it) that, by the instigation of the devil, my wife should go about to wrong me, make me a cuckold downward to the very breech, disgrace me otherwise, steal my goods from me, yea, and lay violently her hands upon me;—she nevertheless should fail of her attempts and not attain to the proposed end of her unreasonable undertakings. The reason which induceth me hereto is grounded totally on this last point, which is extracted from the profoundest privacies of a monastic pantheology, as good Friar Arthur Wagtail told me once upon a Monday morning, as we were (if I have not forgot) eating a bushel of trotter-pies; and I remember well it rained hard. God give him the good morrow! The women at the beginning of the world, or a little after, conspired to flay the men quick, because they found the spirit of mankind inclined to domineer it, and bear rule over them upon the face of the whole earth; and, in pursuit of this their resolution, promised, confirmed, swore, and covenanted amongst them all, by the pure faith they owe to the nocturnal Sanct Rogero. But O the vain enterprises of women! O the great fragility of that sex feminine! They did begin to flay the man, or peel him (as says Catullus), at that member which of all the body they loved best, to wit, the nervous and cavernous cane, and that above five thousand years ago; yet have they not of that small part alone flayed any more till this hour but the head. In mere despite whereof the Jews snip off that parcel of the skin in circumcision, choosing far rather to be called clipyards, rascals, than to be flayed by women, as are other nations. My wife, according to this female covenant, will flay it to me, if it be not so already. I heartily grant my consent thereto, but will not give her leave to flay it all. Nay, truly will I not, my noble king.

CHAPTER 26

PANURGE was indeed very much troubled in mind and disquieted; therefore he made his address to Friar John, in pecking at, rubbing, and scratching his own left ear, he said unto him, Keep me a little jovial and merry, my dear and sweet bully, for I find my brains altogether metagrabolized and confounded, and my spirits in a most dunsical puzzle at the bitter talk of this devilish, hellish, damned fool. Hearken, my dainty.

Mellow C.	Varnished C.	Resolute C.
Lead-coloured C.	Renowned C.	Cabbage-like C.
Knurled C.	Matted C.	Courteous C.
Suborned C.	Genitive C.	Fertile C.
Desired C.	Gigantal C.	Whizzing C.
Stuffed C.	Oval C.	Neat C.
Speckled C.	Claustral C.	Common C.
Finely metalled C.	Virile C.	Brisk C.
Arabian-like C.	Stayed C.	Quick C.
Trussed-up Grey-	Massive C.	Bearlike C.
hound-like C.	Manual C.	Partitional C.
Mounted C.	Absolute C.	Patronymic C.
Sleeked C.	Well-set C.	Cockney C.
Diapered C.	Gemel C.	Auromercuriated C.
Spotted C.	Turkish C.	Robust C.
Master C.	Burning C.	Appetizing C.
Seeded C.	Thwacking C.	Succourable C.
Lusty C.	Urgent C.	Redoubtable C.
Jupped C.	Handsome C.	Affable C.
Milked C.	Prompt C.	Memorable C.

Calfeted C.

Raised C.

Odd C.

Steeled C.

Stale C.

Orange-tawny C.

Embroidered C.

Glazed C.

Interlarded C.

Burgher-like C.

Empowdered C.

Ebonized C.

Brasiliated C.

Organized C.

Passable C.

Trunkified C.

Furious C.

Packed C.

Hooded C.

Fat C.

High-prized C.

Requisite C.

Laycod C.

Hand-filling C.

Insuperable C.

Agreeable C.

Formidable C.

Profitable C.

Notable C.

Musculous C.

Subsidiary C.

Satiric C.

Repercussive C.

Fortunate C.

Boxwood C.

Latten C.

Unbridled C.

Hooked C.

Researched C.

Encompassed C.

Strouting out C.

Jolly C.

Lively C.

Gerundive C.

Franked C.

Polished C.

Powdered Beef C.

Positive C.

Spared C.

Bold C.

Lascivious C.

Gluttonous C.

Boulting C.

Snorting C.

Pilfering C.

Shaking C.

Bobbing C.

Chiveted C.

Fumbling C.

Topsyturvying C.

Raging C.

Piled up C.

Filled up C.

Manly C.

Idle C.

Membrous C.

Palpable C.

Barbable C.

Tragical C.

Transpontine C.

Digestive C.

Active C.

Vital C.

Magistral C.

Monachal C.

Subtle C.

Hammering C.

Clashing C.

Tingling C.

Usual C.

Exquisite C.

Trim C.

Succulent C.

Factious C.

Clammy C.

New-vamped C.

Improved C.

Malling C.

Sounding C.

Battled C.

Burly C.

Seditious C.

Wardian C.

Protective C.

Twinkling C.

Able C.

Algoristical C.

Odoriferous C.

Pranked C.

Convulsive C.	Strong C.	Jocund C.
Restorative C.	Twin C.	Routing C.
Masculinating C.	Belabouring C.	Purloining C.
Incarnative C.	Gentle C.	Frolic C.
Sigillative C.	Stirring C.	Wagging C.
Sallying C.	Confident C.	Ruffling C.
Plump C.	Nimble C.	Jumbling C.
Thundering C.	Roundheaded C.	Rumbling C.
Lechering C.	Figging C.	Thumping C.
Fulminating C.	Helpful C.	Bumping C.
Sparkling C.	Spruce C.	Cringeling C.
Ramming C.	Plucking C.	Berumpling C.
Lusty C.	Ramage C.	Jogging C.
Household C.	Fine C.	Nobbing C.
Pretty C.	Fierce C.	Touzing C.
Astrolabian C.	Brawny C.	Tumbling C.
Algebraical C.	Compt. C.	Fambling C.
Venust C.	Repaired C.	Overturning C.
Aromatizing C.	Soft C.	Shooting C.
Tricksy C.	Wild C.	Culeting C.
Gaillard C.	Renewed C.	Jagged C.
Gaillard C.	Quaint C.	Pinked C.
Broaching C.	Starting C.	Arsiversing C.
Meddle C.	Fleshy C.	Polished C.
Syndicated C.	Auxiliary C.	Slashed C.
Lamed C.	Stuffed C.	Clashing C.
Leisurely C.	Well-fed C.	Wagging C.
Cut C.	Flourished C.	Scriplike C.
Smooth C.	Fallow C.	Encremastered C.
Depending C.	Sudden C.	Bouncing C.
Independent C.	Graspful C.	Levelling C.
Lingering C.	Swillpow C.	Fly-flap C.
Lapping C.	Crushing C.	Perinæ-tegminal C.

Reverend C.	Creaking C.	Squat-couching C.
Nodding C.	Dilting C.	Short-hung C.
Disseminating C.	Ready C.	The hypogastrian C
Affecting C.	Vigorous C.	Witness-bearing C.
Affected C.	Skulking C.	Testigerous C.
Grappled C.	Superlative C.	Instrumental C.

CHAPTER 27

HOW FRIAR JOHN COMFORTETH PANURGE IN THE DOUBTFUI MATTER OF CUCKOLDRY

I UNDERSTAND thee well enough, said Friar John; but time makes all things plain. The most durable marble or porphyry is subject to old age and decay. I see thee waxing a little hoar headed already. Thy beard, by the distinction of grey, white tawny, and black, hath to my thinking the resemblance of a map of the terrestrial globe or geographical chart. Look atten tively upon and take inspection of what I shall show unto thee Behold there Asia. Here are Tigris and Euphrates. Lo there Afric. Here is the mountain of the Moon,—yonder thou mayst perceive the fenny march of Nilus. On this side lieth Europe. Dost thou not see the Abbey of Theleme? This little tuft, which is altogether white, is the Hyperborean Hills By the thirst of my thropple, friend, when snow is on the mountains, I say the head and chin, there is not then any considerable heat to be expected in the valleys and low coun tries of the codpiece. By the kibes of thy heels, quot Panurge, thou dost not understand the topics. When snow i on the tops of the hills, lightning, thunder, tempest, whirl winds, storms, hurricanes, and all the devils of hell rage i the valleys. Wouldst thou see the experience thereof, go t the territory of the Switzers and earnestly perpend with thy

elf there the situation of the lake of Wunderberlich, about
our leagues distant from Berne, on the Syon-side of the land.
Thou twittest me with my grey hairs, yet considerest not how
am of the nature of leeks, which with a white head carry a
green, fresh, straight and vigorous tail. The truth is, nevertheless (why should I deny it), that I now and then discern
in myself some indicative signs of old age. Tell this, I prithee,
to nobody, but let it be kept very close and secret betwixt us
two; for I find the wine much sweeter now, more savoury to
my taste, and unto my palate of a better relish than formerly
was wont to do; and withal, besides mine accustomed manner, I have a more dreadful apprehension than I ever heretofore have had of lighting on bad wine. Note and observe that
this doth argue and portend I know not what of the west and
occident of my time, and signifieth that the south and
meridian of mine age is past. But what then, my gentle companion? That doth but betoken that I will hereafter drink so
much the more. That is not, the devil hale it, the thing that
fear; nor is there where my shoe pinches. The thing that I
doubt most, and have greatest reason to dread and suspect is,
that through some long absence of our King Pantagruel (to
whom I must needs bear company should he go to all the
devils of Barathrum), my future wife shall make me a
cuckold. This is, in truth, the long and short on't. For I am
by all those whom I have spoke to menaced and threatened
with a horned fortune, and all of them affirm it is the lot to
which from heaven I am predestinated. Everyone, answered
Friar John, that would be a cuckold is not one. If it be thy
fate to be hereafter of the number of that horned cattle, then
may I conclude with an Ergo, thy wife will be beautiful, and
Ergo, thou wilt be kindly used by her. Likewise with this
Ergo, thou shalt be blessed with the fruition of many friends
and well-willers. And finally with this other Ergo, thou shalt

be saved and have a place in Paradise. These are monacha
topics and maxims of the cloister. Thou mayst take mor
liberty to sin. Thou shalt be more at ease than ever. Ther
will be never the less left for thee, nothing diminished, bu
thy goods shall increase notably. And if so be, it was pre
ordinated for thee, wouldst thou be so impious as not t
acquiesce in thy destiny? Speak, thou jaded cod.

Faded C.	Louting C.	Appellant C.
Mouldy C.	Discouraged C.	Swagging C.
Musty C.	Surfeited C.	Withered C.
Paltry C.	Peevish C.	Broken-reined C.
Senseless C.	Translated C.	Defective C.
Foundered C.	Forlorn C.	Crestfallen C.
Distempered C.	Unsavoury C.	Felled C.
Bewrayed C.	Worm-eaten C.	Fleeted C.
Inveigled C.	Overtoiled C.	Cloyed C.
Dangling C.	Miserable C.	Squeezed C.
Stupid C.	Steeped C.	Resty C.
Seedless C.	Kneaded-with-cold-	Pounded C.
Soaked C.	water C.	Loose C.
Coldish C.	Hacked C.	Fruitless C.
Pickled C.	Flaggy C.	Riven C.
Churned C.	Scrubby C.	Pursy C.
Filliped C.	Drained C.	Fusty C.
Singlefied C.	Haled C.	Jadish C.
Begrimed C.	Lolling C.	Fistulous C.
Wrinkled C.	Drenched C.	Languishing C.
Fainted C.	Burst C.	Maleficiated C.
Extenuated C.	Stirred up C.	Hectic C.
Grim C.	Mitred C.	Worn out C.
Wasted C.	Peddlingly fur-	Ill-favoured C.
Inflamed C.	nished C.	Duncified C.

Unhinged C.
Scurfy C.
Straddling C.
Putrefied C.
Maimed C.
Overlechered C.
Druggely C.
Titified C.
Goat-ridden C.
Weakened C.
Ass-ridden C.
Puff-pasted C.
St. Anthonified C.
Untriped C.
Blasted C.
Cut off C.
Beveraged C.
Scarified C.
Washed C.
Mashed C.
Infeebled C.
Whore-hunting C.
Deteriorated C.
Chill C.
Scrupulous C.
Crazed C.
Tasteless C.
Sorrowful C.
Murdered C.
Matachin-like C.
Best-toed C.
Customerless C.
Minced C.

Rusty C.
Exhausted C.
Perplexed C.
Unhelved C.
Fizzled C.
Leprous C.
Bruised C.
Spadonic C.
Boughty C.
Mealy C.
Wrangling C.
Gangrened C.
Crust-risen C.
Ragged C.
Quelled C.
Braggadocio C.
Beggarly C.
Trepanned C.
Bedusked C.
Emasculated C.
Corked C.
Transparent C.
Vile C.
Antedated C.
Chopped C.
Pinked C.
Cup-glassified C.
Harsh C.
Beaten C.
Barred C.
Abandoned C.
Confounded C.
Loutish C.

Macerated C.
Paralytic C.
Degraded C.
Benumbed C.
Bat-like C.
Fart-shotten C.
Sunburnt C.
Pacified C.
Blunted C.
Rankling tasted C.
Rooted out C.
Costive C.
Hailed-on C.
Cuffed C.
Buffeted C.
Whirreted C.
Robbed C.
Neglected C.
Lame C.
Confused C.
Unsavoury C.
Overthrown C.
Boulted C.
Trod under C.
Desolate C.
Declining C.
Stinking C.
Crooked C.
Brabbling C.
Rotten C.
Anxious C.
Clouted C.
Tired C.

Exulcerated C.
Patched C.
Stupified C.
Annihilated C.
Spent C.
Foiled C.
Anguished C.
Disfigured C.
Disabled C.
Forceless C.
Censured C.
Cut C.
Rifled C.
Undone C.
Corrected C.
Slit C.
Skittish C.
Spongy C.
Botched C.
Dejected C.
Jagged C.
Pining C.
Deformed C.
Mischieved C.
Cobbled C.
Embased C.
Ransacked C.
Despised C.
Mangy C.
Abased C.
Supine C.
Mended C.
Dismayed C.

Borne down C.
Sparred C.
Abashed C.
Unseasonable C.
Oppressed C.
Grated C.
Falling away C.
Smallcut C.
Disordered C.
Latticed C.
Ruined C.
Exasperated C.
Rejected C.
Belammed C.
Fabricitant C.
Perused C.
Emasculated C.
Roughly handled C.
Examined C.
Cracked C.
Wayward C.
Haggled C.
Gleaning C.
Ill-favoured C.
Pulled C.
Drooping C.
Faint C.
Parched C.
Paltry C.
Cankered C.
Void C.
Vexed C.
Bestunk C.

Proud C.
Fractured C.
Melancholy C.
Coxcombly C.
Base C.
Bleaked C.
Detested C.
Diaphanous C.
Unworthy C.
Checked C.
Mangled C.
Turned over C.
Harried C.
Flawed C.
Froward C.
Ugly C.
Drawn C.
Riven C.
Distasteful C.
Hanging C.
Broken C.
Limber C.
Effeminate C.
Kindled C.
Evacuated C.
Grieved C.
Carking C.
Disorderly C.
Empty C.
Disquieted C.
Besysted C.
Confounded C.
Hooked C.

Divorous C.   Winnowed C.   Unlucky C.
Wearied C.   Decayed C.   Sterile C.
Sad C.   Disastrous C.   Beshitten C.
Cross C.   Unhandsome C.   Appeased C.
Vain-glorious C.   Stummed C.   Caitiff C.
Poor C.   Barren C.   Woeful C.
Brown C.   Wretched C.   Unseemly C.
Shrunken C.   Feeble C.   Heavy C.
Abhorred C.   Cast down C.   Weak C.
Troubled C.   Stopped C.   Prostrated C.
Scornful C.   Kept under C.   Uncomely C.
Dishonest C.   Stubborn C.   Naughty C.
Reproved C.   Ground C.   Laid flat C.
Cocketed C.   Retchless C.   Suffocated C.
Filthy C.   Weather-beaten C.   Held down C.
Shred C.   Flayed C.   Barked C.
Chawned C.   Bald C.   Hairless C.
Short-winded C.   Tossed C.   Flamping C.
Branchless C.   Flapping C.   Hooded C.
Chapped C.   Cleft C.   Wormy C.
Failing C.   Meagre C.   Besysted* C.
Deficient C.   Dumpified C.   Faulty C.
Lean C.   Suppressed C.   Bemealed C.
Consumed C.   Hagged C.   Mortified C.
Used C.   Jawped C.   Scurvy C.
Puzzled C.   Havocked C.   Bescabbed C.
Allayed C.   Astonished C.   Torn C.
Spoiled C.   Dulled C.   Subdued C.
Clagged C.   Slow C.   Sneaking C.
Palsy-stricken C.   Plucked up C.   Bare C.
Amazed C.   Constipated C.   Swart C.

* In his anxiety to swell his catalogue as much as possible Sir Thomas Urquhart has set down this word twice.

Bedunsed C.

Extirpated C.

Banged C.

Stripped C.

Hoary C.

Blotted C.

Sunk in C.

Ghastly C.

Unpointed C.

Beblistered C.

Wizened C.

Beggar-plated C.

Douf C.

Clarty C.

Lumpish C.

Abject C.

Side C.

Choked up C.

Backward C.

Prolix C.

Spotted C.

Crumpled C.

Frumpled C.

Blown C.

Blockified C.

Pommelled C.

All-to-bemauled C.

Fallen away C.

Stale C.

Corrupted C.

Beflowered C.

Amated C.

Blackish C.

Underlaid C.

Loathing C.

Ill-filled C.

Bobbed C.

Mated C.

Tawny C.

Whealed C.

Besmeared C.

Hollow C.

Pantless C.

Guizened C.

Demiss C.

Refractory C.

Smutched C.

Raised up C.

Chopped C.

Flirted C.

Blained C.

Rensy C.

Frowning C.

Limping C.

Ravelled C.

Rammish C.

Gaunt C.

Beskimmered C.

Scraggy C.

Lank C.

Swashering C.

Moiling C.

Swinking C.

Harried C.

Tugged C.

Towed C.

Misused C.

Adamitical C.

CHAPTER 28

HOW PANTAGRUEL CONVOCATED TOGETHER A THEOLOGIAN
PHYSICIAN, LAWYER AND PHILOSOPHER, FOR EXTRICAT-
ING PANURGE OUT OF THE PERPLEXITY WHEREIN HE
WAS

No sooner were they come into the royal palace, but they
to the full made report unto Pantagruel of the success of
their expedition, and showed him the response of Ramina
grobis. When Pantagruel had read it over and over again

the oftener he perused it being the better pleased therewith, he said, in addressing his speech to Panurge, I have not as yet seen any answer framed to your demand which affordeth me more contentment. For in this his succinct copy of verses, he summarily and briefly, yet fully enough expresseth how he would have us to understand that everyone in the project and enterprise of marriage ought to be his own carver, sole arbitrator of his proper thoughts, and from himself alone take counsel in the main and peremptory closure of what his determination should be, in either his assent to or dissent from it. Such always hath been my opinion to you, and when at first you spoke thereof to me I truly told you this same very thing; but tacitly you scorned my advice, and would not harbour it within your mind. I know for certain, and therefore may I with the greater confidence utter my conception of it, that philauty, or self-love, is that which blinds your judgment and deceiveth you.

Let us do otherwise, and that is this: Whatever we are, or have, consisteth in three things—the soul, the body, and the goods. Now, for the preservation of these three, there are three sorts of learned men ordained, each respectively to have care of that one which is recommended to his charge. Theologues are appointed for the soul, physicians for the welfare of the body, and lawyers for the safety of our goods. Hence it is that it is my resolution to have on Sunday next with me at dinner a divine, a physician, and a lawyer, that with those three assembled thus together we may in every point and particle confer at large of your perplexity. By Saint Picot, answered Panurge, we never shall do any good that way, I see it already. And you see yourself how the world is vilely abused, as when with a foxtail one claps another's breech to cajole him. We give our souls to keep to the theologues, who for the greater part are heretics. Our bodies we commit to the physicians, who never themselves take any physic. And then we entrust our goods to the lawyers, who never go to law against one another. You speak like a courtier, quoth Pantagruel. But the first point of your assertion is to be denied; for we daily see how good theologues make it their chief business, their whole and sole employment, by their deeds, their words, and writings, to extirpate errors and heresies out of the hearts of men, and in their stead profoundly plant the true and lively faith. The second point you spoke of I commend; for, whereas the professors of the art of medicine give so good order to the prophylactic, or conservative part of their faculty, in what concerneth their proper healths, that they stand in no need of making use of the other branch, which is the curative or therapeutic, by medicaments. As for the third, I grant it to be true, for learned advocates and counsellors at law are so much taken up with the affairs of others in their consultations, pleadings, and such-like patrocinations of those who are their clients, that they have no leisure to attend any controversies of their own. Therefore, on the next ensuing Sunday, let the divine be our godly Father Hippothadee, the physician our honest Master Rondibilis, and our legist our friend Bridlegoose. Nor will it be (to my thinking) amiss that we enter into the Pythagoric field, and choose for an assistant to the three aforenamed doctors our ancient faithful acquaintance, the philosopher Trouillogan; especially seeing a perfect philosopher, such as is Trouillogan, is able positively to resolve all whatsoever doubts you can propose. Carpalin, have you a care to have them here all four on Sunday next at dinner, without fail.

I believe, quoth Epistemon, that throughout the whole country, in all the corners thereof, you could not have pitched upon such other four. Which I speak not so much in

regard to the most excellent qualifications and accomplishments wherewith all of them are endowed for the respective
discharge and management of each his own vocation and
calling (wherein without all doubt or controversy they are
the paragons of the land, and surpass all others), as for that
Rondibilis is married now, who before was not,—Hippothadee was not before, nor is yet,—Bridlegoose was married
once, but is not now,—and Trouillogan is married now, who
wedded was to another wife before. Sir, if it may stand
with your good liking, I will ease Carpalin of some parcel
of his labour, and invite Bridlegoose myself, with whom I
of a long time have had a very intimate familiarity, and unto
whom I am to speak on behalf of a pretty hopeful youth who
now studieth at Toulouse, under the most learned virtuous
doctor Boissonet. Do what you deem most expedient, quoth
Pantagruel, and tell me if my recommendation can in anything be steadable for the promoval of the good of that
youth, or otherwise serve for bettering of the dignity and
office of the worthy Boissonet, whom I do so love and respect for one of the ablest and most sufficient in his way
that anywhere are extant. Sir, I will use therein my best
endeavours, and heartily bestir myself about it.

CHAPTER 29

HOW THE THEOLOGUE, HIPPOTHADEE, GIVETH COUNSEL TO PANURGE IN THE MATTER AND BUSINESS OF HIS NUPTIAL ENTERPRISE

THE dinner on the subsequent Sunday was no sooner
made ready than that the afore-named invited guests gave
thereto their appearance, all of them, Bridlegoose only excepted, who was the deputy-governor of Fonsbeton. At the
ushering in of the second service Panurge, making a low

reverence, spake thus: Gentlemen, the question I am to pro
pound unto you shall be uttered in very few words—Should
I marry or no? If my doubt herein be not resolved by you
I shall hold it altogether insolvable, as are the *Insolubilia de
Aliaco;* for all of you are elected, chosen, and culled ou
from amongst others, everyone in his own condition and
quality, like so many picked peas on a carpet.

The Father Hippothadee, in obedience to the bidding o
Pantagruel, and with much courtesy to the company, an
swered exceeding modestly after this manner: My friend
you are pleased to ask counsel of us; but first you mus
consult with yourself. Do you find any trouble or disquie
in your body by the importunate stings and pricklings o
the flesh? That I do, quoth Panurge, in a hugely strong and
almost irresistible measure. Be not offended, I beseech you
good father, at the freedom of my expression. No truly
friend, not I, quoth Hippothadee, there is no reason I should
be displeased therewith. But in this carnal strife and debate
of yours have you obtained from God the gift and special
grace of continency? In good faith, not, quoth Panurge. My
counsel to you in that case, my friend, is that you marry
quoth Hippothadee; for you should rather choose to marry
once than to burn still in fires of concupiscence. Then Panurge, with a jovial heart and a loud voice, cried out, That
is spoke gallantly, without circumbilivaginating about and
about, and never hitting it in its centred point. Gramercy
my good father! In truth I am resolved now to marry, and
without fail I shall do it quickly. I invite you to my wedding. By the body of a hen, we shall make good cheer, and
be as merry as crickets. You shall wear the bridegroom's
colours, and, if we eat a goose, my wife shall not roast it for
me. I will entreat you to lead up the first dance of the
bridesmaids, if it may please you to do me so much favour

and honour. There resteth yet a small difficulty, a little scruple, yea, even less than nothing, whereof I humbly crave your resolution. Shall I be a cuckold, father, yea or no? By no means, answered Hippothadee, will you be cuckolded, if it please God. O the Lord help us now, quoth Panurge; whither are we driven to, good folks? To the conditionals, which, according to the rules and precepts of the dialectic faculty, admit of all contradictions and impossibilities. If my Transalpine mule had wings, my Transalpine mule would fly. If it please God, I shall not be a cuckold; but I shall be a cuckold, if it please him. Good God, if this were a condition which I knew how to prevent, my hopes should be as high as ever, nor would I despair. But you here send me to God's privy council, to the closet of his little pleasures. You, my French countrymen, which is the way you take to go thither?

My honest father, I believe it will be your best not to come to my wedding. The clutter and dingle-dangle noise of marriage guests will but disturb you, and break the serious fancies of your brain. You love repose, with solitude and silence; I really believe you will not come. And then you dance but indifferently, and would be out of countenance at the first entry. I will send you some good things to your chamber, together with the bride's favour, and there you may drink our health, if it may stand with your good liking. My friend, quoth Hippothadee, take my words in the sense wherein I meant them, and do not misinterpret me. When I tell you,—If it please God,—do I to you any wrong therein? Is it an ill expression? Is it a blaspheming clause or reserve any way scandalous unto the world? Do not we thereby honour the Lord God Almighty, Creator, Protector, and Conserver of all things? Is not that a mean whereby we do acknowledge him to be the sole giver of all whatsoever is

good? Do not we in that manifest our faith that we believe
all things to depend upon his infinite and incomprehensible
bounty, and that without him nothing can be produced, nor
after its production be of any value, force, or power, without
the concurring aid and favour of his assisting grace? Is it
not a canonical and authentic exception, worthy to be prem-
ised to all our undertakings? Is it not expedient that what
we propose unto ourselves be still referred to what shall
be disposed of by the sacred will of God, unto which all
things must acquiesce in the heavens as well as on the earth?
Is not that verily a sanctifying of his holy name? My friend
you shall not be a cuckold, if it please God, nor shall we
need to despair of the knowledge of his good will and pleasure herein, as if it were such an abstruse and mysteriously
hidden secret that for the clear understanding thereof it were
necessary to consult with those of his celestial privy council
or expressly make a voyage into the empyrean chamber
where order is given for the effectuating of his most holy
pleasures. The great God hath done us this good, that he
hath declared and revealed them to us openly and plainly
and described them in the Holy Bible. There will you find
that you shall never be a cuckold, that is to say, your wife
shall never be a strumpet, if you make choice of one of a
commendable extraction, descended of honest parents, and
instructed in all piety and virtue—such a one as hath not
at any time haunted or frequented the company or conversation of those that are of corrupt and depraved manners,
one loving and fearing God, who taketh a singular delight
in drawing near to him by faith and the cordial observing
of his sacred commandments—and finally, one who, standing in awe of the Divine Majesty of the Most High, will be
loth to offend him and lose the favourable kindness of his
grace through any defect of faith or transgression against

the ordinances of his holy law, wherein adultery is most rigorously forbidden and a close adherence to her husband alone most strictly and severely enjoined; yea, in such sort that she is to cherish, serve, and love him above anything, next to God, that meriteth to be beloved. In the interim, for the better schooling of her in these instructions, and that the wholesome doctrine of a matrimonial duty may take the deeper root in her mind, you must needs carry yourself so on your part, and your behaviour is to be such, that you are to go before her in a good example, by entertaining her unfeignedly with a conjugal amity, by continually approving yourself in all your words and actions a faithful and discreet husband; and by living, not only at home and privately with your own household and family, but in the face also of all men and open view of the world, devoutly, virtuously, and chastely, as you would have her on her side deport and to demean herself towards you, as becomes a godly, loyal, and respectful wife, who maketh conscience to keep inviolable the tie of a matrimonial oath. For as that looking-glass is not the best which is most decked with gold and precious stones, but that which representeth to the eye the liveliest shapes of objects set before it, even so that wife should not be most esteemed who richest is and of the noblest race, but she who, fearing God, conforms herself nearest unto the humour of her husband.

Consider how the moon doth not borrow her light from Jupiter, Mars, Mercury, or any other of the planets, nor yet from any of those splendid stars which are set in the spangled firmament, but from her husband only, the bright sun, which she receiveth from him more or less, according to the manner of his aspect and variously bestowed eradiations. Just so should you be a pattern to your wife in virtue, goodly zeal, and true devotion, that by your radiance in darting on her the aspect of an exemplary goodness, she, in your imitation, may outshine the luminaries of all other women. To this effect you daily must implore God's grace to the protection of you both. You would have me then, quoth Panurge, twisting the whiskers of his beard on either side with the thumb and forefinger of his left hand, to espouse and take to wife the prudent frugal woman described by Solomon. Without all doubt she is dead and truly to my best remembrance I never saw her; the Lord forgive me! Nevertheless, I thank you, father. Eat this slice of marchpane, it will help your digestion; then shall you be presented with a cup of claret hippocras, which is right healthful and stomachal. Let us proceed.

CHAPTER 30

HOW THE PHYSICIAN RONDIBILIS COUNSELLETH PANURGE

PANURGE, continuing his discourse, said, The first word which was spoken by him who gelded the lubberly, quaffing monks of Saussiniac, after that he had unstoned Friar Cauldaureil, was this, To the rest. In like manner, I say, To the rest. Therefore I beseech you, my good Master Rondibilis, should I marry or not? By the raking pace of my mule, quoth Rondibilis, I know not what answer to make to this problem of yours.

You say you feel in you the pricking stings of sensuality by which you are stirred up to venery. I find in our faculty of medicine, and we have founded our opinion therein upon the deliberate resolution and final decision of the ancient Platonics, that carnal concupiscence is cooled and quelled five several ways.

First, By the means of wine. I shall easily believe that quoth Friar John, for when I am well whittled with the juice of the grape I care for nothing else, so I may sleep. When I say, quoth Rondibilis, that wine abateth lust, my meaning is, wine immoderately taken, for by intemperancy proceeding from the excessive drinking of strong liquor there is brought upon the body of such a swill-down boozer a chillness of the blood, a slackening of the sinews, a dissipation of the generative seed, a numbness and hebetation of the senses, with a perversive wryness and convulsion of the muscles—all which are great lets and impediments to the act of generation. Hence it is that Bacchus, the god of bibbers, tipplers, and drunkards, is most commonly painted beardless and clad in a woman's habit, as a person altogether effeminate, or like a libbed eunuch. Wine, nevertheless, taken moderately, worketh quite contrary effects, as is implied by the old proverb, which saith that Venus takes cold when not accompanied with Ceres and Bacchus. The opinion is of great antiquity as appeareth by the testimony of Diodorus the Sicilian, and confirmed by Pausanias, and universally held amongst the Lampsacians, that Don Priapus was the son of Bacchus and Venus.

Secondly, The fervency of lust is abated by certain drugs, plants, herbs, and roots, which make the taker cold, maleficiated, unfit for, and unable to perform the act of generation; as hath been often experimented in the water-lily, heraclea, agnus castus, willow-twigs, hemp-stalks, woodbine, honeysuckle, tamarisk, chaste tree, mandrake, bennet, keckbugloss, the skin of a hippopotam, and many other such. We have nevertheless of those ingredients which, being of a contrary operation, heat the blood, bend the nerves, unite the spirits, quicken the senses, strengthen the muscles, and thereby rouse up, provoke, excite, and enable a man to the vigorous accomplishment of the feat of amorous dalliance. I have no need of those, quoth Panurge, God be thanked, and you, my good master. Howsoever, I pray you, take no exception at these my words; for what I have said was not from any illwill I did bear to you, the Lord he knows.

Thirdly, The ardour of lechery is very much subdued and mated by frequent labour and continual toiling. For by painful exercises and laborious working so great a dissolution is brought upon the whole body, that the blood, which runneth alongst the channels of the veins thereof for the nourishment and alimentation of each of its members, hath neither time, leisure, nor power to afford the seminal resudation, or superfluity of the third concoction, which nature most carefully reserves for the conservation of the individual, whose preservation she more heedfully regardeth than the propagation of the species and the multiplication of human-kind. Whence it is that Diana is said to be chaste, because she is never idle, but always busied about her hunting. For the same reason was a camp or leaguer of old called castrum, as if they would have said castum; because the soldiers, wrestlers, runners, throwers of the bar, and other such-like athletic champions as are usually seen in a military circumvallation, do incessantly travail and turmoil, and are in a perpetual stir and agitation. To this purpose Hippocrates also writeth in his book, *De Aere, Aqua et Locis,* that in his time there were people in Scythia as impotent as eunuchs in the discharge of a venerean exploit, because that without any cessation, pause, or respite they were never from off horse-back, or otherwise assiduously employed in some troublesome and molesting drudgery.

On the other part, in opposition and repugnancy hereto, the philosophers say that idleness is the mother of luxury. When it was asked Ovid, Why Ægisthus became an adulterer? he made no other answer but this, Because he was idle. Who were able to rid the world of loitering and laziness might easily frustrate and disappoint Cupid of all his designs, aims, engines, and devices, and so disable and appall him that his bow, quiver, and darts should from henceforth be a mere needless load and burden to him, for that it could not then lie in his power to strike or wound any of either sex with all the arms he had. He is not, I believe, so expert an archer as that he can hit the cranes flying in the air, or yet the young stags skipping through the thickets, as the Parthians knew well how to do; that is to say, people toiling, stirring, and hurrying up and down, restless, and without repose. He must have those hushed, still, quiet, lying at a stay, lither, and full of ease, whom he is able, though his mother help him, to touch, much less to pierce with all his arrows. In confirmation hereof, Theophrastus, being asked on a time what kind of beast or thing he judged a toyish, wanton love to be? he made answer, that it was a passion of idle and sluggish spirits. From which pretty description of tickling love-tricks that of Diogenes's hatching was not very discrepant, when he defined lechery the occupation of folks destitute of all other occupation. For this cause the Syconian engraver Canachus, being desirous to give us to understand that sloth, drowsiness, negligence, and laziness were the prime guardians and governesses of ribaldry, made the statue of Venus, not standing, as other stone-cutters had used to do, but sitting.

Fourthly, The tickling pricks of incontinency are blunted by an eager study; for from thence proceedeth an incredible resolution of the spirits, that oftentimes there do not remain so many behind as may suffice to push and thrust forward the generative resudation to the places thereto appropriated, and therewithal inflate the cavernous nerve whose office is to ejaculate the moisture for the propagation of human progeny. Lest you should think it is not so, be pleased but to contemplate a little the form, fashion, and carriage of a man exceeding earnestly set upon some learned meditation, and deeply plunged therein, and you shall see how all the arteries of his brains are stretched forth and bent like the string of a crossbow, the more promptly, dexterously, and copiously to suppeditate, furnish, and supply him with store of spirits sufficient to replenish and fill up the ventricles, seats, tunnels, mansions, receptacles, and cellules of the common sense,—of the imagination, apprehension and fancy, —of the ratiocination, arguing, and resolution,—as likewise of the memory, recordation, and remembrance; and with great alacrity, nimbleness, and agility to run, pass, and course from one to the other, through those pipes, windings, and conduits which to skilful anatomists are perceivable at the end of the wonderful net where all the arteries close in a terminating point; which arteries, taking their rise and origin from the left capsule of the heart, bring through several circuits, ambages, and anfractuosities, the vital, to subtilize and refine them to the ethereal purity of animal spirits. Nay, in such a studiously musing person you may espy so extravagant raptures of one as it were out of himself, that all his natural faculties for that time will seem to be suspended from each their proper charge and office, and his exterior senses to be at a stand. In a word, you cannot otherwise choose than think that he is by an extraordinary ecstasy quite transported out of what he was, or should be; and that Socrates did not speak improperly when he said that philosophy was nothing else but a meditation upon death. This possibly is the reason why Democritus deprived himself of the sense of seeing, prizing at a much lower rate the loss of his sight than the diminution of his contemplations, which he frequently had found disturbed by the vagrant, flying-out strayings of his unsettled and roving eyes.

Therefore is it that Pallas, the goddess of wisdom, tutoress and guardianess of such as are diligently studious and painfully industrious, is, and hath been still accounted a virgin. The Muses upon the same consideration are esteemed perpetual maids; and the Graces for the like reason, have been held to continue in a sempiternal pudicity.

I remember to have read that Cupid, on a time being asked of his mother Venus why he did not assault and set upon the Muses, his answer was that he found them so fair, so sweet, so fine, so neat, so wise, so learned, so modest, so discreet, so courteous, so virtuous, and so continually busied and employed,—one in the speculation of the stars,—another in the supputation of numbers,—the third in the dimension of geometrical quantities,—the fourth in the composition of heroic poems,—the fifth in the jovial interludes of a comic strain,—the sixth in the stately gravity of a tragic vein,—the seventh in the melodious disposition of musical airs,—the eighth in the completest manner of writing histories and books on all sorts of subjects,—and the ninth in the mysteries, secrets, and curiosities of all sciences, faculties, disciplines, and arts whatsoever, whether liberal or mechanic,—that approaching near unto them he unbended his bow, shut his quiver, and extinguished his torch, through mere shame and fear that by mischance he might do them some hurt or prejudice. Which done, he thereafter put off the fillet wherewith his eyes were bound to look them in the face, and to hear their melody and poetic odes. There took he the greatest pleasure in the world, that many times he was transported with their beauty and pretty behaviour, and charmed asleep by the harmony; so far was he from assaulting them or interrupting their studies. Under this article may be comprised what Hippocrates wrote in the afore-cited treatise concerning the Scythians; as also that in a book of his entitled, Of Breeding and Production, where he hath affirmed all such men to be unfit for generation as have their parotid arteries cut—whose situation is beside the ears—for the reason given already when I was speaking of the resolution of the spirits and of that spiritual blood whereof the arteries are the sole and proper receptacles, and that likewise he doth maintain a large portion of the parastatic liquor to issue and descend from the brains and backbone.

Fifthly, By the too frequent reiteration of the act of venery. There did I wait for you, quoth Panurge, and shall willingly apply it to myself, whilst anyone that pleaseth, may, for me, make use of any of the four preceding. That is the very same thing, quoth Friar John, which Father Scyllino, Prior of Saint Victor at Marseilles, calleth by the name of maceration and taming of the flesh. I am of the same opinion,—and so was the hermit of Saint Radegonde, a little above Chinon; for, quoth he, the hermits of Thebaide can no more aptly or expediently macerate and bring down the pride of their bodies, daunt and mortify their lecherous sensuality, or depress and overcome the stubbornness and rebellion of the flesh, than by duffling and fanfreluching it five-and-twenty or thirty times a day. I see Panurge, quoth Rondibilis, neatly featured and proportioned in all the members of his body, of a good temperament in his humours, well-complexioned in his spirits, of a competent age, in an opportune time, and of a reasonably forward mind to be married. Truly, if he encounter with a wife of the like nature, temperament, and constitution, he may beget upon her children worthy of some transpontine monarchy; and the sooner he marry it will be the better for him, and the more conducible for his profit if he would see and have his children in his own time well provided for. Sir, my worthy master, quoth

Panurge, I will do it, do not you doubt thereof, and that quickly enough, I warrant you. Nevertheless, whilst you were busied in the uttering of your learned discourse, this flea which I have in mine ear hath tickled me more than ever. I retain you in the number of my festival guests, and promise you that we shall not want for mirth and good cheer enough, yea, over and above the ordinary rate. And, if it may please you, desire your wife to come along with you, together with her she-friends and neighbours—that is to be understood—and there shall be fair play.

CHAPTER 31

HOW RONDIBILIS DECLARETH CUCKOLDRY TO BE NATURALLY ONE OF THE APPENDANCES OF MARRIAGE

THERE remaineth as yet, quoth Panurge, going on in his discourse, one small scruple to be cleared. You have seen heretofore, I doubt not, in the Roman standards, *S. P. Q. R.*, Si, Peu, Que, Rien. Shall not I be a cuckold? By the haven of safety, cried out Rondibilis, what is this you ask of me? If you shall be a cuckold? My noble friend, I am married, and you are like to be so very speedily; therefore be pleased, from my experiment in the matter, to write in your brain with a steel pen this subsequent ditton. There is no married man who doth not run the hazard of being made a cuckold. Cuckoldry naturally attendeth marriage. The shadow doth not more naturally follow the body, than cuckoldry ensueth after marriage to place fair horns upon the husbands' heads.

And when you shall happen to hear any man pronounce these three words, He is married; if you then say he is, hath been, shall be, or may be a cuckold, you will not be accounted an unskilful artist in framing of true consequences. Tripes and bowels of all the devils, cries Panurge, what do you tell me? My dear friend, answered Rondibilis, as Hippocrates on a time was in the very nick of setting forwards from Lango to Polystilo to visit the philosopher Democritus, he wrote a familiar letter to his friend Dionysius, wherein he desired him that he would, during the interval of his absence, carry his wife to the house of her father and mother, who were an honourable couple and of good repute; because I would not have her at my home, said he, to make abode in solitude. Yet, notwithstanding this her residence beside her parents, do not fail, quoth he, with a most heedful care and circumspection to pry into her ways, and to espy what places she shall go to with her mother, and who those be that shall repair unto her. Not, quoth he, that I do mistrust her virtue, or that I seem to have any diffidence of her pudicity and chaste behaviour,—for of that I have frequently had good and real proofs,—but I must freely tell you, She is a woman. There lies the suspicion.

My worthy friend, the nature of women is set forth before our eyes and represented to us by the moon, in divers other things as well as in this, that they squat, skulk, constrain their inclinations, and, with all the cunning they can, dissemble and play the hypocrite in the sight and presence of their husbands; who come no sooner to be out of the way, but that forthwith they take their advantage, pass the time merrily, desist from all labour, frolic it, gad abroad, lay aside their counterfeit garb, and openly declare and manifest the interior of their dispositions, even as the moon, when she is in conjunction with the sun, is neither seen in the heavens nor on the earth, but in her opposition, when remotest from him, shineth in her greatest fulness, and wholly appeareth in her brightest splendour whilst it is night. Thus women are but women.

When I say womankind, I speak of a sex so frail, so variable, so changeable, so fickle, inconstant, and imperfect, that in my opinion Nature, under favour, nevertheless, of the prime honour and reverence which is due unto her, did in a manner mistake the road which she had traced formerly, and stray exceedingly from that excellence of providential judgment by the which she had created and formed all other things, when she built, framed, and made up the woman. And having thought upon it a hundred and five times, I know not what else to determine therein, save only that in the devising, hammering, forging, and composing of the woman she hath had a much tenderer regard, and by a great deal more respectful heed to the delightful consortship and sociable delectation of the man, than to the perfection and accomplishment of the individual womanishness or muliebrity. The divine philosopher Plato was doubtful in what rank of living creatures to place and collocate them, whether amongst the rational animals, by elevating them to an upper seat in the specifical classis of humanity, or with the irrational, by degrading them to a lower bench on the opposite side, of a brutal kind, and mere bestiality. For nature hath posited in a privy, secret, and intestine place of their bodies, a sort of member, by some not impertinently termed an animal, which is not to be found in men. Therein sometimes are engendered certain humours so saltish, brackish, clammy, sharp, nipping, tearing, prickling, and most eagerly tickling, that by their stinging acrimony, rending nitrosity, figging itch, wriggling mordicancy, and smarting salsitude, their whole body is shaken and ebrangled, their senses totally ravished and transported, the operations of their judgment and understanding utterly confounded and all disordinate passions and perturbations of the mind thoroughly and absolutely allowed, admitted, and approved of; yea, in such sort that if nature had not been so favourable unto them as to have sprinkled their forehead with a little tincture of bashfulness and modesty, you should see them in a so frantic mood run mad after lechery, and hie apace up and down with haste and lust, in quest of and to fix some chamber-standard in their Paphian ground, that never did the Prœtides, Mimallonides, nor Lyæan Thyades deport themselves in the time of their bacchanalian festivals more shamelessly, or with a so affronted and brazen-faced impudency; because this terrible animal is knit unto, and hath an union with all the chief and most principal parts of the body, as to anatomists is evident. Let it not here be thought strange that I should call it an animal, seeing therein I do no otherwise than follow and adhere to the doctrine of the academic and peripatetic philosophers. For if a proper motion be a certain mark and infallible token of the life and animation of the mover, as Aristotle writeth, and that any such thing as moveth of itself ought to be held animated and of a living nature, then assuredly Plato with very good reason did give it the denomination of an animal, for that he perceived and observed in it the proper and self-stirring motions of suffocation, precipitation, corrugation, and of indignation so extremely violent, that oftentimes by them is taken and removed from the woman all other sense and moving whatsoever, as if she were in a swounding lipothymy, benumbing syncope, epileptic, apoplectic palsy, and true resemblance of a pale-faced death.

Furthermore, in the said member there is a manifest discerning faculty of scents and odours very perceptible to women, who feel it fly from what is rank and unsavoury, and follow fragrant and aromatic smells. It is not unknown to me how Cl. Galen striveth with might and main to prove that these are not proper and particular notions proceeding intrinsically from the—thing itself, but accidentally and by chance. Nor hath it escaped my notice how others of that sect have laboured hardly, yea, to the utmost of their abilities, to demonstrate that it is not a sensitive discerning or perception in it of the difference of wafts and smells, but merely a various manner of virtue and efficacy passing forth and flowing from the diversity of odoriferous substances applied near unto it. Nevertheless, if you will studiously examine and seriously ponder and weigh in Critolaus's balance the strength of their reasons and arguments, you shall find that they, not only in this, but in several other matters also of the like nature, have spoken at random, and rather out of an ambitious envy to check and reprehend their betters than for any design to make inquiry into the solid truth.

I will not launch my little skiff any further into the wide ocean of this dispute, only will I tell you that the praise and commendation is not mean and slender which is due to those honest and good women who, living chastely and without blame, have the power and virtue to curb, range, and subdue that unbridled, heady, and wild animal to an obedient, submissive, and obsequious yielding unto reason. Therefore here will I make an end of my discourse thereon, when I shall have told you that the said animal being once satiated—if it be possible that it can be contented or satisfied—by that ailment which nature hath provided for it out of the epididymal storehouse of man, all its former and irregular and disordered motions are at an end, laid, and assuaged, all its vehement and unruly longings lulled, pacified, and quieted, and all the furious and raging lusts, appetites and desires thereof appeased, calmed, and extinguished. For this cause let it seem nothing strange unto you if we be in a perpetual danger of being cuckolds, that is to say, such of us as have not wherewithal fully to satisfy the appetite and expectation of that voracious animal. Odds fish! quoth Panurge, have you no preventive cure in all your medicinal art for hindering one's head to be horny-graffed at home whilst his feet are plodding abroad? Yes, that I have, my gallant friend, answered Rondibilis, and that which is a sovereign remedy, whereof I frequently make use myself; and, that you may the better relish, it is set down and written in the book of a most famous author, whose renown is of a standing of two thousand years. Hearken and take good heed. You are, quoth Panurge, by cocks-hobby, a right honest man, and I love you with all my heart. Eat a little of this quince-pie; it is very proper and convenient for the shutting up of the orifice of the ventricle of the stomach, because of a kind of astringent stypticity which is in that sort of fruit, and is helpful to the first concoction. But what? I think I speak Latin before clerks. Stay till I give you somewhat to drink out of this Nestorian goblet. Will you have another draught of white hippocras? Be not afraid of the squinzy, no. There is neither squinant, ginger, nor grains it in; only a little choice cinnamon, and some of the best refined sugar, with the delicious white wine of the growth of that vine which was set in the slips of the great sorbapple above the walnut-tree.

CHAPTER 32

HOW THE PHILOSOPHER TROUILLOGAN HANDLETH THE DIFFICULTY OF MARRIAGE

As this discourse was ended, Pantagruel said to the philosopher Trouillogan, Our loyal, honest, true, and trusty friend, the lamp from hand to hand is come to you. It falleth to your turn to give an answer: Should Panurge, pray you, marry, yea or no? He should do both, quoth Trouillogan. What say you? asked Panurge. That which you have heard, answered Trouillogan. What have I heard? replied Panurge. That which I have said, replied Trouillogan. Ha, ha, ha! are we come to that pass? quoth Panurge. Let it go nevertheless, I do not value it at a rush, seeing we can make no better of the game. But howsoever tell me, Should I marry or no? Neither the one nor the other, answered Trouillogan. The devil take me, quoth Panurge, if these odd answers do not make me dote, and may he snatch me presently away if I do understand you. Stay awhile until I fasten these spectacles of mine on this left ear, that I may hear you better. With this Pantagruel perceived at the door of the great hall, which was that day their dining-room, Gargantua's little dog, whose name was Kyne; for so was Toby's dog called, as is recorded. Then did he say to these who were there present, Our King is not far off,—let us all rise.

That word was scarcely sooner uttered, than that Gargantua with his royal presence graced that banqueting and stately hall. Each of the guests arose to do their king that reverence and duty which became them. After that Gargantua had most affably saluted all the gentlemen there present, he said, Good friends, I beg this favour of you, and therein you will very much oblige me, that you leave not the places where you sate nor quit the discourse you were upon. Let a chair be brought hither unto this end of the table, and reach me a cupful of the strongest and best wine you have, that I may drink to all the company. You are, in faith, all welcome, gentlemen. Now let me know what talk you were about. To this Pantagruel answered that at the beginning of the second service Panurge had proposed a problematic theme, to wit, whether he should marry, or not marry? that Father Hippothadee and Doctor Rondibilis had already despatched their resolutions thereupon; and that, just as his majesty was coming in, the faithful Trouillogan in the delivery of his opinion hath thus far proceeded, that when Panurge asked whether he ought to marry, yea or no? at first he made this answer, Both together.

When this same question was again propounded, his second
answer was, Neither the one nor the other. Panurge ex-
claimeth that those answers are full of repugnancies and contradictions, protesting that he understands them not, nor
what it is that can be meant by them. If I be not mistaken,
quoth Gargantua, I understand it very well. The answer is
not unlike to that which was once made by a philosopher in
ancient times, who being interrogated if he had a woman
whom they named him to his wife? I have her, quoth he, but
she hath not me,—possessing her, by her I am not possessed.
Such another answer, quoth Pantagruel, was once made by
a certain bouncing wench of Sparta, who being asked if at
any time she had had to do with a man? No, quoth she, but
sometimes men have had to do with me. Well then, quoth
Rondibilis, let it be a neuter in physic, as when we say a
body is neuter, when it is neither sick nor healthful, and a
mean in philosophy; that, by an abnegation of both extremes,
and this by the participation of the one and of the other.
Even as when lukewarm water is said to be both hot and
cold; or rather, as when time makes the partition, and equally
divides betwixt the two, a while in the one, another while as
long in the other opposite extremity. The holy Apostle, quoth
Hippothadee, seemeth, as I conceive, to have more clearly
explained this point when he said, Those that are married,
let them be as if they were not married; and those that have
wives, let them be as if they had no wives at all. I thus interpret, quoth Pantagruel, the having and not having of a wife.
To have a wife is to have the use of her in such a way as
nature hath ordained, which is for the aid, society, and solace
of man, and propagating of his race. To have no wife is not
to be uxorious, play the coward, and be lazy about her, and
not for her sake to disdain the lustre of that affection which
man owes to God, or yet for her to leave those offices and

duties which he owes unto his country, unto his friends and kindred, or for her to abandon and forsake his precious studies, and other businesses of account, to wait still on her will, her beck, and her buttocks. If we be pleased in this sense to take having and not having of a wife, we shall indeed find no repugnancy nor contradiction in the terms at all.

CHAPTER 33

A CONTINUATION OF THE ANSWER OF THE EPHECTIC AND PYRRHONIAN PHILOSOPHER TROUILLOGAN

You speak wisely, quoth Panurge, if the moon were green cheese. Such a tale once pissed my goose. I do not think but that I am let down into that dark pit in the lowermost bottom whereof the truth was hid, according to the saying of Heraclitus. I see no whit at all, I hear nothing, understand as little, my senses are altogether dulled and blunted; truly I do very shrewdly suspect that I am enchanted. I will now alter the former style of my discourse, and talk to him in another strain. Our trusty friend, stir not, nor imburse any; but let us vary the chance, and speak without disjunctives. I see already that these loose and ill-joined members of an enunciation do vex, trouble, and perplex you.

Now go on, in the name of God! Should I marry?

TROUILLOGAN.   There is some likelihood therein.

PANURGE.   But if I do not marry?

TROUIL.   I see in that no inconvenience.

PAN.   You do not?

TROUIL.   None, truly, if my eyes deceive me not.

PAN.   Yea, but I find more than five hundred.

TROUIL.   Reckon them.

PAN.   This is an impropriety of speech, I confess; for I do no more thereby but take a certain for an uncertain number, and posit the determinate term for what is indeterminate. When I say, therefore, five hundred, my meaning is many.

TROUIL.   I hear you.

PAN.   Is it possible for me to live without a wife, in the name of all the subterranean devils?

TROUIL.   Away with these filthy beasts.

PAN.   Let it be, then, in the name of God; for my Salmigondinish people use to say, To lie alone, without a wife, is certainly a brutish life. And such a life also was it assevered to be by Dido in her lamentations.

TROUIL.   At your command.

PAN.   By the pody cody, I have fished fair; where are we now? But will you tell me? Shall I marry?

TROUIL.   Perhaps.

PAN.   Shall I thrive and speed well withal?

TROUIL.   According to the encounter.

PAN.   But if in my adventure I encounter aright, as I hope I will, shall I be fortunate?

TROUIL.   Enough.

PAN.   Let us turn the clean contrary way, and brush our former words against the wool: what if I encounter ill?

TROUIL.   Then blame not me.

PAN.   But, of courtesy, be pleased to give me some advice. I heartily beseech you, what must I do?

TROUIL.   Even what thou wilt.

PAN.   Wishy, washy; trolly, trolly.

TROUIL.   Do not invocate the name of anything, I pray you.

PAN.   In the name of God, let it be so! My actions shall be regulated by the rule and square of your counsel. What is it that you advise and counsel me to do?

TROUIL.   Nothing.

PAN. Shall I marry?

TROUIL. I have no hand in it.

PAN. Then shall I not marry?

TROUIL. I cannot help it.

PAN. If I never marry, I shall never be a cuckold.

TROUIL. I thought so.

PAN. But put the case that I be married.

TROUIL. Where shall we put it?

PAN. Admit it to be so, then, and take my meaning in that sense.

TROUIL. I am otherwise employed.

PAN. By the death of a hog, and mother of a toad, O Lord! if I durst hazard upon a little fling at the swearing game, though privily and under thumb, it would lighten the burden of my heart and ease my lights and reins exceedingly. A little patience nevertheless is requisite. Well then, if I marry, I shall be a cuckold.

TROUIL. One would say so.

PAN. Yet if my wife prove a virtuous, wise, discreet, and chaste woman, I shall never be cuckolded.

TROUIL. I think you speak congruously.

PAN. Hearken.

TROUIL. As much as you will.

PAN. Will she be discreet and chaste? This is the only point I would be resolved in.

TROUIL. I question it.

PAN. You never saw her?

TROUIL. Not that I know of.

PAN. Why do you then doubt of that which you know not?

TROUIL. For a cause.

PAN. And if you should know her?

TROUIL. Yet more.

PAN. Page, my pretty little darling, take here my cap,— I give it thee. Have a care you do not break the spectacles that are in it. Go down to the lower court. Swear there half an hour for me, and I shall in compensation of that favour swear hereafter for thee as much as thou wilt. But who shall cuckold me?

TROUIL. Somebody.

PAN. By the belly of the wooden horse at Troy, Master Somebody, I shall bang, belam thee, and claw thee well for thy labour.

TROUIL. You say so.

PAN. Nay, nay, that Nick in the dark cellar, who hath no white in his eye, carry me quite away with him if, in that case, whensoever I go abroad from the palace of my domestic residence, I do not, with as much circumspection as they use to ring mares in our country to keep them from being sallied by stoned horses, clap a Bergamasco lock upon my wife.

TROUIL. Talk better.

PAN. It is *bien chien, chie chante,* well cacked and cackled, shitten, and sung in matter of talk. Let us resolve on somewhat.

TROUIL. I do not gainsay it.

PAN. Have a little patience. Seeing I cannot on this side draw any blood of you, I will try if with the lancet of my judgment I be able to bleed you in another vein. Are you married, or are you not?

TROUIL. Neither the one nor the other, and both together.

PAN. O the good God help us! By the death of a buffle-ox, I sweat with the toil and travail that I am put to, and find my digestion broke off, disturbed, and interrupted, for all my phrenes, metaphrenes, and diaphragms, back, belly, midriff, muscles, veins, and sinews are held in suspense and for a while discharged from their proper offices to stretch forth their several powers and abilities for incornifistibulating and laying up into the hamper of my understanding your various sayings and answers.

TROUIL. I shall be no hinderer thereof.

PAN. Tush, for shame! Our faithful friend, speak; are you married?

TROUIL. I think so.

PAN. You were also married before you had this wife?

TROUIL. It is possible.

PAN. Had you good luck in your first marriage?

TROUIL. It is not impossible.

PAN. How thrive you with this second wife of yours?

TROUIL. Even as it pleaseth my fatal destiny.

PAN. But what, in good earnest? Tell me—do you prosper well with her?

TROUIL. It is likely.

PAN. Come on, in the name of God. I vow, by the burden of Saint Christopher, that I had rather undertake the fetching of a fart forth of the belly of a dead ass than to draw out of you a positive and determinate resolution. Yet shall I be sure at this time to have a snatch at you, and get my claws over you. Our trusty friend, let us shame the devil of hell, and confess the verity. Were you ever a cuckold? I say, you who are here, and not that other you who playeth below in the tennis-court?

TROUIL. No, if it was not predestinated.

PAN. By the flesh, blood, and body, I swear, reswear, forswear, abjure, and renounce, he evades and avoids, shifts, and escapes me, and quite slips and winds himself out of my grips and clutches.

At these words Gargantua arose and said, Praised be the

good God in all things, but especially for bringing the world
into that height of refinedness beyond what it was when I
first came to be acquainted therewith, that now the learnedst
and most prudent philosophers are not ashamed to be seen
entering in at the porches and frontispieces of the schools
of the Pyrrhonian, Aporrhetic, Sceptic, and Ephectic sects.
Blessed be the holy name of God! Veritably, it is like henceforth to be found an enterprise of much more easy undertaking to catch lions by the neck, horses by the mane, oxen
by the horns, bulls by the muzzle, wolves by the tail, goats
by the beard, and flying birds by the feet, than to entrap
such philosophers in their words. Farewell, my worthy, dear,
and honest friends.

When he had done thus speaking, he withdrew himself
from the company. Pantagruel and others with him would
have followed and accompanied him, but he would not permit
them so to do. No sooner was Gargantua departed out of
the banqueting hall than that Pantagruel said to the invited
guests: Plato's Timæus, at the beginning always of a solemn
festival convention, was wont to count those that were called
thereto. We, on the contrary, shall at the closure and end
of this treatment reckon up our number. One, two, three;
where is the fourth? I miss my friend Bridlegoose. Was not
he sent for? Epistemon answered that he had been at his
house to bid and invite him, but could not meet with him;
for that a messenger from the parliament of Mirlingois, in
Mirlingues, was come to him with a writ of summons to cite
and warn him personally to appear before the reverend
senators of the high court there, to vindicate and justify
himself at the bar of the crime of prevarication laid to his
charge, and to be peremptorily instanced against him in a
certain decree, judgment, or sentence lately awarded, given,
and pronounced by him; and that, therefore, he had taken

horse and departed in great haste from his own house, to
the end that without peril or danger of falling into a default or contumacy he might be the better able to keep the
prefixed and appointed time.

I will, quoth Pantagruel, understand how that matter
goeth. It is now above forty years that he hath been con-
stantly the judge of Fonsbeton, during which space of time
he hath given four thousand definitive sentences, of two
thousand three hundred and nine whereof, although appeal
was made by the parties whom he had judicially condemned
from his inferior judicatory to the supreme court of the
parliament of Mirlingois, in Mirlingues, they were all of
them nevertheless confirmed, ratified, and approved of by
an order, decree, and final sentence of the said sovereign
court, to the casting of the appellants, and utter overthrow
of the suit, wherein they had been foiled at law, for ever
and a day. That now in his old age he should be personally
summoned, who in all the foregoing time of his life hath
demeaned himself so unblamably in the discharge of the
office and vocation he had been called unto, it cannot assuredly be that such a change hath happened without some
notorious misfortune and disaster. I am resolved to help and
assist him in equity and justice to the uttermost extent of
my power and ability. I know the malice, despite, and
wickedness of the world to be so much more nowadays exasperated, increased, and aggravated by what it was not
long since, that the best cause that is, how just and equitable
soever it be, standeth in great need to be succoured, aided,
and supported. Therefore, presently, from this very instant
forth, do I purpose, till I see the vent and closure thereof,
most heedfully to attend and wait upon it, for fear of some
underhand tricky surprisal, cavilling pettifoggery, or fallacious quirks in law, to his detriment, hurt, or disadvantage.

Then dinner being done, and the tables drawn and removed, when Pantagruel had very cordially and affectionately thanked his invited guests for the favour which he had enjoyed of their company, he presented them with several rich and costly gifts, such as jewels, rings set with precious stones, gold and silver vessels, with a great deal of other plate besides, and lastly, taking leave of all, retired himself to an inner chamber.

CHAPTER 34

HOW PANTAGRUEL WAS PRESENT AT THE TRIAL OF JUDGE BRIDLEGOOSE, WHO DECIDED CAUSES AND CONTROVERSIES IN LAW BY THE CHANCE AND FORTUNE OF THE DICE

On the day following, precisely at the hour appointed, Pantagruel came to Mirelingues. At his arrival the presidents, senators, and counsellors prayed him to do them the honour to enter in with them, to hear the decision of all the causes, arguments, and reasons which Bridlegoose in his own defence would produce, why he had pronounced a certain sentence against the subsidy-assessor, Toucheronde, which did not seem very equitable to that centumviral court. Pantagruel very willingly condescended to their desire, and accordingly entering in, found Bridlegoose sitting within the middle of an enclosure of the said court of justice; who immediately upon the coming of Pantagruel, accompanied with the senatorian members of that worshipful judicatory, arose, went to the bar, had his indictment read, and for all his reasons, defences, and excuses, answered nothing else but that he was become old, and that his sight of late was very much failed, and become dimmer than it was wont to be; instancing therewithal many miseries and calamities which old age bringeth along with it, and are concomitant to

wrinkled elders; which *not. per Archid. d. lxxxvi. c. tanta.*
By reason of which infirmity he was not able so clearly to
discern the points and blots of the dice as formerly he had
been accustomed to do; whence it might very well have
happened, said he, as old dim-sighted Isaac took Jacob for
Esau, that, after the same manner, at the decision of causes
and controversies in law, should have been mistaken in taking a quatre for a cinque, or a trey for a deuce. This I beseech
your worships, quoth he, to take into your serious consideration, and to have the more favourable opinion of my
uprightness, notwithstanding the prevarication whereof I
am accused in the matter of Toucheronde's sentence, that
at the time of that decree's pronouncing I only had made
use of my small dice; and your worships, said he, know very
well how by the most authentic rules of the law it is provided that the imperfections of nature should never be im-
puted unto any for crimes and transgressions; as appeareth,
ff. *de re milit. l. qui cum uno. ff. de reg. Jur. l. fere. ff. de*
œdil. edict. per totum. ff. de term. mod. l. Divus Adrianus,
resolved by *Lud. Rom. in l. si vero. ff. Sol. Matr.* And who
would offer to do otherwise, should not thereby accuse the
man, but nature, and the all-seeing providence of God, as is
evident in *l. Maximum Vitium, c. de lib. præter.*

What kind of dice, quoth Trinquamelle, grand-president of
the said court, do you mean, my friend Bridlegoose? The dice,
quoth Bridlegoose, of sentences at law, decrees and peremptory judgments, *Alea Judiciorum,* whereof is written, *Per*
Doct. 26. *qu.* 2. *cap sort. l. nec emptio ff. de contrahend. empt.*
l. quod debetur. ff. de pecul. et ibi Bartol., and which your
worships do, as well as I, use, in this glorious sovereign court
of yours. So do all other righteous judges in their decision of
processes and final determination of legal differences, observing that which hath been said thereof by D. Henri, Ferran-

dat, *et not. gl. in c. fin. de sortil. et l. sed cum ambo. ff. de jud. Ubi Docto.* Mark, that chance and fortune are good, honest, profitable, and necessary for ending of and putting a final closure to dissensions and debates in suits at law. The same hath more clearly been declared by Bald. Bartol. et Alex. c. *communia de leg. l. Si duo.* But how is it that you do these things? asked Trinquamelle. I very briefly, quoth Bridle-goose, shall answer you, according to the doctrine and instructions of *Leg. ampliorem §. in refutatoriis. c. de appel.;* which is conform to what is said in *Gloss. l. 1. ff. quod met. causa. Gaudent brevitate moderni.* My practice is therein the same with that of your other worships, and as the custom of the judicatory requires, unto which our law commandeth us to have regard, and by the rule thereof still to direct and regulate our actions and procedures; *ut not. extra. de consuet. in c. ex. litertis et ibi innoc.* For having well and exactly seen, surveyed, overlooked, reviewed, recognized, read, and read over again, turned and tossed over, seriously perused and examined the bills of complaint, accusations, impeachments, indictments, warnings, citations, summonings, comparitions, appearances, mandates, commissions, delegations, instructions, informations, inquests, preparatories, productions, evidences, proofs, allegations, depositions, cross speeches, contradictions, supplications, requests, petitions, inquiries, instruments of the deposition of witnesses, rejoinders, replies, confirmations of former assertions, duplies, triplies, answers to rejoinders, writings, deeds, reproaches, disabling of exceptions taken, grievances, salvation bills, re-examination of witnesses, confronting of them together, declarations, denunciations, libels, certificates, royal missives, letters of appeal, letters of attorney, instruments of compulsion, delineatories, anticipatories, evocations, messages, dimissions, issues, exceptions, dilatory pleas, demurs, compositions, injunctions reliefs, reports, returns, confessions, acknowledgements, exploits, executions, and other such-like confects and spiceries, both at the one and the other side, as a good judge ought to do, conform to what hath been noted thereupon. *Spec. de ordination. Paragr.* 3. *et Tit. de Offi. omn. jud. paragr. fin. et de rescriptis præsentat parag.* 1.—I posit on the end of a table in my closet all the pokes and bags of the defendant, and then allow unto him the first hazard of the dice according to the usual manner of your other worships. And it is mentioned, *l. favorabiliores. ff. de reg. jur. et in cap. cum sunt eod. tit. lib.* 6., which saith, *Quum sunt partium jura obscura, reo potius favendum est quam actori.* That being done, I thereafter lay down upon the other end of the same table the bags and satchels of the plaintiff, as your other worships are accustomed to do, *visum visu,* just over against one another; for *Opposita juxta se posita clarius elucescunt: ut not. in lib.* 1. *parag. Videamus. ff. de his qui sunt sui vel alieni juris, et in l. munerum.* § *mixta. ff. de mun. et hon.* Then do I likewise and semblably throw the dice for him, and forthwith livre him his chance. But, quoth Trinquamelle, my friend, how come you to know, understand, and resolve the obscurity of these various and seeming contrary passages in law, which are laid claim to by the suitors and pleading parties? Even just, quoth Bridlegoose, after the fashion of your other worships; to wit, when there are many bags on the one side and on the other, I then use my little small dice, after the customary manner of your other worships, in obedience to the law, *Semper in stipulationibus ff. de reg. jur.* And the law ver[s]ified versifieth that, *Eod. tit. Semper in obscuris quod minimum est sequimur;* canonized in *c. in obscuris. eod. tit. lib.* 6. I have other large great dice, fair and goodly ones, which I employ in the fashion that your other worships use to do, when the matter is more plain, clear, and liquid, that is to say, when there are fewer bags. But when you have done all these fine things, quoth Trinquamelle, how do you, my friend, award your decrees, and pronounce judgment? Even as your other worships, answered Bridlegoose; for I give out sentence in his favour unto whom hath befallen the best chance by dice, judiciary, tribunian, pretorial, what comes first. So our laws command, *ff. qui pot, in pign. l. creditor*, c. *de consul.* 1. *Et de regul. jur. in* 6. *Qui prior est tempore potior est jure.*

CHAPTER 35

HOW BRIDLEGOOSE GIVETH REASONS WHY HE LOOKED UPON THOSE LAW-ACTIONS WHICH HE DECIDED BY THE CHANCE OF THE DICE

YEA but, quoth Trinquamelle, my friend, seeing it is by the lot, chance, and throw of the dice that you award your judgments and sentences, why do not you livre up these fair throws and chances at the very same day and hour, without any further procrastination or delay, that the controverting party-pleaders appear before you? To what use can those writings serve you, those papers and other procedures contained in the bags and pokes of the law-suitors? To the very same use, quoth Bridlegoose, that they serve your other worships. They are behooveful unto me, and serve my turn in three things very exquisite, requisite, and authentical. First, for formality sake, the omission whereof, that it maketh all, whatever is done, to be of no force or value, is excellently well proved, by Spec. 1. *tit. de instr. edit. et tit. de rescript. præsent.* Besides that, it is not unknown to you, who have had many more experiments thereof than I, how oftentimes, in judicial proceedings, the formalities utterly destroy the materialities and substances of the causes and matters agitated; for *Forma mutata, mutatur substantia. ff.*

ad exhib. l. Julianus. ff. ad leg. Fal. l. si is qui quadraginta. Et extra de decim. c. ad, audientiam, et de celebrat. miss. c. in quadam.

Secondly they are useful and steadable to me, even as unto your other worships, in lieu of some other honest and healthful exercise The late Master Othoman Vadet [Vadere], a prime physician, as you would say, *Cod. de Comit. et Archi. lib.* 12, hath frequently told me that the lack and default of bodily exercise is the chief, if not the sole and only cause of the little health and short lives of all officers of justice, such as your worships and I am. Which observation was singularly well before him noted and remarked by Bartholus *in lib.* 1. *c. de sent. quæ pro eo quod.* Therefore is it that the practice of such-like exercitations is appointed to be laid hold on by your other worships, and consequently not to be denied unto me, who am of the same profession. *Quia accessorium naturam sequitur principalis. de reg. jur. l. 6. et l. cum principalis. et l. nihil dolo. ff. eod. tit. ff. de fide-juss. l. fide-juss. et extra de officio deleg. cap.* 1. Let certain honest and recreative sports and plays of corporeal exercises be allowed and approved of; and so far, [*ff. de allus. et aleat l. solent. et authent.*] *ut omnes obed. in princ. coll.* 7. *et ff. de præscript. verb. l. si gratuitam et l.* 1. *cod. de spect. l.* 11. Such also is the opinion of D. Thom. *in secunda, secundæ Q.* I. 168. Quoted in very good purpose by D. Albert de Rosa, who *fuit magnus practicus,* and a solemn doctor, as Barbatias attesteth in *principiis consil.* Wherefore the reason is evidently and clearly deduced and set down before us in *glos. in proœmio ff. par. ne autem tertii.*

Interpone tuis interdum gaudia curis.

In very deed, once, in the year a thousand four hundred fourscore and ninth, having business concerning the portion

and inheritance of a younger brother depending in the court
and chamber of the four high treasurers of France whereinto
as soon as ever I got leave to enter by a pecuniary permission
of the usher thereof,—as your other worships know very
well, that *Pecuniæ obediunt omnia,* and there says Baldus,
in *l. singularia. ff. si cert. pet. et Salic. in l. receptitia. Cod.
de constit. pecuni. et Card. in Clem. 1. de baptism.*—I found
them all recreating and diverting themselves at the play
called muss, either before or after dinner; to me, truly, it is
a thing altogether indifferent whether of the two it was,
provided that *hic not.,* that the game of the muss is honest,
healthful, ancient and lawful, *a Muscho inventore, de quo
cod. de petit. hæred. l. si post mortem. et Muscarii.* Such as
play and sport it at the muss are excusable in and by law,
lib. 1. c. de excus. artific. lib. 10. And at the very same time
was Master Tielman Picquet one of the players of that game
of muss. There is nothing that I do better remember for
he laughed heartily when his fellow members of the aforesaid judicial chamber spoiled their caps in swingeing of his
shoulders. He, nevertheless, did even then say unto them,
that the banging and flapping of him, to the waste and havoc
of their caps, should not, at their return from the palace to
their own houses, excuse them from their wives, *Per. c.
extra. de præsumpt. et ibi gloss.* Now, *resolutorie loquendo,*
I should say, according to the style and phrase of your other
worships, that there is no exercise, sport, game, play, nor
recreation in all this palatine, palatial, or parliamentary
world, more aromatizing and fragrant than to empty and
void bags and purses, turn over papers and writings, quote
margins and backs of scrolls and rolls, fill panniers, and take
inspection of causes, *Ex. Bart. et Joan. de Pra. in l. falsa. de
condit. et demonst. ff.*

Thirdly, I consider, as your own worships use to do, that

ime ripeneth and bringeth all things to maturity, that by
ime everything cometh to be made manifest and patent,
nd that time is the father of truth and virtue. *Gloss. in l.
. cod. de servit. authent. de restit. et ea quæ pa. et spec. tit.
'e requisit. cons.* Therefore is it that, after the manner and
ashion of your other worships, I defer, protract, delay,
prolong, intermit, surcease, pause, linger, suspend, prorogate,
drive out, wire-draw, and shift off the time of giving a
definitive sentence, to the end that the suit or process, being
well fanned and winnowed, tossed, and canvassed to and fro,
narrowly, precisely, and neatly garbled, sifted, searched, and
examined, and on all hands exactly argued, disputed, and
debated, may, by succession of time, come at last to its full
ripeness and maturity. By means whereof, when the fatal
hazard of the dice ensueth thereupon, the parties cast or
condemned by the said aleatory chance will with much
greater patience, and more mildly and gently, endure and
bear up the disastrous load of their misfortune, than if they
had been sentenced at their first arrival unto the court, as
ot. gl. ff. de excus. tut. l. tria. onera.

Portatur leviter quod portat quisque libenter.

On the other part, to pass a decree or sentence when the
action is raw, crude, green, unripe, and unprepared, as at
the beginning, a danger would ensue of a no less inconveniency than that which the physicians have been wont to
say befalleth to him in whom an imposthume is pierced
before it be ripe, or unto any other whose body is purged of
a strong predominating humour before its digestion. For as
t is written, *in authent. hæc constit. in Innoc. de constit.
princip.*, so is the same repeated *in gloss. in c. cæterum. extra.
de juram. calumn. Quod medicamenta morbis exhibent, hoc*

jura negotiis. Nature furthermore admonisheth and teacheth us to gather and reap, eat, and feed on fruits when they are ripe, and not before. *Instit. de rer. div. paragr. is ad quem. et ff. de action. empt. l. Julianus.* To marry likewise our daughters when they are ripe, and no sooner, *ff. de donation. inter vir. et uxor. l. cum hic status. paragr. si quis sponsam. et 27 qu. 1. c. sicut dicit. gl.*

> *Jam matura thoro plenis adoleverat annis*
> *Virginitas.*

And, in a word, she instructeth us to do nothing of any considerable importance, but in a full maturity and ripeness, 23, q. § *ult. et 23. de c. ultimo.*

CHAPTER 36

HOW BRIDLEGOOSE RELATETH THE HISTORY OF THE RECONCILERS OF PARTIES AT VARIANCE IN MATTERS OF LAW

I REMEMBER to the same purpose, quoth Bridlegoose, in continuing his discourse, that in the time when at Poictiers I was a student of law under Brocadium Juris, there was at Semerve one Peter Dandin, a very honest man, careful labourer of the ground, fine singer in a church-desk, of good repute and credit, and older than the most aged of all your worships; who was wont to say that he had seen the great and goodly good man, the Council of Lateran, with his wide and broad-brimmed red hat. As also, that he had beheld and looked upon the fair and beautiful Pragmatical Sanction his wife, with her huge rosary or patenotrian chaplet of jet beads hanging at a large sky-coloured ribbon. This honest man compounded, atoned, and agreed more differences, controversies, and variances at law than had been determined, voided, and finished during his time in the whole palace of Poictiers, in the auditory of Montmorillon, and in the town-house of the old Partenay. This amicable disposition of his rendered him venerable and of great estimation, sway, power, and authority throughout all the neighbouring places of Chauvigny, Nouaillé, Legugé, Vivonne, Mezeaux, Estables, and other bordering and circumjacent towns, villages, and hamlets. All their debates were pacified by him; he put an end to their brabbling suits at law and wrangling differences. By his advice and counsels were accords and reconcilements no less firmly made than if the verdict of a sovereign judge had been interposed therein, although, in very deed, he was no judge at all, but a right honest man, as you may well conceive,—*arg. in l. sed si unius. ff. de jure-jur. et de verbis obligatoriis l. continuus.* There was not a hog killed within three parishes of him whereof he had not some part of the haslet and puddings. He was almost every day invited either to a marriage banquet, christening feast, an uprising or woman-churching treatment, a birthday's anniversary solemnity, a merry frolic gossiping, or otherwise to some delicious entertainment in a tavern, to make some accord and agreement between persons at odds and in debate with one another. Remark what I say; for he never yet settled and compounded a difference betwixt any two at variance, but he straight made the parties agreed and pacified to drink together as a sure and infallible token and symbol of a perfect and completely well-cemented reconciliation, sign of sound and sincere amity and proper mark of a new joy and gladness to follow thereupon,—*Ut not, per [Doct.] ff. de peric. et com. rei vend. l.* 1. He had a son, whose name was Tenot Dandin, a lusty, young, sturdy, frisking roister, so help me God! who likewise, in imitation of his peace-making father, would have undertaken and meddled with the making up

of variances and deciding of controversies betwixt disagree
ing and contentious party-pleaders; as you know,

> *Sœpe solet similis filius esse patri.*
> *Et sequitur leviter filia matris iter.*

Ut ait gloss. 6. quœst. I. c. Si quis. gloss. de cons. dist. 5
c. 2. fin. et est. not. per Doct. cod. de impub. et aliis substit
l. ult. et l. legitime. ff. de stat. hom. gloss. in l. quod si noli
ff. de œdil. edict. l. quisquis c. ad leg. Jul. Majest. Excipi
filios a Moniali susceptos ex Monacho. per gloss. in c. im
pudicas. 27. *quœstione.* 1. And such was his confidence to
have no worse success than his father, he assumed unto him
self the title of Law-strife-settler. He was likewise in these
pacificatory negotiations so active and vigilant—for, *Vigi*
lantibus jura subveniunt. ex l. pupillus. ff. quœ in fraud. crea
et ibid. l. non enim. et instit. in proœm.—that when he ha
smelt, heard, and fully understood—*ut ff. si quando pauţ*
fec l. Agaso. gloss. in verb. olfecit, id est, nasum ad culun
posuit—and found that there was anywhere in the country
debatable matter at law, he would incontinently thrust in hi
advice, and so forwardly intrude his opinion in the business
that he made no bones of making offer, and taking upo
him to decide it, how difficult soever it might happen to b
to the full contentment and satisfaction of both partie
It is written, *Qui non laborat non manducat;* and the sai
gl. ff. de damn. infect. l. quamvis, and *Currere plus quele pa*
vetulam compellit egestas. gloss. ff. de lib. agnosc. l. si qui
pro qua facit. l. si plures. c. de cond. incert. But so hugel
great was his misfortune in this undertaking, that he neve
composed any difference, how little soever you may imagin
it might have been, but that, instead of reconciling th
parties at odds, he did incense, irritate, and exasperate the

to a higher point of dissension and enmity than ever they
were at before. Your worships know, I doubt not, that,

Sermo datur cunctis, animi sapientia paucis

Gl. ff. de alien. jud. mut. caus. fa. lib. 2. This administered
unto the tavern-keepers, wine-drawers, and vintners of Semerve an occasion to say, that under him they had not in the
space of a whole year so much reconciliation-wine, for so
were they pleased to call the good wine of Legugé, as under
his father they had done in one half-hour's time. It happened a little while thereafter that he made a most heavy
regret thereof to his father, attributing the causes of his
bad success in pacificatory enterprises to the perversity,
stubbornness, forward, cross, and backward inclinations of
the people of his time; roundly, boldly, and irreverently up-
braiding, that if but a score of years before the world had
been so wayward, obstinate, pervicacious, implacable, and
out of all square, frame, and order as it was then, his father
had never attained to and acquired the honour and title of
Strife-appeaser so irrefragably, inviolably, and irrevocably
as he had done. In doing whereof Tenot did heinously trans-
gress against the law which prohibiteth children to reproach
the actions of their parents; *per gl. et Bart. l.* 3. *paragr. si
quis. ff. de cond. ob caus. et authent. de nupt. par. sed quod
sancitum. col.* 4. To this the honest old father answered
thus: My son Dandin, when Don Oportet taketh place, this
is the course which we must trace, *gl. c. de appell. l. eos etiam.*
For the road that you went upon was not the way to the
fuller's mill, nor in any part thereof was the form to be
found wherein the hare did sit. Thou hast not the skill and
dexterity of settling and composing differences. Why? Because thou takest them at the beginning, in the very in-

fancy and bud as it were, when they are green, raw, and indigestible. Yet I know handsomely and featly how to compose and settle them all. Why? Because I take them at their decadence, in their weaning, and when they are pretty well digested. So saith Gloss:

Dulcior est fructus post multa pericula ductus.

L. non moriturus. c. de contrahend. et committ. stip. Didst' thou ever hear the vulgar proverb, *Happy is the physician whose coming is desired at the declension of a disease?* For the sickness being come to a crisis is then upon the decreasing hand, and drawing towards an end, although the physician should not repair thither for the cure thereof; whereby, though nature wholly do the work, he bears away the palm and praise thereof. My pleaders, after the same manner, before I did interpose my judgment in the reconciling of them, were waxing faint in their contestations. Their altercation heat was much abated, and, in declining from their former strife, they of themselves inclined to a firm accommodation of their differences; because there wanted fuel to that fire of burning rancour and despiteful wrangling whereof the lower sort of lawyers were the kindlers. That is to say, their purses were emptied of coin, they had not a win in their fob, nor penny in their bag, wherewith to solicit and present their actions.

Deficiente pecu, deficit omne, nia.

There wanted then nothing but some brother to supply the place of a paranymph, brawl-broker, proxenete, or mediator, who, acting his part dexterously, should be the first broacher of the motion of an agreement, for saving both the one and the other party from that hurtful and pernicious shame whereof he could not have avoided the imputation

when it should have been said that he was the first who
yielded and spoke of a reconcilement, and that therefore,
his cause not being good, and being sensible where his shoe
did pinch him, he was willing to break the ice, and make
the greater haste to prepare the way for a condescendment
to an amicable and friendly treaty. Then was it that I came
in pudding time, Dandin, my son, nor is the fat of bacon
more relishing to boiled peas than was my verdict then
agreeable to them. This was my luck, my profit, and good
fortune. I tell thee, my jolly son Dandin, that by this rule
and method I could settle a firm peace, or at least clap up a
cessation of arms and truce for many years to come, betwixt
the Great King and the Venetian State, the Emperor and the
Cantons of Switzerland, the English and the Scots, and betwixt the Pope and the Ferrarians. Shall I go yet further?
Yea, as I would have God to help me, betwixt the Turk and
the Sophy, the Tartars and the Muskoviters. Remark well
what I am to say unto thee. I would take them at that very
instant nick of time when both those of the one and the
other side should be weary and tired of making war, when
they had voided and emptied their own cashes and coffers
of all treasure and coin, drained and exhausted the purses
and bags of their subjects, sold and mortgaged their domains
and proper inheritances, and totally wasted, spent, and consumed the munition, furniture, provision, and victuals that
were necessary for the continuance of a military expedition.
There, I am sure, by God, or by his Mother, that, would
they, would they not, in spite of all their teeth, they should
be forced to have a little respite and breathing time to
moderate their fury and cruel rage of their ambitious aims.
This is the doctrine in *Gl.* 37. *d. c. si quando.*

Odero, si potero; si non, invitus amabo.

CHAPTER 37

HOW SUITS AT LAW ARE BRED AT FIRST, AND HOW THEY COME AFTERWARDS TO THEIR PERFECT GROWTH

FOR this cause, quoth Bridlegoose, going on in his discourse, I temporize and apply myself to the times, as your other worships use to do, waiting patiently for the maturity of the process, full growth and perfection thereof in all its members, to wit, the writings and the bags. *Arg. in l. si major. c. commun. divid. et de cons. di.* 1. *c. solemnitates, et ibi gl.* A suit in law at its production, birth, and first beginning, seemeth to me, as unto your other worships, shapeless, without form or fashion, incomplete, ugly and imperfect, even as a bear at his first coming into the world hath neither hands, skin, hair, nor head, but is merely an inform, rude, and ill-favoured piece and lump of flesh, and would remain still so, if his dam, out of the abundance of her affection to her hopeful cub, did not with much licking put his members into that figure and shape which nature had provided for those of an arctic and ursinal kind; *ut not. Doct. ff. ad l. Aquil. l.* 3. *in fin.* Just so do I see, as your other worships do, processes and suits in law, at their first bringing forth, to be numberless, without shape, deformed, and disfigured, for that then they consist only of one or two writings, or copies of instruments, through which defect they appear unto me, as to your other worships, foul, loathsome, filthy, and misshapen beasts. But when there are heaps of these legiformal papers packed, piled, laid up together, impoked, insatchelled, and put up in bags, then is it that with a good reason we may term that suit, to which, as pieces, parcels, parts, portions, and members thereof, they do pertain and belong, well-formed and fashioned, big-limbed, strong-set, and in all and each of its dimensions most completely mem-

bered. Because *forma dat esse. rei. l. si is qui. ff. ad leg.
Falcid. in c. cum dilecta. de rescript. Barbat. consil.* 12. *lib.*
2, and before him, *Baldus, in c. ult. extra de consuet. et l.
Julianus ad exhib. ff. et l. quæsitum. ff. de leg.* 3. The manner
is such as is set down in *gl. p. quæst.* 1. *c. Paulus.*

Debile principium melior fortuna sequetur.

Like your other worships, also the sergeants, catchpoles,
pursuivants, messengers, summoners, apparitors, ushers,
door-keepers, pettifoggers, attorneys, proctors, commission-
ers, justices of the peace, judge delegates, arbitrators, over-
seers, sequestrators, advocates, inquisitors, jurors, searchers,
examiners, notaries, tabellions, scribes, scriveners, clerks,
pregnotaries, secondaries, and expedanean judges, *de quibus
tit. est. l.* 3. *c.*, by sucking very much, and that exceeding
forcibly, and licking at the purses of the pleading parties,
they, to the suits already begot and engendered, form,
fashion, and frame, head, feet, claws, talons, beaks, bills,
teeth, hands, veins, sinews, arteries, muscles, humours, and
so forth, through all the similary and dissimilary parts of the
whole; which parts, particles, pendicles, and appurtenances
are the law pokes and bags, *gl. de cons. d.* 4. *c. accepisti.
Qualis vestis erit, talia corda gerit. Hic notandum est,* that
in this respect the pleaders, litigants, and law-suitors are
happier than the officers, ministers, and administrators of
justice. For *beatius est dare quam accipere. ff. commun. l.*
3. *extra. de celebr. Miss. c. cum Marthæ. et* 24. *quæst.* 1. *cap.
Od. gl.*

Affectum dantis pensat censura tonantis.

Thus becometh the action or process by their care and industry to be of a complete and goodly bulk, well shaped,

framed, formed, and fashioned according to the canonical
gloss.

Accipe, sume, cape, sunt verba placentia Papæ.

Which speech hath been more clearly explained by Albert
de Ros, *in verbo Roma.*

Roma manus rodit, quas rodere non valet, odit.
Dantes custodit, non dantes spernit, et odit.

The reason whereof is thought to be this:

Ad præsens ova cras pullis sunt meliora.

ut est gl. in l. quam hi. ff. de transact. Nor is this all; for
the inconvenience of the contrary is set down in *gloss. c.
de allu. l. fin.*

Quum labor in damno est, crescit mortalis egestas.

In confirmation whereof we find that the true etymology
and exposition of the word *process* is *purchase,* viz. of good
store of money to the lawyers, and of many pokes—*id est,
prou-sacks*—to the pleaders, upon which subject we have
most celestial quips, gibes, and girds.

Ligitando jura crescunt, ligitando jus acquiritur.
*Item gl. in cap. illud extrem. de præsumpt. et c. de prob. l.
instrum. l. non epistolis. l. non nudis.*
Et si non prosunt singula, multa juvant.

Yea, but, asked Trinquamelle, how do you proceed, my
friend, in criminal causes, the culpable and guilty party
being taken and seized upon *flagrante crimine?* Even as

your other worships use to do, answered Bridlegoose. First, I permit the plaintiff to depart from the court, enjoining him not to presume to return thither till he preallably should have taken a good sound and profound sleep, which is to serve for the prime entry and introduction to the legal carrying on of the business. In the next place, a formal report is to be made to me of his having slept. Thirdly, I issue forth a warrant to convene him before me. Fourthly, he is to produce a sufficient and authentic attestation of his having thoroughly and entirely slept, conform to the *Gloss.* 37. *Quest.* 7. *c. Si quis cum.*

Quandoque bonus dormitat Homerus.

Being thus far advanced in the formality of the process, I find that this consopiating act engendereth another act, whence ariseth the articulating of a member. That again produceth a third act, fashionative of another member; which third bringing forth a fourth, procreative of another act. New members in a no fewer number are shapen and framed, one still breeding and begetting another—as, link after link, the coat of mail at length is made—till thus, piece after piece, by little and little, by information and upon information, the process be completely well formed and perfect in all his members. Finally, having proceeded this length, I have recourse to my dice, nor is it to be thought that this interruption, respite, or interpellation is by me occasioned without very good reason inducing me thereunto, and a notable experience of a most convincing and irrefragable force.

I remember, on a time, that in the camp at Stockholm there was a certain Gascon named Gratianauld, native of the town of St. Sever, who having lost all his money at play, and consecutively being very angry thereat—as you know,

Pecunia est alter sanguis, ut ait Anto. de Burtio, in c. ac-
cedens. 2. extra ut lit. non contest. et Bald. in l. si tuis. c.
de opt. leg. per tot. in l. advocati. c. de advoc. div. jud.
Pecunia est vita hominis et optimus fide-jussor in neces-
sitatibus—did, at his coming forth of the gaming-house, in
the presence of the whole company that was there, with a
very loud voice speak in his own language these following
words: Pao cap de bious hillots, que maux de pipes bous
tresbire: ares que de pergudes sont les mires bingt, et quou-
atre bagnelles, ta pla donnerien pics, trucs, et patacts, Sey
degun de bous aulx, qui boille truquar ambe iou a bels embis.
Finding that none would make him any answer, he passed
from thence to that part of the leaguer where the huff-snuff,
honder sponder, swashbuckling High Germans were, to whom
he renewed these very terms, provoking them to fight with
him; but all the return he had from them to his stout challenge was only, *Der Gasconner thut sich ausz mit ein jedem*
zu schlagen, aber er ist geneigter zu stehlen, darum, liebe
frauen, habt sorg zu euerm hauszrath. Finding also that none
of that band of Teutonic soldiers offered himself to the combat, he passed to that quarter of the leaguer where the
French freebooting adventurers were encamped, and reiterat-
ing unto them what he had before repeated to the Dutch
warriors, challenged them likewise to fight with him, and
therewithal made some pretty little Gasconado frisking gam-
bols to oblige them the more cheerfully and gallantly to cope
with him in the lists of a duellizing engagement; but no
answer at all was made unto him. Whereupon the Gascon,
despairing of meeting with any antagonists, departed from
thence, and laying himself down not far from the pavilions
of the grand Christian cavalier Crissie, fell fast asleep. When
he had thoroughly slept an hour or two, another adventurous and all-hazarding blade of the forlorn hope of the

lavishingly wasting gamesters, having also lost all his moneys, sallied forth with a sword in his hand, of a firm resolution to fight with the aforesaid Gascon, seeing he had lost as well as he.

Ploratur lachrymis amissa pecunia veris,

saith the *Gl. de pœnitent. distinct 3. c. sunt plures.* To this effect having made inquiry and search for him throughout the whole camp, and in sequel thereof found him asleep, he said unto him, Up, ho, good fellow, in the name of all the devils of hell, rise up, rise up, get up! I have lost my money as well as thou hast done; let us therefore go fight lustily together, grapple and scuffle it to some purpose. Thou mayst look and see that my tuck is no longer than thy rapier. The Gascon, altogether astonished at his unexpected provocation, without altering his former dialect spoke thus: Cap de Saint Arnault, quau seys tu, qui me rebeillez? Que mau de taberne te gire. Ho Saint Siobé, cap de Gascoigne, ta pla dormy jou, quand aquoest taquain me bingut estée. The venturous roister inviteth him again to the duel, but the Gascon, without condescending to his desire, said only this: Hé paovert jou tesquinerie ares, que son pla reposat. Vayne un pauque te pausar com jou, peusse truqueren. Thus, in forgetting his loss, he forgot the eagerness which he had to fight. In conclusion, after that the other had likewise slept a little, they, instead of fighting, and possibly killing one another, went jointly to a sutler's tent, where they drank together very amicably, each upon the pawn of his sword. Thus by a little sleep was pacified the ardent fury of two warlike champions. There, gossip, comes the golden word of John Andr. *in cap. ult. de sent. et re. judic. l. sexto.*

Sedendo, et dormiendo fit anima prudens.

CHAPTER 38

HOW PANTAGRUEL EXCUSETH BRIDLEGOOSE IN THE MATTER OF SENTENCING ACTIONS AT LAW BY THE CHANCE OF THE DICE

WITH this Bridlegoose held his peace. Whereupon Trinquamelle bid him withdraw from the court—which accordingly was done—and then directed his discourse to Pantagruel after this manner: It is fitting, most illustrious prince, not only by reason of the deep obligations wherein this present parliament, together with the whole marquisate of Mirelingues, stand bound to your royal highness for the innumerable benefits which, as effects of mere grace, they have received from your incomparable bounty, but for that excellent wit also, prime judgment, and admirable learning wherewith Almighty God, the giver of all good things, hath most richly qualified and endowed you, we tender and present unto you the decision of this new, strange, and paradoxical case of Bridlegoose; who, in your presence, to your both hearing and seeing, hath plainly confessed his final judging and determinating of suits of law by the mere chance and fortune of the dice. Therefore do we beseech you that you may be pleased to give sentence therein as unto you shall seem most just and equitable. To this Pantagruel answered: Gentlemen, it is not unknown to you how my condition is somewhat remote from the profession of deciding law controversies; yet seeing you are pleased to do me the honour to put that task upon me, instead of undergoing the office of a judge I will become your humble supplicant. I observe, gentlemen, in this Bridlegoose several things which induce me to represent before you that it is my opinion he should be pardoned. In the first place, his old age; secondly, his simplicity; to both which qualities our

statute and common laws, civil and municipal together, allow
many excuses for any slips or escapes which, through the
invincible imperfection of either, have been inconsiderately
stumbled upon by a person so qualified. Thirdly, gentlemen,
I must needs display before you another case, which in equity
and justice maketh much for the advantage of Bridlegoose,
to wit, that this one, sole and single fault of his ought to be
quite forgotten, abolished, and swallowed up by that immense and vast ocean of just dooms and sentences which
heretofore he hath given and pronounced his demeanours,
for these forty years and upwards that he hath been a judge,
having been so evenly balanced in the scales of uprightness,
that envy itself till now could not have been so impudent as
to accuse and twit him with an act worthy of a check or
reprehension; as, if a drop of the sea were thrown into the
Loire, none could perceive or say that by this single drop the
whole river should be salt or brackish.

Truly, it seemeth to me, that in the whole series of Bridlegoose's juridical decrees there hath been I know not what
of extraordinary savouring of the unspeakable benignity of
God, that all those his preceding sentences, awards, and
judgments, have been confirmed and approved of by yourselves in this your own venerable and sovereign court. For
it is usual, as you know well, with him whose ways are in-
scrutable, to manifest his own ineffable glory in blunting the
perspicacy of the eyes of the wise, in weakening the strength
of potent oppressors, in depressing the pride of rich extor-
tioners, and in erecting, comforting, protecting, supporting,
upholding, and shoring up the poor, feeble, humble, silly, and
foolish ones of the earth. But waiving all these matters, I
shall only beseech you, not by the obligations which you
pretend to owe to my family, for which I thank you, but
for that constant and unfeigned love and affection which you

have always found in me, both on this and on the other side
of the Loire, for the maintenance and establishment of your
places, offices and dignities, that for this one time you would
pardon and forgive him upon these two conditions. First,
that he satisfy, or put a sufficient surety for the satisfaction
of the party wronged by the injustice of the sentence in question. For the fulfilment of this article I will provide sufficiently. And, secondly, that for his subsidiary aid in the
weighty charge of administrating justice you would be pleased
to appoint and assign unto him some pretty little virtuous
counsellor, younger, learneder, and wiser than he, by the
square and rule of whose advice he may regulate, guide,
temper, and moderate in times coming all his judiciary procedures; or otherwise, if you intend totally to depose him
from his office, and to deprive him altogether of the state
and dignity of a judge, I shall cordially entreat you to make
a present and free gift of him to me, who shall find in my
kingdoms charges and employment enough wherewith to
embusy him, for the bettering of his own fortunes and fur-
therance of my service. In the meantime, I implore the
Creator, Saviour, and Sanctifier of all good things, in his
grace, mercy, and kindness, to preserve you all now and
evermore, world without end.

These words thus spoken, Pantagruel, vailing his cap and
making a leg with such a majestic garb as became a person
of his paramount degree and eminency, farewelled Trinquamelle, the president and master-speaker of that Mirelingue-
sian parliament, took his leave of the whole court, and went
out of the chamber; at the door whereof finding Panurge,
Epistemon, Friar John, and others, he forthwith, attended
by them, walked to the outer gate, where all of them immediately took horse to return towards Gargantua. Pantagruel by the way related to them from point to point the

manner of Bridlegoose's sententiating differences at law. Friar John said that he had seen Peter Dandin, and was acquainted with him at that time when he sojourned in the monastery of Fontaine le Comte, under the noble Abbot Ardillon. Gymnast likewise affirmed that he was in the tent of the grand Christian cavalier De Crissie, when the Gascon, after his sleep, made answer to the adventurer. Panurge was somewhat incredulous in the matter of believing that it was morally possible Bridlegoose should have been for such a long space of time so continually fortunate in that aleatory way of deciding law debates. Epistemon said to Pantagruel, Such another story, not much unlike to that in all the circumstances thereof, is vulgarly reported of the provost of Montlehery. In good sooth, such a perpetuity of good luck is to be wondered at. To have hit right twice or thrice in a judgment so given by haphazard might have fallen out well enough, especially in controversies that were ambiguous, intricate, abstruse, perplexed, and obscure.

CHAPTER 39

HOW PANURGE TAKETH ADVICE OF TRIBOULET

On the sixth day thereafter Pantagruel was returned home at the very same hour that Triboulet was by water come from Blois. Panurge, at his arrival, gave him a hog's bladder puffed up with wind, and resounding because of the hard peas that were within it. Moreover he did present him with a gilt wooden sword, a hollow budget made of a tortoise shell, an osier-wattled wicker-bottle full of Breton wine, and five-and-twenty apples of the orchard of Blandureau.

If he be such a fool, quoth Carpalin, as to be won with apples, there is no more wit in his pate than in the head of an ordinary cabbage. Triboulet girded the sword and scrip to his side, took the bladder in his hand, ate some few of the apples, and drunk up all the wine. Panurge very wistly and heedfully looking upon him said, I never yet saw a fool, and I have seen ten thousand francs worth of that kind of cattle who did not love to drink heartily, and by good long draughts. When Triboulet had done with his drinking, Panurge laid out before him and exposed the sum of the business wherein he was to require his advice, in eloquent and choicely-sorted terms, adorned with flourishes of rhetoric. But, before he had altogether done, Triboulet with his fist gave him a bouncing whirret between the shoulders, rendered back into his hand again the empty bottle, filliped and flirted him on the nose with the hog's bladder, and lastly, for a final resolution, shaking and wagging his head strongly and disorderly, he answered nothing else but this, By God, God, mad fool, beware the monk, Buzansay hornpipe! These words thus finished, he slipped himself out of the company, went aside, and, rattling the bladder, took a huge delight in the melody of the rickling crackling noise of the peas. After which time it lay not in the power of them all to draw out of his chaps the articulate sound of one syllable, insomuch that, when Panurge went about to interrogate him further, Triboulet drew his wooden sword, and would have stuck him therewith. I have fished fair now, quoth Panurge, and brought my pigs to a fine market. Have I not got a brave determination of all my doubts, and a response in all things agreeable to the oracle that gave it? He is a great fool, that is not to be denied, yet is he a greater fool who brought him hither to me,—That bolt, quoth Carpalin, levels point-blank at me,—but of the three I am the greatest fool, who did impart the secret of my thoughts to such an idiot ass and native ninny.

Without putting ourselves to any stir or trouble in the

least, quoth Pantagruel, let us maturely and seriously consider and perpend the gestures and speech which he hath
made and uttered. In them, veritably, quoth he, have I remarked and observed some excellent and notable mysteries;
yea, of such important worth and weight, that I shall never
henceforth be astonished, nor think strange, why the Turks
with a great deal of worship and reverence honour and respect natural fools equally with their primest doctors, muftis,
divines, and prophets. Did not you take heed, quoth he, a
little before he opened his mouth to speak, what a shogging,
shaking, and wagging his head did keep? By the approved
doctrine of the ancient philosophers, the customary ceremonies of the most expert magicians, and the received
opinions of the learnedest lawyers, such a brangling agitation
and moving should by us all be judged to proceed from, and
be quickened and suscitated by the coming and inspiration
of the prophetizing and fatidical spirit, which, entering
briskly and on a sudden into a shallow receptacle of a debile
substance (for, as you know, and as the proverb shows it, a
little containeth not much brains), was the cause of that
commotion. This is conform to what is avouched by the
most skilful physicians, when they affirm that shakings and
tremblings fall upon the members of a human body, partly
because of the heaviness and violent impetuosity of the
burden and load that is carried, and, other part, by reason
of the weakness and imbecility that is in the virtue of the
bearing organ. A manifest example whereof appeareth in
those who, fasting, are not able to carry to their heads a
great goblet full of wine without a trembling and a shaking
in the hand that holds it. This of old was accounted a pre-
figuration and mystical pointing out of the Pythian diviner-
ess, who used always, before the uttering of a response from
the oracle, to shake a branch of her domestic laurel. Lam-

pridius also testifieth that the Emperor Heliogabalus, to acquire unto himself the reputation of a soothsayer, did, on several holy days of prime solemnity, in the presence of the fanatic rabble, make the head of his idol by some slight within the body thereof publicly to shake. Plautus, in his Asinaria, declareth likewise, that Saurias, whithersoever he walked, like one quite distracted of his wits kept such a furious lolling and mad-like shaking of his head that he commonly affrighted those who casually met him in his way. The said author in another place, showing a reason why Charmides shook and brangled his head, assevered that he was transported and in an ecstasy. Catullus after the same manner maketh mention, in his Berecynthia and Atys, of the place wherein the Menades, Bacchical women, she-priests of the Lyæan god, and demented prophetesses, carrying ivy boughs in their hands, did shake their heads. As in the like case, amongst the Galli, the gelded priests of Cybele were wont to do in the celebrating of their festivals. Whence, too, according to the sense of the ancient theologues, she herself has her denomination; for *chubistan* signifieth to turn round, whirl about, shake the head, and play the part of one that is wry-necked.

Semblably Titus Livius writeth that, in the solemnization time of the Bacchanalian holidays at Rome, both men and women seemed to prophetize and vaticinate, because of an affected kind of wagging of the head, shrugging of the shoulders, and jectigation of the whole body, which they used then most punctually. For the common voice of the philosophers, together with the opinion of the people, asserteth for an irrefragable truth that vaticination is seldom by the heavens bestowed on any without the concomitancy of a little frenzy and a head-shaking, not only when the said presaging virtue is infused, but when the person also therewith inspired declareth and manifesteth it unto others. The learned lawyer Julian, being asked on a time if that slave might be truly esteemed to be healthful and in a good plight who had not only conversed with some furious maniac, and enraged people, but in their company had also prophesied, yet without a noddle-shaking concussion, answered that, seeing there was no head-wagging at the time of his predictions, he might be held for sound and competent enough. Is it not daily seen how school masters, teachers, tutors, and instructors of children shake the heads of their disciples, as one would do a pot in holding it by the lugs, that by this erection, vellication, stretching, and pulling their ears, which, according to the doctrine of the sage Egyptians, is a member consecrated to the memory, they may stir them up to recollect their scattered thoughts, bring home those fancies of theirs which perhaps have been extravagantly roaming abroad upon strange and uncouth objects, and totally range their judgments, which possibly by disordinate affections have been made wild, to the rule and pattern of a wise, discreet, virtuous, and philosophical discipline. All which Virgil acknowledgeth to be true, in the branglement of Apollo Cynthius.

CHAPTER 40

HOW PANTAGRUEL AND PANURGE DIVERSELY INTERPRET THE WORDS OF TRIBOULET

He says you are a fool. And what kind of fool? A mad fool, who in your old age would enslave yourself to the bondage of matrimony, and shut your pleasures up within a wedlock whose key some ruffian carries in his codpiece. He says furthermore, Beware of the monk. Upon mine honour, it gives me in my mind that you will be cuckolded by a monk. Nay, I will engage mine honour, which is the most precious pawn I could have in my possession although I were sole and peaceable dominator over all Europe, Asia, and Africa, that, if you marry, you will surely be one of the horned brotherhood of Vulcan. Hereby you may perceive how much I do attribute to the wise foolery of our morosoph Triboulet. The other oracles and responses did in the general prognosticate you a cuckold, without descending so near to the point of a particular determination as to pitch upon what vocation amongst the several sorts of men he should profess who is to be the copesmate of your wife and hornifier of your proper self. Thus noble Triboulet tells it us plainly, from whose words we may gather with all ease imaginable that your cuckoldry is to be infamous, and so much the more scandalous that your conjugal bed will be incestuously contaminated with the filthiness of a monkery lecher. Moreover, he says that you will be the hornpipe of Buzansay, that is to say, well-horned, hornified, and cornuted. And, as Triboulet's uncle asked from Louis the Twelfth, for a younger brother of his own who lived at Blois, the hornpipes of Buzansay, for the organ pipes, through the mistake of one word for another, even so, whilst you think to marry a wise, humble, calm, discreet, and honest wife, you shall unhappily stumble upon one witless, proud, loud, obstreperous, bawling, clamorous, and more unpleasant than any Buzansay hornpipe. Consider withal how he flirted you on the nose with the bladder, and gave you a sound thumping blow with his fist upon the ridge of the back. This denotates and presageth that you shall be banged, beaten, and fillipped by her, and that also she will steal of your goods from you, as you stole the hog's bladder from the little boys of Vaubreton.

Flat contrary, quoth Panurge;—not that I would impudently exempt myself from being a vassal in the territory of

olly. I hold of that jurisdiction, and am subject thereto, I
onfess it. And why should I not? For the whole world is
oolish. In the old Lorraine language, *fou* for *tou*, all and
ool, were the same thing. Besides, it is avouched by Solomon
hat infinite is the number of fools. From an infinity nothing
an be deducted or abated, nor yet, by the testimony of
Aristotle, can anything thereto be added or subjoined. There-
ore were I a mad fool if, being a fool, I should not hold
myself a fool. After the same manner of speaking, we may
aver the number of the mad and enraged folks to be in-
inite. Avicenna maketh no bones to assert that the several
kinds of madness are infinite. Though this much of Tribou-
et's words tend little to my advantage, howbeit the prejudice which I sustain thereby be common with me to all
other men, yet the rest of his talk and gesture maketh altogether for me. He said to my wife, Be wary of the monkey;
that is as much as if she should be cheery, and take as much
delight in a monkey as ever did the Lesbia of Catullus in
her sparrow; who will for his recreation pass his time no
ess joyfully at the exercise of snatching flies than heretofore did the merciless fly-catcher Domitian. Withal he meant,
by another part of his discourse, that she should be of a
jovial country-like humour, as gay and pleasing as a harmonious hornpipe of Saulieau or Buzansay. The veridical Triboulet did therein hint at what I liked well, as perfectly
knowing the inclinations and propensions of my mind, my
natural disposition, and the bias of my interior passions and
affections. For you may be assured that my humour is much
better satisfied and contented with the pretty, frolic, rural,
dishevelled shepherdess, whose bums through their coarse
canvas smocks smell of the clover grass of the field, than
with those great ladies in magnific courts, with their flandan
topknots and sultanas, their polvil, pastillos, and cosmetics.

The homely sound, likewise of a rustical hornpipe is more agreeable to my ears than the curious warbling and musical quavering of lutes, theorbos, viols, rebecs, and violins. He gave me a lusty rapping thwack on my back,—what then. Let it pass, in the name and for the love of God, as an abatement of and deduction from so much of my future pains in purgatory. He did it not out of any evil intent. He thought belike, to have hit some of the pages. He is an honest fool and an innocent changeling. It is a sin to harbour in the heart any bad conceit of him. As for myself, I heartily pardon him. He flirted me on the nose. In that there is no harm; for it importeth nothing else but that betwixt my wife and me there will occur some toyish wanton tricks which usually happen to all new-married folks.

CHAPTER 41

HOW PANTAGRUEL AND PANURGE RESOLVED TO MAKE A VISIT TO THE ORACLE OF THE HOLY BOTTLE

THERE is as yet another point, quoth Panurge, which you have not at all considered on, although it be the chief and principal head of the matter. He put the bottle in my hand and restored it to me again. How interpret you that passage? What is the meaning of that? He possibly, quoth Pantagruel, signifieth thereby that your wife will be such a drunkard as shall daily take in her liquor kindly, and ply the pots and bottles apace. Quite otherwise, quoth Panurge; for the bottle was empty. I swear to you, by the prickling brambly thorn of St. Fiacre in Brie, that our unique morosoph, whom I formerly termed the lunatic Triboulet, referreth me, for attaining to the final resolution of my scruple, to the response-giving bottle. Therefore do I renew afresh the first vow which I made, and here in your presence protest and make oath, by Styx and Acheron, to carry still spectacles in my cap, and never to wear a codpiece in my breeches, until upon the enterprise in hand of my nuptial undertaking I shall have obtained an answer from the holy bottle. I am acquainted with a prudent, understanding, and discreet gentleman, and besides a very good friend of mine, who knoweth the land, country, and place where its temple and oracle is built and posited. He will guide and conduct us thither sure and safely. Let us go thither, I beseech you. Deny me not, and say not nay; reject not the suit I make unto you, I entreat you. I will be to you an Achates, a Damis, and heartily accompany you all along in the whole voyage, both in your going forth and coming back. I have of a long time known you to be a great lover of peregrination, desirous still to learn new things, and still to see what you had never seen before.

Very willingly, quoth Pantagruel, I condescend to your request. But before we enter in upon our progress towards the accomplishment of so far a journey, replenished and fraught with eminent perils, full of innumerable hazards, and every way stored with evident and manifest dangers,— What dangers? quoth Panurge, interrupting him. Dangers fly back, run from, and shun me whithersoever I go, seven leagues around, as in the presence of the sovereign a subordinate magistracy is eclipsed; or as clouds and darkness quite evanish at the bright coming of a radiant sun; or as all sores and sicknesses did suddenly depart at the approach of the body of St. Martin à Quande. Nevertheless, quoth Pantagruel, before we adventure to set forward on the road of our projected and intended voyage, some few points are to be discussed, expedited, and despatched. First, let us send back Triboulet to Blois. Which was instantly done, after that Pantagruel had given him a frieze coat. Secondly, our design must be backed with the advice and counsel of the

king my father. And, lastly, it is most needful and expedie
for us that we search for and find out some sibyl to ser
us for a guide, truchman, and interpreter. To this Panur
made answer, that his friend Xenomanes would abundant
suffice for the plenary discharge and performance of t
sibyl's office; and that, furthermore, in passing through t
Lanternatory revelling country, they should take along wi
them a learned and profitable Lanternesse, which would l
no less useful to them in their voyage than was the sibyl
Æneas in his descent to the Elysian fields. Carpalin, in th
interim, as he was upon the conducting away of Triboule
in his passing by hearkened a little to the discourse they we
upon; then spoke out, saying, Ho, Panurge, master freemar
take my Lord Debitis at Calais alongst with you, for he
goud-fallot, a good fellow. He will not forget those who hav
been debitors; these are Lanternes. Thus shall you not lac
for both fallot and lanterne. I may safely with the skill
have, quoth Pantagruel, prognosticate that by the way w
shall engender no melancholy. I clearly perceive it already
The only thing that vexeth me is, that I cannot speak th
Lanternatory language. I shall, answered Panurge, spea
for you all. I understand it every whit as well as I do min
own maternal tongue; I have been no less used to it than t
the vulgar French.

> *Briszmarg dalgotbrick nubstzne zos,*
> *Isquebsz prusq: albok crinqs zacbac.*
> *Mizbe dilbarskz morp nipp stancz bos,*
> *Strombtz, Panurge, walmap quost gruszbac.*

Now guess, friend Epistemon, what this is. They are
quoth Epistemon, names of errant devils, passant devils, an
rampant devils. These words of thine, dear friend of mine

are true, quoth Panurge; yet are they terms used in the language of the court of the Lanternish people. By the way, as we go upon our journey, I will make to thee a pretty little dictionary, which, notwithstanding, shall not last you much longer than a pair of new shoes. Thou shalt have learned it sooner than thou canst perceive the dawning of the next subsequent morning. What I have said in the foregoing tetrastich is thus translated out of the Lanternish tongue into our vulgar dialect:

> *All miseries attended me, whilst I*
> *A lover was, and had no good thereby.*
> *Of better luck the married people tell;*
> *Panurge is one of those, and knows it well.*

There is little more, then, quoth Pantagruel, to be done, but that we understand what the will of the king my father will be therein, and purchase his consent.

CHAPTER 42

HOW GARGANTUA SHOWETH THAT THE CHILDREN OUGHT NOT TO MARRY WITHOUT THE SPECIAL KNOWLEDGE AND ADVICE OF THEIR FATHERS AND MOTHERS

No sooner had Pantagruel entered in at the door of the great hall of the castle, than that he encountered full butt with the good honest Gargantua coming forth from the council board, unto whom he made a succinct and summary narrative of what had passed and occurred, worthy of his observation, in his travels abroad, since their last interview; then, acquainting him with the design he had in hand, besought him that it might stand with his goodwill and pleasure to grant him leave to prosecute and go throughstitch with the enterprise which he had undertaken. The good man Gargantua, having in one hand two great bundles of petitions endorsed and answered, and in the other some remembrancing notes and bills, to put him in mind of such other requests of supplicants, which, albeit presented, had nevertheless been neither read nor heard, he gave both to Ulric Gallet, his ancient and faithful Master of Requests; then drew aside Pantagruel, and, with a countenance more serene and jovial than customary, spoke to him thus: I praise God, and have great reason so to do, my most dear son, that he hath been pleased to entertain in you a constant inclination to virtuous actions. I am well content that the voyage which you have motioned to me be by you accomplished, but withal I could wish you would have a mind and desire to marry, for that I see you are of competent years. Panurge in the meanwhile was in a readiness of preparing and providing for remedies, salves, and cures against all such lets, obstacles, and impediments as he could in the height of his fancy conceive by Gargantua be cast in the way of their itinerary design. Is it your pleasure, most dear father, that you speak? answered Pantagruel. For my part, I have not yet thought upon it. In all this affair I wholly submit and rest in your good liking and paternal authority. For I shall rather pray unto God that he would throw me down stark dead at your feet, in your pleasure, than that against your pleasure I should be found married alive. I never yet heard that by any law, whether sacred or profane, yea, amongst the rudest and most barbarous nations in the world, it was allowed and approved of that children may be suffered and tolerated to marry at their own goodwill and pleasure, without the knowledge, advice, or consent asked and had thereto of their fathers, mothers, and nearest kindred. All legislators, everywhere upon the face of the whole earth, have taken away and removed this licentious liberty from children, and totally reserved it to the discretion of the parents.

My dearly beloved son, quoth Gargantua, I believe you, and from my heart thank God for having endowed you with the grace of having both a perfect notice of and entire liking to laudable and praiseworthy things; and that through the windows of your exterior senses he hath vouchsafed to transmit unto the interior faculties of your mind nothing but what is good and virtuous. For in my time there hath been found on the continent a certain country, wherein are I know not what kind of Pastophorian mole-catching priests, who, albeit averse from engaging their proper persons into a matrimonial duty, like the pontifical flamens of Cybele in Phrygia, as if they were capons, and not cocks full of lasciviousness, salacity, and wantonness, who yet have, nevertheless, in the matter of conjugal affairs, taken upon them to prescribe laws and ordinances to married folks. I cannot goodly determine what I should most abhor, detest, loathe, and abominate,—whether the tyrannical presumption of those dreaded sacerdotal mole-catchers, who, not being willing to contain and coop up themselves within the grates and trellises of their own mysterious temples, do deal in, meddle with, obtrude upon, and thrust their sickles into harvests of secular businesses quite contrary and diametrically opposite to the quality, state, and condition of their callings, professions, and vocations; or the superstitious stupidity and senseless scrupulousness of married folks, who have yielded obedience, and submitted their bodies, fortunes, and estates to the discretion and authority of such odious, perverse, barbarous, and unreasonable laws. Nor do they see that which is clearer than the light and splendour of the morning star,—how all these nuptial and connubial sanctions, statutes, and ordinances have been decreed, made, and instituted for the sole benefit, profit, and advantage of the flaminal mysts and mysterious flamens, and nothing at all for the good, utility or emolument of the silly hoodwinked married people. Which administereth unto others a sufficient cause for rendering these churchmen suspicious of iniquity, and of an unjust and fraudulent manner of dealing, no more to be connived at nor countenanced, after that it be well weighed in the scales of reason, than if with a reciprocal temerity the laics by way of compensation, would impose laws to be followed and observed by those mysts and flamens, how they should behave themselves in the making and performance of their rites and ceremonies, and after what manner they ought to proceed in the offering and immolating of their various oblations, victims, and sacrifices; seeing that, besides the decimation and tithe-haling of their goods, they cut off and take parings, shreddings, and clippings of the gain proceeding from the labour of their hands and sweat of their brows, therewith to entertain themselves the better. Upon which consideration, in my opinion, their injunctions and commands would not prove so pernicious and impertinent as those of the ecclesiastic power unto which they had tendered their blind obedience. For, as you have very well said, there is no place in the world where, legally, a license is granted to the children to marry without the advice and consent of their parents and kindred. Nevertheless, by those wicked laws and mole-catching customs, whereat there is a little hinted in what I have already spoken to you, there is no scurvy measly, leprous, or pocky ruffian, pander, knave, rogue, skellum, robber, or thief, pilloried, whipped, and burn-marked in his own country for his crimes and felonies who may not violently snatch away and ravish what maid soever he had a mind to pitch upon, how noble, how fair, how rich, honest and chaste soever she be, and that out of the house of her

wn father, in his own presence, from the bosom of her
nother, and in the sight and despite of her friends and kindred looking on a so woeful spectacle, provided that the
ascal villain be so cunning as to associate unto himself some
mystical flamen, who, according to the covenant made be-
wixt them two, shall be in hope some day to participate of
he prey.

Could the Goths, the Sycths, or Massagets do a worse or
nore cruel act to any of the inhabitants of a hostile city,
when, after the loss of many of their most considerable com-
manders, the expense of a great deal of money, and a long
siege, they shall have stormed and taken it by a violent and
impetuous assault? May not these fathers and mothers,
hink you, be sorrowful and heavy-hearted when they see an
unknown fellow, a vagabond-stranger, a barbarous lout, a
ude cur, rotten, fleshless, putrefied, scraggy, boily, botchy,
poor, a forlorn caitiff and miserable sneak, by an open rapt
snatch away before their own eyes their so fair, delicate,
neat, well-behavioured, richly-provided-for and healthful
daughters, on whose breeding and education they had spared
no cost nor charges, by bringing them up in an honest discipline to all the honourable and virtuous employments becom-
ing one of their sex descended of a noble parentage, hoping
by those commendable and industrious means in an opportune and convenient time to bestow them on the worthy
sons of their well-deserving neighbours and ancient friends,
who had nourished, entertained, taught, instructed, and
schooled their children with the same care and solicitude, to
make them matches fit to attain to the felicity of a so happy
marriage, that from them might issue an offspring and
progeny no less heirs to the laudable endowments and exquisite qualifications of their parents, whom they every way
resemble, than to their personal and real estates, movables,

and inheritances? How doleful, trist, and plangorous would
such a sight and pageantry prove unto them? You shall not
need to think that the collachrymation of the Romans and
their confederates at the decease of Germanicus Drusus was
comparable to this lamentation of theirs? Neither would I
have you to believe that the discomfort and anxiety of the
Lacedæmonians, when the Greek Helen, by the perfidious-
ness of the adulterous Trojan, Paris, was privily stolen away
out of their country, was greater or more pitiful than this
ruthful and deplorable collugency of theirs? Ceres at the
ravishment of her daughter Proserpina was not more at-
tristed, sad, nor mournful than they. Trust me, and your own
reason, that the loss of Osiris was not so regrettable to Isis,
nor did Venus so deplore the death of Adonis, nor yet did
Hercules so bewail the straying of Hylas, nor was the rapt
of Polyxena more throbbingly resented and condoled by
Priamus and Hecuba, than this aforesaid accident would be
sympathetically bemoaned, grievous, ruthful, and anxious to
the woefully desolate and disconsolate parents.

Notwithstanding all this, the greater part of so vilely
abused parents are so timorous and afraid of devils and hobgoblins, and so deeply plunged in superstition, that they dare
not gainsay nor contradict, much less oppose and resist those
unnatural and impious actions, when the mole-catcher hath
been present at the perpetrating of the fact, and a party
contractor and covenanter in that detestable bargain. What
do they do then? They wretchedly stay at their own miserable homes, destitute of their well-beloved daughters, the
fathers cursing the days and the hours wherein they were
married, and the mothers howling and crying that it was
not their fortune to have brought forth abortive issues when
they happened to be delivered of such unfortunate girls, and
in this pitiful plight spend at best the remainder of their

ime with tears and weeping for those their children, of and
rom whom they expected, (and, with good reason, should
ave obtained and reaped,) in these latter days of theirs,
oy and comfort. Other parents there have been, so impatient of that affront and indignity put upon them and their
amilies, that, transported with the extremity of passion, in
, mad and frantic mood, through the vehemency of a
grievous fury and raging sorrow, have drowned, hanged,
illed, and otherwise put violent hands on themselves. Others,
gain, of that parental relation have, upon the reception of
he like injury, been of a more magnanimous and heroic
pirit, who, in imitation and at the example of the children
f Jacob revenging upon the Sichemites the rapt of their sister
Dinah, having found the rascally ruffian in the association
f his mystical mole-catcher closely and in hugger-
mugger conferring, parleying, and coming with their daugh-
ers, for the suborning, corrupting, depraving, perverting,
nd enticing these innocent unexperienced maids unto filthy
ewdnesses, have, without any further advisement on the
natter, cut them instantly into pieces, and thereupon forthwith thrown out upon the fields their so dismembered bodies,
o serve for food unto the wolves and ravens. Upon the
chivalrous, bold, and courageous achievement of a so valiant,
tout, and manlike act, the other mole-catching symmysts
ave been so highly incensed, and have so chafed, fretted,
nd fumed thereat, that, bills of complaint and accusations
aving been in a most odious and detestable manner put in
before the competent judges, the arm of secular authority
ath with much importunity and impetuosity been by them
mplored and required, they proudly contending that the
ervants of God would become contemptible if exemplary
punishment were not speedily taken upon the persons of

the perpetrators of such an enormous, horrid, sacrilegiou
crying, heinous, and execrable crime.

Yet neither by natural equity, by the law of nations, no
by any imperial law whatsoever, hath there been found s
much as one rubric, paragraph, point, or tittle, by the whic
any kind of chastisement or correction hath been adjudge
due to be inflicted upon any for their delinquency in tha
kind. Reason opposeth, and nature is repugnant. For ther
is no virtuous man in the world who both naturally and wit
good reason will not be more hugely troubled in min
hearing of the news of the rapt, disgrace, ignominy, and di
honour of his daughter, than of her death. Now any ma
finding in hot blood one who with a fore-thought felor
hath murdered his daughter, may, without tying himse
to the formalities and circumstances of a legal proceedin
kill him on a sudden and out of hand without incurring an
hazard of being attainted and apprehended by the office
of justice for so doing. What wonder is it then? Or ho
little strange should it appear to any rational man, if
lechering rogue, together with his mole-catching abetto
be entrapped in the flagrant act of suborning his daughte
and stealing her out of his house, though herself conser
thereto, that the father in such a case of stain and infam
by them brought upon his family, should put them both t
a shameful death; and cast their carcasses upon dunghil
to be devoured and eaten up by dogs and swine, or otherwis
fling them a little further off to the direption, tearing, seve
ing and rending asunder of their joints and members by th
wild beasts and birds of prey of the field [as unworthy t
receive the gentle, the desired, the last kind embraces of th
great Alma Mater, the earth, commonly called burial].

Dearly beloved son, have an especial care that after m
decease none of these laws be received in any of your kin

loms; for whilst I breathe, by the grace and assistance of God, I shall give good order. Seeing, therefore, you have totally referred unto my discretion the disposure of you in marriage, I am fully of an opinion that I shall provide sufficiently well for you in that point. Make ready and prepare yourself for Panurge's voyage. Take along with you Epistemon, Friar John, and such others as you will choose. Do with my treasures what unto yourself shall seem most expedient. None of your actions, I promise you, can in any manner of way displease me. Take out of my arsenal Thalasse whatsoever equipage, furniture, or provision you please, together with such pilots, mariners, and truchmen as you have a mind to, and with the first fair and favourable wind set sail and make out to sea in the name of God, our Saviour. In the meanwhile, during your absence, I shall not be neglective of providing a wife for you, nor of those preparations which are requisite to be made for the more sumptuous solemnizing of your nuptials with a most splendid feast, if ever there was any in the world, since the days of Ahasuerus.

CHAPTER 43

HOW PANTAGRUEL DID PUT HIMSELF IN A READINESS TO GO TO SEA; AND OF THE HERB NAMED PANTAGRUELION

WITHIN very few days after that Pantagruel had taken his leave of the good Gargantua, who devoutly prayed for his son's happy voyage, he arrived at the seaport, near to Sammalo, accompanied with Panurge, Epistemon, Friar John of the Funnels, Abbot of Theleme, and others of the royal house, especially with Xenomanes, the great traveller and thwarter of dangerous ways, who was come at the bidding and appointment of Panurge, of whose castlewick of Salmigondin he did hold some pretty inheritance by the tenure of a mesne fee. Pantagruel, being come thither, prepared and made ready for launching a fleet of ships, to the number of those which Ajax of Salamine had of old equipped in convoy of the Grecian soldiery against the Trojan state. He likewise picked out for his use so many mariners, pilots, sailors, interpreters, artificers, officers, and soldiers, as he thought fitting, and therewithal made provision of so much victuals of all sorts, artillery, munition of divers kinds, clothes, moneys, and other such luggage, stuff, baggage, chaffer and furniture, as he deemed needful for carrying on the design of a so tedious, long, and perilous voyage. Amongst other things, it was observed how he caused some of his vessels to be fraught and loaded with a great quantity of an herb of his called Pantagruelion, not only of the green and raw sort of it, but of the confected also, and of that which was notably well befitted for present use after the fashion of conserves. The herb Pantagruelion hath a little root somewhat hard and rough, roundish, terminating in an obtuse and very blunt point, and having some of its veins, strings, or filaments coloured with some spots of white, never fixeth itself into the ground above the profoundness almost of a cubit, or foot and a half. From the root thereof proceedeth the only stalk, orbicular, cane-like, green without, whitish within, and hollow like the stem of smyrnium, olus atrum, beans, and gentian, full of long threads, straight, easy to be broken, jagged, snipped, nicked, and notched a little after the manner of pillars and columns, slightly furrowed, chamfered, guttered, and channelled, and full of fibres, or hairs like strings, in which consisteth the chief value and dignity of the herb, especially in that part thereof which is termed mesa, as he would say the mean, and in that other, which hath got the denomination of milasea. Its height is commonly of five or six foot. Yet sometimes it is of such a tall

growth as doth surpass the length of a lance, but that is only
when it meeteth with a sweet, easy, warm, wet, and well-
soaked soil—as is the ground of the territory of Olone, and
that of Rasea, near to Preneste in Sabinia—and that it want
not for rain enough about the season of the fishers' holidays
and the estival solstice. There are many trees whose height
is by it very far exceeded, and you might call it dendroma-
lache by the authority of Theophrastus. The plant every
year perisheth,—the tree neither in the trunk, root, bark,
or boughs being durable.

From the stalk of this Pantagruelion plant there issue forth
several large and great branches, whose leaves have thrice
as much length as breadth, always green, roughish, and
rugged like the orcanet, or Spanish bugloss, hardish, slit
round about like unto a sickle, or as the saxifragum, betony,
and finally ending as it were in the points of a Macedonian
spear, or of such a lancet as surgeons commonly make use
of in their phlebotomizing tiltings. The figure and shape of
the leaves thereof is not much different from that of those
of the ash-tree, or of agrimony; the herb itself being so like
the Eupatorian plant that many skilful herbalists have called
it the Domestic Eupator, and the Eupator the Wild Pantagruelion. These leaves are in equal and parallel distances
spread around the stalk by the number in every rank either
of five or seven, nature having so highly favoured and cherished this plant that she has richly adorned it with these
two odd, divine, and mysterious numbers. The smell thereof
is somewhat strong, and not very pleasing to nice, tender,
and delicate noses. The seed enclosed therein mounteth up
to the very top of its stalk, and a little above it.

This is a numerous herb; for there is no less abundance
of it than of any other whatsoever. Some of these plants
are spherical, some rhomboid, and some of an oblong shape,

and all of those either black, bright-coloured, or tawny, rude to the touch, and mantled with a quickly-blasted-away coat, yet such a one as is of a delicious taste and savour to all shrill and sweetly-singing birds, such as linnets, goldfinches, larks, canary birds, yellow-hammers, and others of that airy chirping choir.

The Third Book of

RABELAIS

Treating of the Heroic Deeds and Sayings
of the Good Pantagruel.

CHAPTER 1

In the month of June, on Vesta's holiday, the very numerical day on which Brutus, conquering Spain, taught its
strutting dons to truckle under him, and that niggardly miser
Crassus was routed and knocked on the head by the Parthians, Pantagruel took his leave of the good Gargantua, his
royal father. The old gentleman, according to the laudable
custom of the primitive Christians, devoutly prayed for the
happy voyage of his son and his whole company, and then
they took shipping at the port of Thalassa. Pantagruel had
with him Panurge, Friar John des Entomeures, alias of the
Funnels, Epistemon, Gymnast, Eusthenes, Rhizotome, Carpalin, *cum multis aliis*, his ancient servants and domestics;
also Xenomanes, the great traveller, who had crossed so
many dangerous roads, dikes, ponds, seas, and so forth, and
was come some time before, having been sent for by Panurge.

For certain good causes and considerations him thereunto
moving, he had left with Gargantua, and marked out, in his
great and universal hydrographical chart, the course which
they were to steer to visit the oracle of the Holy Bottle
Bacbuc. The number of ships were such as I described in the
third book, convoyed by a like number of triremes, men of
war, galleons, and feluccas, well-rigged, caulked, and stored
with a good quantity of Pantagruelion.

All the officers, droggermen, pilots, captains, mates, boat-
swains, midshipmen, quartermasters, and sailors, met in the
Thalamege, Pantagruel's principal flag-ship, which had in

her stern for her ensign a huge large bottle, half silver well polished, the other half gold enamelled with carnation; whereby it was easy to guess that white and red were the colours of the noble travellers, and that they went for the word of the Bottle.

Or the stern of the second was a lantern like those of the ancients, industriously made with diaphanous stone, implying that they were to pass by Lanternland. The third ship had for her device a fine deep china ewer. The fourth, a double-handed jar of gold, much like an ancient urn. The fifth, a famous can made of sperm of emerald. The sixth, a monk's mumping bottle made of the four metals together. The seventh, an ebony funnel, all embossed and wrought with gold after the Tauchic manner. The eighth, an ivy goblet, very precious, inlaid with gold. The ninth, a cup of fine Obriz gold. The tenth, a tumbler of aromatic agoloch (you call it lignum aloes) edged with Cyprian gold, after the Azemine make. The eleventh, a golden vine-tub of mosaic work. The twelfth, a runlet of unpolished gold, covered with a small vine of large Indian pearl of Topiarian work. Insomuch that there was not a man, however in the dumps, musty, sour-looked, or melancholic he were, not even excepting that blubbering whiner Heraclitus, had he been there, but seeing this noble convoy of ships and their devices, must have been seized with present gladness of heart, and, smiling at the conceit, have said that the travellers were all honest topers, true-pitcher men, and have judged by a most sure prognostication that their voyage, both outward and homeward bound, would be performed in mirth and perfect health.

In the Thalamege, where was the general meeting, Pantagruel made a short but sweet exhortation, wholly backed with authorities from Scripture upon navigation; which being ended, with an audible voice prayers were said in the presence and hearing of all the burghers of Thalassa, who had flocked to the mole to see them take shipping. After the prayers was melodiously sung a psalm of the holy King David, which begins, *When Israel went out of Egypt;* and that being ended, tables were placed upon deck, and a feast speedily served up. The Thalassians, who had also borne a chorus in the psalm, caused store of belly-timber to be brought out of their houses. All drank to them; they drank all; which was the cause that none of the whole company gave up what they had eaten, nor were sea-sick, with a pain at the head and stomach; which inconveniency they could not so easily have prevented by drinking, for some time before, salt water, either alone or mixed with wine; using quinces, citron peel, juice of pomegranates, sourish sweetmeats, fasting a long time, covering their stomachs with paper, or following such other idle remedies as foolish physicians prescribe to those that go to sea.

Having often renewed their tipplings, each mother's son retired on board his own ship, and set sail all so fast with a merry gale at south-east; to which point of the compass the chief pilot, James Brayer by name, had shaped his course, and fixed all things accordingly. For seeing that the Oracle of the Holy Bottle lay near Cathay, in the Upper India, his advice, and that of Xenomanes also, was not to steer the course which the Portuguese use, while sailing through the torrid zone, and Cape Bona Speranza, at the south point of Africa, beyond the equinoctial line, and losing sight of the northern pole, their guide, they make a prodigious long voyage; but rather to keep as near the parallel of the said India as possible, and to tack to the westward of the said pole, so that winding under the north, they might find themselves in the latitude of the port of Olone, without coming nearer it for fear of being shut up in the frozen sea;

whereas, following this canonical turn, by the said parallel, they must have that on the right to the eastward, which at their departure was on their left.

This proved a much shorter cut; for without shipwreck, danger, or loss of men, with uninterrupted good weather, except one day near the island of the Macreons, they performed in less than four months the voyage of Upper India, which the Portuguese, with a thousand inconveniences and innumerable dangers, can hardly complete in three years. And it is my opinion, with submission to better judgments, that this course was perhaps steered by those Indians who sailed to Germany, and were honourably received by the King ot Swedes, while Quintus Metellus Celer was proconsul of the Gauls; as Cornelius Nepos, Pomponius Mela, and Pliny after them tell us.

CHAPTER 2

HOW PANTAGRUEL BOUGHT MANY RARITIES IN THE ISLAND OF MEDAMOTHY

THAT day and the two following they neither discovered land nor anything new; for they had formerly sailed that way: but on the fourth they made an island called Medamothy, of a fine and delightful prospect, by reason of the vast number of lighthouses and high marble towers in its circuit, which is not less than that of Canada [sic]. Pantagruel, inquiring who governed there, heard that it was King Philophanes, absent at that time on account of the marriage of his brother Philotheamon with the infanta of the kingdom of Engys.

Hearing this, he went ashore in the harbour, and while every ship's crew watered, passed his time in viewing divers pictures, pieces of tapestry, animals, fishes, birds, and other

exotic and foreign merchandises, which were along the walks
of the mole and in the markets of the port. For it was the
third day of the great and famous fair of the place, to which
the chief merchants of Africa and Asia resorted. Out of
these Friar John bought him two rare pictures; in one of
which the face of a man that brings in an appeal was drawn
to the life; and in the other a servant that wants a master,
with every needful particular, action, countenance, look, gait,
feature, and deportment, being an original by Master Charles
Charmois, principal painter to King Megistus; and he paid
for them in the court fashion, with congé and grimace. Panurge bought a large picture copied and done from the needle
work formerly wrought by Philomela, showing to her sister
Progne how her brother-in-law Tereus had by force hand-
selled her copyhold, and then cut out her tongue that she
might not (as women will) tell tales. I vow and swear by
the handle of my paper lantern that it was a gallant, a
mirific, nay, a most admirable piece. Nor do you think, I
pray you, that in it was the picture of a man playing the
beast with two backs with a female; this had been too silly
and gross: no, no; it was another-guise thing, and much
plainer. You may, if you please, see it at Theleme, on the
left hand as you go into the high gallery. Epistemon bought
another, wherein were painted to the life the ideas of Plato
and the atoms of Epicurus. Rhizotome purchased another,
wherein Echo was drawn to the life. Pantagruel caused to
be bought, by Gymnast, the life and deeds of Achilles, in
seventy-eight pieces of tapestry, four fathom long, and three
fathom broad, all of Phrygian silk, embossed with gold and
silver; the work beginning at the nuptials of Peleus and
Thetis, continuing to the birth of Achilles; his youth, described by Statius Papinius; his warlike achievements, celebrated by Homer; his death and obsequies, written by Ovid

and Quintus Calaber; and ending at the appearance of his ghost, and Polyxena's sacrifice, rehearsed by Euripides.

He also caused to be bought three fine young unicorns; one of them a male of a chestnut colour, and two grey dappled females; also a tarand, whom he bought of a Scythian of the Gelones' country.

A tarand is an animal as big as a bullock, having a head like a stag, or a little bigger, two stately horns with large branches, cloven feet, hair long like that of a furred Muscovite, I mean a bear, and a skin almost as hard as steel armour. The Scythian said that there are but few tarands to be found in Scythia, because it varieth its colour according to the diversity of the places where it grazes and abides, and represents the colour of the grass, plants, trees, shrubs, flowers, meadows, rocks, and generally of all things near which it comes. It hath this common with the sea-pulp, or polypus, with the thoes, with the wolves of India, and with the chameleon, which is a kind of lizard so wonderful that Democritus hath written a whole book on its figure and anatomy, as also of its virtue and propriety in magic. This I can affirm, that I have seen it change its colour, not only at the approach of things that have a colour, but by its own voluntary impulse, according to its fear or other affections; as, for example, upon a green carpet I have certainly seen it become green; but having remained there some time, it turned yellow, blue, tanned, and purple in course, in the same manner as you see a turkey-cock's comb change colour according to its passions. But what we find most surprising in this tarand is, that not only its face and skin, but also its hair could take whatever colour was about it. Near Panurge, with his kersey coat, its hair used to turn grey; near Pantagruel with his scarlet mantle, its hair and skin grew red; near the pilot, dressed after the fashion of the Isiacs of Anubis in

Egypt, its hair seemed all white, which two last colours the
chameleon cannot borrow.

When the creature was free from any fear or affection, the
colour of its hair was just such as you see that of the asses
of Meung.

CHAPTER 3

HOW PANTAGRUEL WENT ASHORE AT THE ISLAND OF CHELY,
WHERE HE SAW KING ST. PANIGON

WE sailed right before the wind, which we had at west,
leaving those odd alliancers with their ace-of-clubs snouts,
and having taken height by the sun, stood in for Chely, a
large, fruitful, wealthy, and well-peopled island. King St.
Panigon, first of the name, reigned there, and, attended by
the princes his sons and the nobles of his court, came as far
as the port to receive Pantagruel, and conducted him to his
palace; near the gate of which the queen, attended by the
princesses her daughters and the court ladies, received us.
Panigon directed her and all her retinue to salute Pantagruel
and his men with a kiss; for such was the civil custom of
the country; and they were all fairly bussed accordingly,
except Friar John, who stepped aside and sneaked off among
the king's officers. Panigon used all the entreaties imaginable
to persuade Pantagruel to tarry there that day and the next;
but he would needs be gone, and excused himself upon the
opportunity of wind and weather, which, being oftener desired than enjoyed, ought not to be neglected when it comes.
Panigon, having heard these reasons, let us go, but first made
us take off some five-and-twenty or thirty bumpers each.

Pantagruel, returning to the port, missed Friar John, and
asked why he was not with the rest of the company. Panurge
could not tell how to excuse him, and would have gone

back to the palace to call him, when Friar John overtook them, and merrily cried, Long live the noble Panigon! As I love my belly, he minds good eating, and keeps a noble house and a dainty kitchen. I have been there, boys. Everything goes about by dozens. I was in good hopes to have stuffed my puddings there like a monk. What! always in a kitchen, friend? said Pantagruel. By the belly of St. Cramcapon, quoth the friar, I understand the customs and ceremonies which are used there much better than all the formal stuff, antique postures, and nonsensical fiddle-faddle that must be used with those women, *magni magna, shittencumshita,* cringes, grimaces, scrapes, bows, and congées; double honours this way, triple salutes that way, the embrace, the grasp, the squeeze, the hug, the leer, the smack, *baso las manos de vostra merce, de vostra maesta.* You are most *tarabin, tarabas, Strout;* that's downright Dutch. Why all this ado? I don't say but a man might be for a bit by the bye and away, to be doing as well as his neighbours; but this little nasty cringing and courtesying made me as mad as any March devil. You talk of kissing ladies; by the worthy and sacred frock I wear, I seldom venture upon it, lest I be served as was the Lord of Guyercharois. What was it? said Pantagruel; I know him. He is one of the best friends I have.

He was invited to a sumptuous feast, said Friar John, by a relation and neighbour of his, together with all the gentlemen and ladies in the neighbourhood. Now some of the latter expecting his coming, dressed the pages in women's clothes, and finified them like any babies; then ordered them to meet my lord at his coming near the drawbridge. So the complimenting monsieur came, and there kissed the petticoated lads with great formality. At last the ladies, who minded passages in the gallery, burst out with laughing, and made

signs to the pages to take off their dress; which the good
lord having observed, the devil a bit he durst make up to
true ladies to kiss them, but said, that since they had disguised the pages, by his great grandfather's helmet, these
were certainly the very footmen and grooms still more cun-
ningly disguised. Odds fish, *da jurandi,* why do not we rather
remove our humanities into some good warm kitchen of
God, that noble laboratory, and there admire the turning
of the spits, the harmonious rattling of the jacks and fenders,
criticise on the position of the lard, the temperature of the
pottages, the preparation for the dessert, and the order
of the wine service? *Beati immaculati in via.* Matter of
breviary, my masters.

CHAPTER 4

WHY MONKS LOVE TO BE IN KITCHENS

THIS, said Epistemon, is spoke like a true monk; I mean
like a right monking monk, not a bemonked monastical
monkling. Truly you put me in mind of some passages that
happened at Florence, some twenty years ago, in a company of studious travellers, fond of visiting the learned, and
seeing the antiquities of Italy, among whom I was. As we
viewed the situation and beauty of Florence, the structure
of the dome, the magnificence of the churches and palaces,
we strove to outdo one another in giving them their due;
when a certain monk of Amiens, Bernard Lardon, by name,
quite angry, scandalized, and out of all patience, told us,
I don't know what the devil you can find in this same town,
that is so much cried up; for my part I have looked and
pored and stared as well as the best of you; I think my eye-
sight is as clear as another's body; and what can one see
after all? There are fine houses, indeed, and that's all. But

the cage does not feed the birds. God and Monsieur St. Bernard, our good patron, be with us! in all this same town I have not seen one poor lane of roasting cooks; and yet I have not a little looked about and sought for so necessary a part of a commonwealth: ay, and I dare assure you that I have pried up and down with the exactness of an informer; as ready to number, both to the right and left, how many, and on what side, we might find most roasting cooks, as a spy would be to reckon the bastions of a town. Now at Amiens, in four, nay, five times less ground than we have trod in our contemplations, I could have shown you above fourteen streets of roasting cooks, most ancient, savoury, and aromatic. I cannot imagine what kind of pleasure you can have taken in gazing on the lions and Africans (so methinks you call their tigers) near the belfry, or in ogling the porcupines and estridges in the Lord Philip Strozzi's palace. Faith and truth I had rather see a good fat goose at the spit. This porphyry, those marbles are fine; I say nothing to the contrary; but our cheesecakes at Amiens are far better in my mind. These ancient statues are well made; I am willing to believe it; but, by St. Ferreol of Abbeville, we have young wenches in our country which please me better a thousand times.

What is the reason, asked Friar John, that monks are always to be found in kitchens, and kings, emperors, and popes are never there? Is there not, said Rhizotome, some latent virtue and specific propriety hid in the kettles and pans, which, as the loadstone attracts iron, draws the monks there, and cannot attract emperors, popes, or kings? Or is it a natural induction and inclination, fixed in the frocks and cowls, which of itself leads and forceth those good religious men into kitchens, whether they will or no? He would speak of forms following matter, as Averroes calls them, answered Epistemon. Right, said Friar John.

I will not offer to solve this problem, said Pantagruel; for it is somewhat ticklish, and you can hardly handle it without coming off scurvily; but I will tell you what I have heard.

Antigonus, King of Macedon, one day coming into one of the tents, where his cooks used to dress his meat, and finding there poet Antagoras frying a conger, and holding the pan himself, merrily asked him, Pray, Mr. Poet, was Homer frying congers when he wrote the deeds of Agamemnon? Antagoras readily answered: But do you think, sir, that when Agamemnon did them he made it his business to know if any in his camp were frying congers? The king thought it an indecency that a poet should be thus a-frying in a kitchen; and the poet let the king know that it was a more indecent thing for a king to be found in such a place. I'll clap another story upon the neck of this, quoth Panurge, and will tell you what Breton Villandry answered one day to the Duke of Guise.

They were saying that at a certain battle of King Francis against Charles the Fifth, Breton, armed cap-à-pie to the teeth, and mounted like St. George, yet sneaked off, and played least in sight during the engagement. Blood and oons, answered Breton, I was there, and can prove it easily; nay, even where you, my lord, dared not have been. The duke began to resent this as too rash and saucy; but Breton easily appeased him, and set them all a-laughing. Egad, my lord, quoth he, I kept out of harm's way; I was all the while with your page Jack, skulking in a certain place where you had not dared hide your head as I did. Thus discoursing, they got to their ships, and left the island of Chely.

CHAPTER 5

HOW PANTAGRUEL PASSED BY THE LAND OF PETTIFOGGING,
AND OF THE STRANGE WAY OF LIVING AMONG THE
CATCHPOLES

STEERING our course forwards the next day, we passed
through Pettifogging, a country all blurred and blotted, so
that I could hardly tell what to make on't. There we saw
some pettifoggers and catchpoles, rogues that will hang
their father for a groat. They neither invited us to eat or
drink; but, with a multiplied train of scrapes and cringes,
said they were all at our service for the *Legem pone*.

One of our droggermen related to Pantagruel their strange
way of living, diametrically opposed to that of our modern
Romans; for at Rome a world of folks get an honest liveli-
hood by poisoning, drubbing, lambasting, stabbing, and
murthering; but the catchpoles earn theirs by being thrashed;
so that if they were long without a tight lambasting, the
poor dogs with their wives and children would be starved.
This is just, quoth Panurge, like those who, as Galen tells
us, cannot erect the cavernous nerve towards the equinoctial
circle unless they are soundly flogged. By St. Patrick's slipper, whoever should jerk me so, would soon, instead of setting me right, throw me off the saddle, in the devil's name.

The way is this, said the interpreter. When a monk,
levite, close-fisted usurer, or lawyer owes a grudge to some
neighbouring gentleman, he sends to him one of those catchpoles or apparitors, who nabs, or at least cites him, serves
a writ or warrant upon him, thumps, abuses, and affronts
him impudently by natural instinct, and according to his
pious instructions; insomuch, that if the gentleman hath but
any guts in his brains, and is not more stupid than a gyrin
frog, he will find himself obliged either to apply a faggot-

stick or his sword to the rascal's jobbernowl, give him the gentle lash, or make him cut a caper out at the window, by way of correction. This done, Catchpole is rich for four months at least, as if bastinadoes were his real harvest; for the monk, levite, usurer, or lawyer will reward him roundly; and my gentleman must pay him such swingeing damages that his acres must bleed for it, and he be in danger of miserably rotting within a stone doublet, as if he had struck the king.

Quoth Panurge, I know an excellent remedy against this, used by the Lord of Basché. What is it? said Pantagruel. The Lord of Basché, said Panurge, was a brave, honest, noble-spirited gentleman, who, at his return from the long war in which the Duke of Ferrara, with the help of the French, bravely defended himself against the fury of Pope Julius the Second, was every day cited, warned, and prosecuted at the suit and for the sport and fancy of the fat prior of St. Louant.

One morning, as he was at breakfast with some of his domestics (for he loved to be sometimes among them) he sent for one Loire, his baker, and his spouse, and for one Oudart, the vicar of his parish, who was also his butler, as the custom was then in France; then said to them before his gentlemen and other servants: You all see how I am daily plagued with these rascally catchpoles. Truly, if you do not lend me your helping hand, I am fully resolved to leave the country, and go fight for the sultan, or the devil, rather than be thus eternally teased. Therefore, to be rid of their damned visits, hereafter, when any of them come here, be ready, you baker and your wife, to make your personal appearance in my great hall, in your wedding clothes, as if you were going to be affianced. Here, take these ducats, which I give you to keep you in a fitting garb. As for you, Sir

Oudart, be sure you make your personal appearance there in your fine surplice and stole, not forgetting your holy water, as if you were to wed them. Be you there also, Trudon, said he to his drummer, with your pipe and tabor. The form of matrimony must be read, and the bride kissed; then all of you, as the witnesses use to do in this country, shall give one another the remembrance of the wedding, which you know is to be a blow with your fist, bidding the party struck remember the nuptials by that token. This will but make you have the better stomach to your supper; but when you come to the catchpole's turn, thrash him thrice and threefold, as you would a sheaf of green corn; do not spare him; maul him, drub him, lambast him, swinge him off, I pray you. Here, take these steel gauntlets, covered with kid. Head, back, belly, and sides, give him blows innumerable; he that gives him most shall be my best friend. Fear not to be called to an account about it; for the blows must seem to be given in jest, as it is customary among us at all weddings.

Ay, but how shall we know the catchpole? said the man of God. All sorts of people daily resort to this castle. I have taken care of that, replied the lord. When some fellow, either on foot, or on a scurvy jade, with a large broad silver ring on his thumb, comes to the door, he is certainly a catchpole; the porter having civilly let him in, shall ring the bell; then be all ready, and come into the hall, to act the tragi-comedy whose plot I have now laid for you.

That numerical day, as chance would have it, came an old fat ruddy catchpole. Having knocked at the gate, and then pissed, as most men will do, the porter soon found him out, by his large greasy spatterdashes, his jaded hollow-flanked mare, his bagful of writs and informations dangling at his girdle, but, above all, by the large silver hoop on his left thumb.

The porter was civil to him, admitted him in kindly, and
rung the bell briskly. As soon as the baker and his wife
heard it, they clapped on their best clothes, and made their
personal appearance in the hall, keeping their gravities like a
new-made judge. The dominie put on his surplice and stole,
and as he came out of his office, met the catchpole, had him
in there, and made him suck his face a good while, while the
gauntlets were drawing on all hands; and then told him,
You are come just in pudding-time; my lord is in his right
cue. We shall feast like kings anon; here is to be swingeing
doings; we have a wedding in the house; here, drink and
cheer up; pull away.

While these two were at it hand-to-fist, Basché, seeing
all his people in the hall in their proper equipage, sends for
the vicar. Oudart comes with the holy-water pot, followed
by the catchpole, who, as he came into the hall, did not
forget to make good store of awkward cringes, and then
served Basché with a writ. Basché gave him grimace for
grimace, slipped an angel into his mutton-fist, and prayed
him to assist at the contract and ceremony; which he did.
When it was ended, thumps and fisticuffs began to fly about
among the assistants; but when it came to the catchpole's
turn, they all laid on him so unmercifully with their gauntlets that they at last settled him, all stunned and battered,
bruised and mortified, with one of his eyes black and blue,
eight ribs bruised, his brisket sunk in, his omoplates in
four quarters, his under jawbone in three pieces; and all
this in jest, and no harm done. God wot how the levite belaboured him, hiding within the long sleeve of his canonical
shirt his huge steel gauntlet lined with ermine; for he was a
strong-built bull, and an old dog at fisticuffs. The catchpole,
all of a bloody tiger-like stripe, with much ado crawled home
to L'Isle Bouchart, well pleased and edified, however, with

Basché's kind reception; and, with the help of the good surgeons of the place, lived as long as you would have him. From that time to this, not a word of the business, the memory of it was lost with the sound of the bells that rung with joy at his funeral.

CHAPTER 6

HOW PANTAGRUEL MET WITH A GREAT STORM AT SEA

THE next day we espied nine sail that came spooning before the wind; they were full of Dominicans, Jesuits, Capuchins, Hermits, Austins, Bernardins, Egnatins, Celestins, Theatins, Amadeans, Cordeliers, Carmelites, Minims, and the devil and all of other holy monks and friars who were going to the Council of Chesil, to sift and garble some new articles of faith against the new heretics. Panurge was overjoyed to see them, being most certain of good luck for that day and a long train of others. So having courteously saluted the blessed fathers, and recommended the salvation of his precious soul to their devout prayers and private ejaculations, he caused seventy-eight dozen of Westphalia hams, units of pots of caviare, tens of Bologna sausages, hundreds of botargoes, and thousands of fine angels, for the souls of the dead, to be thrown on board their ships. Pantagruel seemed metagrabolized, dozing, out of sorts, and as melancholic as a cat. Friar John, who soon perceived it, was inquiring of him whence should come this unusual sadness; when the master, whose watch it was, observing the fluttering of the ancient above the poop, and seeing that it began to overcast, judged that we should have wind; therefore he bid the boatswain call all hands upon deck, officers, sailors, foremast-men, swabbers, and cabin-boys, and even the passengers; made them first settle their topsails, take in their spritsail; then he cried, In with your topsails, lower the foresail, tallow under the parrels, braid up close all them sails, strike your topmasts to the cap, make all sure with your sheeps-feet, lash your guns fast. All this was nimbly done. Immediately it blowed a storm; the sea began to roar and swell mountain-high; the rut of the sea was great, the waves breaking upon our ship's quarter; the northwest wind blustered and overblowed; boisterous gusts, dreadful clashing, and deadly scuds of wind whistled through our yards and made our shrouds rattle again. The thunder grumbled so horridly that you would have thought heaven had been tumbling about our ears; at the same time it lightened, rained, hailed; the sky lost its transparent hue, grew dusky, thick, and gloomy, so that we had no other light than that of the flashes of lightning and rending of the clouds. The hurricanes, flaws, and sudden whirlwinds began to make a flame about us by the lightnings, fiery vapours, and other aerial ejaculations. Oh, how our looks were full of amazement and trouble, while the saucy winds did rudely lift up above us the mountainous waves of the main! Believe me, it seemed to us a lively image of the chaos, where fire, air, sea, land, and all the elements were in a refractory confusion. Poor Panurge having with the full contents of the inside of his doublet plentifully fed the fish, greedy enough of such odious fare, sat on the deck all in a heap, with his nose and arse together, most sadly cast down, moping and half dead; invoked and called to his assistance all the blessed he- and she-saints he could muster up; swore and vowed to confess in time and place convenient, and then bawled out frightfully, steward, maitre d'hotel, see ho! my friend, my father, my uncle, prithee let us have a piece of powdered beef or pork; we shall drink but too much anon, for aught I see. Eat little and drink the more will hereafter be my motto, I fear.

Would to our dear Lord, and to our blessed, worthy, and sacred Lady, I were now, I say, this very minute of an hour, well on shore, on terra firma, hale and easy. O twice and thrice happy those that plant cabbages! O destinies, why did you not spin me for a cabbage-planter? Oh how few are there to whom Jupiter hath been so favourable as to predestinate them to plant cabbages! They have always one foot on the ground, and the other not far from it. Dispute who will of felicity and *summum bonum*, for my part whosoever plants cabbages is now, by my decree, proclaimed most happy; for as good a reason as the philosopher Pyrrho, being in the same danger, and seeing a hog near the shore eating some scattered oats, declared it happy in two respects; first, because it had plenty of oats, and besides that, was on shore. Ha, for a divine and princely habitation, commend me to the cows' floor.

Murder! This wave will sweep us away, blessed Saviour! O my friends! a little vinegar. I sweat again with mere agony. Alas! the mizen-sail's split, the gallery's washed away, the masts are sprung, the maintop-masthead dives into the sea; the keel is up to the sun; our shrouds are almost all broke, and blown away. Alas! alas! where is our main course? *Al is verlooren, by Godt!* our topmast is run adrift. Alas! who shall have this wreck? Friend, lend me here behind you one of these whales. Your lantern is fallen, my lads. Alas! do not let go the main-tack nor the bowline. I hear the block crack; is it broke? For the Lord's sake, let us have the hull, and let all the rigging be damned. Be, be, be, bous, bous, bous. Look to the needle of your compass, I beseech you, good Sir Astrophil, and tell us, if you can, whence comes this storm. My heart's sunk down below my midriff. By my troth, I am in a sad fright, bou, bou, bou, bous, bous, I am lost for ever. I conskite myself for mere madness and fear. Bou, bou, bou, bou, Otto to to to to ti. Bou, bou, bou, ou, ou, ou, bou, bou, bous. I sink, I'm drowned, I'm gone, good people, I'm drowned.

CHAPTER 7

WHAT COUNTENANCES PANURGE AND FRIAR JOHN KEPT DURING THE STORM

PANTAGRUEL, having first implored the help of the great and Almighty Deliverer, and prayed publicly with fervent devotion, by the pilot's advice held tightly the mast of the ship. Friar John had stripped himself to his waistcoat, to help the seamen. Epistemon, Ponocrates, and the rest did as much. Panurge alone sat on his breech upon deck, weeping and howling. Friar John espied him going on the quarter-deck, and said to him, Odzoons! Panurge the calf, Panurge the whiner, Panurge brayer, would it not become thee much better to lend us here a helping hand than to lie lowing like a cow, as thou dost, sitting on thy stones like a bald-breeched baboon? Be, be, be, bous, bous, bous, returned Panurge; Friar John, my friend, my good father, I am drowning, my dear friend! I drown! I am a dead man, my dear father in God; I am a dead man, my friend; your cutting anger cannot save me from this; alas! alas! we are above ela. Above the pitch, out of tune, and off the hinges. Be, be, be, bou, bous. Alas! we are now above *g sol re ut*. I sink, I sink, ha, my father, my uncle, my all. The water is got into my shoes by the collar; bous, bous, bous, paish, hu, hu, hu, he, he, he, ha, ha, I drown. Alas! alas! Hu, hu, hu, hu, hu, hu, hu, be, be, bous, bous, bobous, bobous, ho, ho, ho, ho, ho, alas! alas! Now I am like your tumblers, my feet stand higher than my head. Would to heaven I were now with those good holy fathers bound for the council whom we met this morning, so godly, so fat, so merry, so plump and comely. Holos, bolos, holas, holas, alas! This devilish wave (*mea culpa Deus*), I mean this wave of God, will sink our vessel. Alas! Friar John, my father, my friend, confession. Here I am down on my knees; *confiteor;* your holy blessing. Come hither and be damned, thou pitiful devil, and help us, said Friar John (who fell a-swearing and cursing like a tinker), in the name of thirty legions of black devils, come; will you come? Do not let us swear at this time, said Panurge; holy father, my friend, do not swear, I beseech you; to-morrow as much as you please. Holos, holos, alas! our ship leaks. I drown, alas! alas! I will give eighteen hundred thousand crowns to anyone that will set me on shore, all berayed and bedaubed as I am now. If ever there was a man in my country in the like pickle. *Confiteor,* alas! a word or two of testament or codicil at least. A thousand devils seize the cuckoldy cow-hearted mongrel, cried Friar John. Ods-belly, art thou talking here of making thy will now we are in danger, and it behoveth us to bestir our stumps lustily, or never? Wilt thou come, ho devil? Midshipman, my friend; O the rare lieutenant; here Gymnast, here on the poop. We are, by the mass, all beshit now; our light is out. This is hastening to the devil as fast as it can. Alas, bou, bou, bou, bou, bou, alas, alas, alas, alas, said Panurge; was it here we were born to perish? Oh! ho! good people, I drown, I die. *Consummatum est.* I am sped— *Magna, gna, gna,* said Friar John. Fie upon him, how ugly the shitten howler looks. Boy, younker, see hoyh. Mind the pumps, or the devil choke thee. Hast thou hurt thyself? Zoons, here fasten it to one of these blocks. On this side, in the devil's name, hay—so, my boy. Ah, Friar John, said Panurge, good ghostly father, dear friend, don't let us swear, you sin. Oh, ho, oh, ho, be be be bous, bous, bhous, I sink, I die, my friends. I die in charity with all the world. Farewell, *in manus.* Bohus, bohous, bhousowauswaus. St. Michael of Aure! St. Nicholas! now, now or never, I here make you a solemn vow, and to our Saviour, that if you stand by me this time, I mean if you set me ashore out of this danger, I will build you a fine large little chapel or two, between Quande and Montsoreau, where neither cow nor calf shall feed. Oh ho, oh ho. Above eighteen pailfuls or two of it are got down my gullet; bous, bhous, bhous, bhous, how damned bitter and salt it is! By the virtue, said Friar John, of the blood, the flesh, the belly, the head, if I hear thee again howling, thou cuckoldy cur, I'll maul thee worse than any sea-wolf. Odsfish, why don't we take him up by the lugs and throw him overboard to the bottom of the sea? Hear, sailor; ho, honest fellow. Thus, thus, my friend, hold fast above. In truth, here is a sad lightning and thundering; I think that all the devils are got loose; it is holiday with them; or else Madame Proserpine is in child's labour: all the devils dance a morrice.

CHAPTER 8

HOW THE PILOTS WERE FORSAKING THEIR SHIPS IN THE GREATEST STRESS OF WEATHER

OH, said Panurge, you sin, Friar John, my former crony! former, I say, for at this time I am no more, you are no more. It goes against my heart to tell it you; for I believe this swearing doth your spleen a great deal of good; as it is a great ease to a wood-cleaver to cry hem at every blow, and as one who plays at ninepins is wonderfully helped if, when he hath not thrown his bowl right, and is like to make a bad cast, some ingenious stander-by leans and scews his body halfway about on that side which the bowl should have took to hit the pins. Nevertheless, you offend, my sweet friend.

But what do you think of eating some kind of cabirotadoes? Wouldn't this secure us from this storm? I have read that the ministers of the gods Cabiri, so much celebrated by Orpheus, Apollonius, Pherecydes, Strabo, Pausanias, and Herodotus were always secure in time of storm. He dotes, he raves, the poor devil! A thousand, a million, nay, a hundred million of devils seize the hornified doddipole. Lend's a hand here, hoh, tiger, wouldst thou? Here, on the starboard side. Ods-me, thou buffalo's head stuffed with relics, what ape's paternoster art thou muttering and chattering here between thy teeth? That devil of a sea-calf is the cause of all this storm, and is the only man who doth not lend a helping hand. By G—, if I come near thee, I'll fetch thee out by the head and ears with a vengeance, and chastise thee like any tempestative devil. Here, mate, my lad, hold fast, till I have made a double knot. O brave boy! Would to heaven thou wert abbot of Talemouze, and that he that is were guardian of Croullay. Hold, brother Ponocrates, you will hurt yourself, man. Epistemon, prithee stand off out of the hatchway. Methinks I saw the thunder fall there but just now. Con the ship, so ho—Mind your steerage. Well said, thus, thus, steady, keep her thus, get the long-boat clear—steady. Ods-fish, the beak-head is staved to pieces. Grumble, devils. If this be weather, the devil's a ram. Nay by G—, a little more would have washed me clear away into the current. I think all the legions of devils hold here their provincial chapter, or are polling, canvassing, and wrangling for the election of a new rector. Starboard; well said. Take heed; have a care of your noddle, lad, in the devil's name. So ho, starboard, starboard. Be, be, be, bous, bous, bous, cried Panurge; bous, bous, be, be, be, bous, bous, I am lost. I see neither heaven nor earth; of the four elements we have here only fire and water left. Bou, bou, bou, bous, bous, bous

Would it were the pleasure of the worthy divine bounty that I were at this present hour in the close at Sevillé, or at Innocent's the pastry-cook over against the painted wine-vault at Chinon, though I were to strip to my doublet, and bake the petti-pasties myself.

Honest man, could not you throw me ashore? you can do a world of good things, they say. I give you all Salmigondinois, and my large shore full of whelks, cockles, and periwinkles, if, by your industry, I ever set foot on firm ground. Alas! alas! I drown. Harkee, my friends, since we cannot get safe into port, let us come to an anchor into some road, no matter whither. Drop all your anchors; let us be out of danger, I beseech you. Here, honest tar, get you into the chains, and heave the lead, an't please you. Let us know how many fathom water we are in. Sound, friend, in the Lord Harry's name. Let us know whether a man might here drink easily without stooping. I am apt to believe one might. Helm a-lee, hoh, cried the pilot. Helm a-lee; a hand or two at the helm; about ships with her; helm a-lee, helm a-lee. Stand off from the leech of the sail. Hoh! belay, here make fast below; hoh, helm a-lee, lash sure the helm a-lee, and let her drive. Is it come to that? said Pantagruel; our good Saviour then help us. Let her lie under the sea, cried James Brahier, our chief mate; let her drive. To prayers, to prayers; let all think on their souls, and fall to prayers; nor hope to escape but by a miracle: Let us, said Panurge, make some good pious kind of vow; alas, alas, alas! bou, bou, be, be, be, bous, bous, bous, oho, oho, oho, oho, let us make a pilgrim; come, come, let every man club his penny towards it, come on. Here, here, on this side, said Friar John, in the devil's name. Let her drive, for the Lord's sake unhang the rudder; hoh, let her drive, let her drive, and let us drink, I say, of the best and most cheering; d'ye hear, steward, produce, exhibit; for, d'ye see this, and all the rest will as well go to the devil out of hand. A pox on that wind-broker Æolus, with his fluster-blusters. Sirrah, page, bring me here my drawer (for so he called his breviary); stay a little here; haul, friend, thus. Odzoons, here is a deal of hail and thunder to no purpose. Hold fast above, I pray you. When have we All-saints day? I believe it is the unholy holiday of all the devil's crew. Alas! said Panurge, Friar John damns himself here as black as butter-milk for the nonce. Oh, what a good friend I lose in him. Alas! alas! this is another gatsbout than last year's. We are falling out of Scylla into Charybdis. Oho! I drown. *Confiteor;* one poor word or two by way of testament, Friar John, my ghostly father; good Mr. Abstractor, my crony, my Achates, Xenomanes, my all. Alas! I drown; two words of testament here upon this ladder.

CHAPTER 9

A CONTINUATION OF THE STORM, WITH A SHORT DISCOURSE ON THE SUBJECT OF MAKING TESTAMENTS AT SEA

To make one's last will, said Epistemon, at this time that we ought to bestir ourselves and help our seamen, on the penalty of being drowned, seems to me as idle and ridiculous a maggot as that of some of Cæsar's men, who, at their coming into the Gauls, were mightily busied in making wills and codicils; bemoaned their fortune and the absence of their spouses and friends at Rome, when it was absolutely necessary for them to run to their arms and use their utmost strength against Ariovistus their enemy.

This also is to be as silly as that jolt-headed loblolly of a carter, who, having laid his waggon fast in a slough, down on his marrow-bones was calling on the strong-backed deity,

Hercules, might and main, to help him at a dead lift, but all the while forgot to goad on his oxen and lay his shoulder to the wheels, as it behooved him; as if a Lord have mercy upon us alone would have got his cart out of the mire.

What will it signify to make your will now? for either we shall come off or drown for it. If we 'scape, it will not signify a straw to us; for testaments are of no value or authority but by the death of the testators. If we are drowned, will it not be drowned too? Prithee, who will transmit it to the executors? Some kind wave will throw it ashore, like Ulysses, replied Panurge; and some king's daughter, going to fetch a walk in the fresco, on the evening will find it, and take care to have it proved and fulfilled; nay, and have some stately cenotaph erected to my memory, as Dido had to that of her goodman Sichæus, Æneas to Deiphobus, upon the Trojan shore, near Rhœte; Andromache to Hector, in the city of Buthrot; Aristotle to Hermias and Eubulus; the Athenians to the poet Euripides; the Romans to Drusus in Germany, and to Alexander Severus, their emperor, in the Gauls; Argentier to Callaischre; Xenocrates to Lysidices; Timares to his son Teleutagoras; Eupolis and Aristodice to their son Theotimus; Onestus to Timocles; Callimachus to Sopolis, the son of Dioclides; Catullus to his brother; Statius to his father; Germain of Brie to Hervé, the Breton tarpaulin. Art thou mad, said Friar John, to run on at this rate? Help, here, in the name of five hundred thousand millions of cartloads of devils, help! may a shanker gnaw thy moustachios, and the three rows of pockroyals and cauliflowers cover thy bum and turd-barrel instead of breeches and codpiece. Codsooks, our ship is almost overset. Odsdeath, how shall we clear her? it is well if she do not founder. What a devilish sea there runs! She'll never try nor hull; the sea will overtake her, so we shall never 'scape; the devil 'scape me. Then

Pantagruel was heard to make a sad exclamation, saying, with a loud voice, Lord save us, we perish; yet not as we would have it, but thy holy will be done. The Lord and the blessed Virgin be with us, said Panurge. Holos, alas, I drown; be be be bous, be bous, bous; *in manus*. Good heavens, send me some dolphin to carry me safe on shore, like a pretty little Arion. I shall make shift to sound the harp, if it be not unstrung. Let nineteen legions of black devils seize me, said Friar John. (The Lord be with us! whispered Panurge, between his chattering teeth.) If I come down to thee, I'll show thee to some purpose that the badge of thy humanity dangles at a calf's breech, thou ragged, horned, cuckoldy booby—-mgna, mgnan, mgnan—come thither and help us, thou great weeping calf, or may thirty millions of devils leap on thee. Wilt thou come, sea-calf? Fie! how ugly the howling whelp looks. What, always the same ditty? Come on now, my bonny drawer. This he said, opening his breviary. Come forward, thou and I must be somewhat serious for a while; let me pursue thee stiffly. *Beatus vir qui non abiit.* Pshaw, I know all this by heart, let us see the legend of Mons. St. Nicholas.

Horrida tempestas montem turbavit acutum.

Tempest was a mighty flogger of lads at Mountagu College. If pedants be damned for whipping poor little innocent wretches their scholars, he is, upon my honour, by this time fixed within Ixion's wheel, lashing the cropeared, bobtailed cur that gives it motion. If they are saved for having whipped innocent lads, he ought to be above the——

CHAPTER 10

AN END OF THE STORM

Shore, shore, cried Pantagruel. Land to, my friends, I
see land! Pluck up a good spirit, boys, 'tis within a kenning.
So! we are not far from a port.—I see the sky clearing up
to the northwards.—Look to the southeast! Courage, my
hearts, said the pilot; now she'll bear the hullock of a sail;
the sea is much smoother; some hands aloft to the maintop.
Put the helm a-weather. Steady! steady! Haul your after-
mizen bowlines. Haul, haul, haul! Thus, thus, and no near.
Mind your steerage; bring your main-tack aboard. Clear
your sheets; clear your bowlines; port, port. Helm a-lee.
Now to the sheet on the starboard side, thou son of a
whore. Thou art mightily pleased, honest fellow, quoth Friar
John, with hearing make mention of thy mother. Luff, luff,
cried the quartermaster that conned the ship, keep her full,
luff the helm. Luff. It is, answered the steersman. Keep her
thus. Get the bonnets fixed. Steady, steady.

That is well said, said Friar John; now, this is something
like a tansy. Come, come, come, children, be nimble. Good.
Luff, luff, thus. Helm a-weather. That's well said and thought
on. Methinks the storm is almost over. It was high time,
faith; however, the Lord be thanked. Our devils begin to
scamper. Out with all your sails. Hoist your sails. Hoist.
That is spoke like a man, hoist, hoist. Here, a God's name,
honest Ponocrates; thou art a lusty fornicator; the whore-
son will get none but boys. Eusthenes, thou art a notable
fellow. Run up to the fore-topsail. Thus, thus. Well said, i'
faith; thus, thus. I dare not fear anything all this while, for
it is holiday. Vea, vea, vea! huzza! This shout of the seamen is not amiss, and pleases me, for it is holiday. Keep her
full thus. Good. Cheer up, my merry mates all, cried out

Epistemon; I see already Castor on the right. Be, be, bous, bous, bous, said Panurge; I am much afraid it is the bitch Helen. It is truly Mixarchagenas, returned Epistemon, if thou likest better that denomination, which the Argives give him. Ho, ho! I see land too; let her bear in with the harbour; I see a good many people on the beach; I see a light on an obeliscolychny. Shorten your sails, said the pilot; fetch the sounding-line; we must double that point of land, and mind the sands. We are clear of them, said the sailors. Soon after, Away she goes, quoth the pilot, and so doth the rest of our fleet; help came in good season.

By St. John, said Panurge, this is spoke somewhat like. O the sweet word! there is the soul of music in it. Mgna, mgna, mgna, said Friar John; if ever thou taste a drop of it, let the devil's dam taste me, thou ballocky devil. Here, honest soul, here's a full sneaker of the very best. Bring the flagons; dost hear, Gymnast? and that same large pasty jambic, gammonic, as you will have it. Take heed you pilot her in right.

Cheer up, cried out Pantagruel; cheer up, my boys; let us be ourselves again. Do you see yonder, close by our ship, two barks, three sloops, five ships, eight pinks, four yawls, and six frigates making towards us, sent by the good people of the neighbouring island to our relief? But who is this Ucalegon below, that cries and makes such a sad moan? Were it not that I hold the mast firmly with both hands, and keep it straighter than two hundred tacklings—I would—— It is, said Friar John, that poor devil Panurge, who is troubled with a calf's ague; he quakes for fear when his belly's full. If, said Pantagruel, he hath been afraid during this dreadful hurricane and dangerous storm, provided (waiving that) he hath done his part like a man, I do not value him a jot the less for it. For as to fear in all encounters is the mark of a heavy and cowardly heart, as Agamemnon did, who for that reason is ignominiously taxed by Achilles with having dog's eyes and a stag's heart; so, not to fear when the case is evidently dreadful is a sign of want or smallness of judgment. Now, if anything ought to be feared in this life, next to offending God, I will not say it is death. I will not meddle with the disputes of Socrates and the academics, that death of itself is neither bad nor to be feared, but I will affirm that this kind of shipwreck is to be feared, or nothing is. For, as Homer saith, it is a grievous, dreadful and unnatural thing to perish at sea. And indeed Æneas, in the storm that took his fleet near Sicily, was grieved that he had not died by the hand of the brave Diomedes, and said that those were three, nay four times happy, who perished in the conflagration at Troy. No man here hath lost his life, the Lord our Saviour be eternally praised for it! but in truth here is a ship sadly out of order. Well, we must take care to have the damage repaired. Take heed we do not run aground and bulge her.

CHAPTER 11

HOW PANURGE PLAYED THE GOOD FELLOW WHEN THE STORM WAS OVER

WHAT cheer, ho, fore and aft? quoth Panurge. Oh ho! all is well, the storm is over. I beseech ye, be so kind as to let me be the first that is sent on shore; for I would by all means a little untruss a point. Shall I help you still? Here, let me see, I will coil this rope; I have plenty of courage, and of fear as little as may be. Give it me yonder, honest tar. No, no, I have not a bit of fear. Indeed, that same decumane wave that took us fore and aft somewhat altered my pulse. Down with your sails; well said. How now, Friar

John? you do nothing. Is it time for us to drink now? Wh
can tell but St. Martin's running footman Belzebuth ma
still be hatching us some further mischief? Shall I come an
help you again? Pork and peas choke me, if I do heartil
repent, though too late, not having followed the doctrin
of the good philosopher who tells us that to walk by the se
and to navigate by the shore are very safe and pleasan
things; just as 'tis to go on foot when we hold our horse b
the bridle. Ha! ha! ha! by G—, all goes well. Shall I hel
you here too? Let me see, I will do this as it should be, o
the devil's in't.

Epistemon, who had the inside of one of his hands a
flayed and bloody, having held a tackling with might an
main, hearing what Pantagruel had said, told him: You ma
believe, my lord, I had my share of fear as well as Panurge
yet I spared no pains in lending my helping hand. I con
sidered that, since by fatal and unavoidable necessity w
must all die, it is the blessed will of God that we die thi
or that hour, and this or that kind of death. Nevertheless
we ought to implore, invoke, pray, beseech, and supplicat
him; but we must not stop there; it behoveth us also to us
our endeavours on our side, and, as the holy writ saith, t
co-operate with him.

You know what C. Flaminius, the consul, said when b
Hannibal's policy he was penned up near the lake of Peruse
alias Thrasymene. Friends, said he to his soldiers, you mus
not hope to get out of this place barely by vows or prayer
to the gods; no, 'tis by fortitude and strength we must es
cape and cut ourselves a way with the edge of our sword
through the midst of our enemies.

Sallust likewise makes M. Portius Cato say this: Th
help of the gods is not obtained by idle vows and womanis
complaints; 'tis by vigilance, labour, and repeated endeav

ours that all things succeed according to our wishes and designs. If a man in time of need and danger is negligent, heartless, and lazy, in vain he implores the gods; they are then justly angry and incensed against him. The devil take me, said Friar John,—I'll go his halves, quoth Panurge,—if the close of Sevillé had not been all gathered, vintaged, gleaned, and destroyed, if I had only sung *contra hostium insidias* (matter of breviary) like all the rest of the monking devils, and had not bestirred myself to save the vineyard as I did, despatching the truant picaroons of Lerné with the staff of the cross.

Let her sink or swim a God's name, said Panurge, all's one to Friar John; he doth nothing; his name is Friar John Do-little; for all he sees me here a-sweating and puffing to help with all my might this honest tar, first of the name.— Hark you me, dear soul, a word with you; but pray be not angry. How thick do you judge the planks of our ship to be? Some two good inches and upwards, returned the pilot; don't fear. Odskilderkins, said Panurge, it seems then we are within two fingers' breadth of damnation.

Is this one of the nine comforts of matrimony? Ah, dear soul, you do well to measure the danger by the yard of fear. For my part, I have none on't; my name is William Dread-nought. As for heart, I have more than enough on't. I mean none of your sheep's heart; but of wolf's heart—the courage of a bravo. By the pavilion of Mars, I fear nothing but danger.

CHAPTER 12

HOW PANURGE WAS SAID TO HAVE BEEN AFRAID WITHOUT REASON DURING THE STORM

Good morrow, gentlemen, said Panurge; good morrow to you all; you are in very good health, thanks to heaven and

yourselves; you are all heartily welcome, and in good time.
Let us go on shore.—Here, coxswain, get the ladder over
the gunnel; man the sides; man the pinnace, and get her by
the ship's side. Shall I lend you a hand here? I am stark
mad for want of business, and would work like any two
yokes of oxen. Truly this is a fine place, and these look like
a very good people. Children, do you want me still in anything? do not spare the sweat of my body, for God's sake.
Adam—that is, man—was made to labour and work, as the
birds were made to fly. Our Lord's will is that we get our
bread with the sweat of our brows, not idling and doing
nothing, like this tatterdemalion of a monk here, this Friar
Jack who is fain to drink to hearten himself up, and dies for
fear.—Rare weather.—I now find the answer of Anarcharsis,
the noble philosopher, very proper. Being asked what ship
he reckoned the safest, he replied: That which is in the
harbour. He made a yet better repartee, said Pantagruel,
when somebody inquiring which is greater, the number of
the living or that of the dead, he asked them amongst which
of the two they reckoned those that are at sea, ingeniously
implying that they are continually in danger of death, dying
alive, and living die. Portius Cato also said that there were
but three things of which he would repent: if he had trusted
his wife with his secret, if he had idled away a day, and if
he had ever gone by sea to a place which he could visit by
land. By this dignified frock of mine, said Friar John to
Panurge, friend, thou hast been afraid during the storm
without cause or reason; for thou wert not born to be
drowned, but rather to be hanged and exalted in the air, or
to be roasted in the midst of a jolly bonfire. My lord, would
you have a good cloak for the rain; leave me off your wolf
and badger-skin mantle; let Panurge but be flayed, and cover
yourself with his hide. But do not come near the fire, nor

near your blacksmith's forges, a God's name; for in a moment you will see it in ashes. Yet be as long as you please in the rain, snow, hail, nay, by the devil's maker, throw yourself or dive down to the very bottom of the water, I'll engage you'll not be wet at all. Have some winter boots made of it, they'll never take in a drop of water; make bladders of it to lay under boys to teach them to swim, instead of corks, and they will learn without the least danger. His skin, then, said Pantagruel, should be like the herb called true maiden's hair, which never takes wet nor moistness, but still keeps dry, though you lay it at the bottom of the water as long as you please; and for that reason is called Adiantos.

Friend Panurge, said Friar John, I pray thee never be afraid of water; thy life for mine thou art threatened with a contrary element. Ay, ay, replied Panurge, but the devil's cooks dote sometimes, and are apt to make horrid blunders as well as others; often putting to boil in water what was designed to be roasted on the fire; like the head-cooks of our kitchen, who often lard partridges, queests, and stock-doves with intent to roast them, one would think; but it happens sometimes that they e'en turn the partridges into the pot to be boiled with cabbages, the queests with leek pottage, and the stock-doves with turnips. But hark you me, good friends, I protest before this noble company, that as for the chapel which I vowed to Mons. St. Nicholas between Quande and Montsoreau, I honestly mean that it shall be a chapel of rose-water, which shall be where neither cow nor calf shall be fed; for between you and I, I intend to throw it to the bottom of the water. Here is a rare rogue for you, said Eusthenes; here is a pure rogue, a rogue in grain, a rogue enough, a rogue and a half. He is resolved to make good the Lombardic proverb, *Passato el pericolo, gabbato el santo.*

The devil was sick, the devil a monk would be;
The devil was well, the devil a monk was he.

CHAPTER 13

HOW, AFTER THE STORM, PANTAGRUEL WENT ON SHORE IN
THE ISLANDS OF THE MACREONS

IMMEDIATELY after we went ashore at the port of an
island which they called the island of the Macreons.

The good people of the place received us very honourably.
An old Macrobius (so they called their eldest elderman)
desired Pantagruel to come to the town-house to refresh
himself and eat something, but he would not budge a foot
from the mole till all his men were landed. After he had
seen them, he gave order that they should all change clothes,
and that some of all the stores in the fleet should be brought
on shore, that every ship's crew might live well; which was
accordingly done, and God wot how well they all toped and
caroused. The people of the place brought them provisions
in abundance. The Pantagruelists returned them more; as
the truth is, theirs were somewhat damaged by the late
storm. When they had well stuffed the insides of their doublets, Pantagruel desired everyone to lend their help to repair
the damage; which they readily did. It was easy enough to
refit there; for all the inhabitants of the island were car-
penters and all such handicrafts as are seen in the arsenal
at Venice. None but the largest island was inhabited, having
three ports and ten parishes; the rest being overrun with
wood and desert, much like the forest of Arden. We entreated the old Macrobius to show us what was worth seeing
in the island; which he did; and in the desert and dark
forest we discovered several old ruined temples, obelisks,
pyramids, monuments, and ancient tombs, with divers in-

scriptions and epitaphs; some of them in hieroglyphic characters; others in the Ionic dialect; some in the Arabic, Agarenian, Slavonian, and other tongues; of which Epistemon took an exact account. In the interim, Panurge said to Friar John, Is this the island of the Macreons? Macreon signifies in Greek an old man, or one much stricken in years. What is that to me? said Friar John; how can I help it? I was not in the country when they christened it. Now I think on't, quoth Panurge, I believe the name of mackerel* was derived from it; for procuring is the province of the old, as buttock-riggling is that of the young. Therefore I do not know but this may be the bawdy or Mackerel Island, the original and prototype of the island of that name at Paris. Let's go and dredge for cock-oysters. Old Macrobius asked, in the Ionic tongue, How, and by what industry and labour, Pantagruel got to their port that day, there having been such blustering weather and such a dreadful storm at sea? Pantagruel told him that the Almighty Preserver of mankind had regarded the simplicity and sincere affection of his servants, who did not travel for gain or sordid profit, the whole design of their voyage being a studious desire to know, see, and visit the Oracle of Bacbuc, and take the word of the Bottle upon some difficulties offered by one of the company; nevertheless this had not been without great affliction and evident danger of shipwreck. After that, he asked him what he judged to be the cause of that terrible tempest, and if the adjacent seas were thus frequently subject to storms; as in the ocean are the Ratz of Sammaieu, Maumusson, and in the Mediterranean sea the Gulf of Sataly, Montargentan, Piombino, Capo Melio in Laconia, the Straits of Gibraltar, Faro di Messina, and others.

* Motteux adds, between brackets,—"that's a *bawd* in French."

CHAPTER 14

HOW THE GOOD MACROBIUS GAVE US AN ACCOUNT OF THE MANSION AND DECEASE OF THE HEROES

THE good Macrobius then answered, Friendly strangers, this island is one of the Sporades; not of your Sporades that lie in the Carpathian sea, but one of the Sporades of the ocean; in former times rich, frequented, wealthy, populous, full of traffic, and in the dominions of the rulers of Britain, but now, by course of time, and in these latter ages of the world, poor and desolate, as you see. In this dark forest, above seventy-eight thousand Persian leagues in compass, is the dwelling-place of the demons and heroes that are grown old, and we believe that some one of them died yesterday; since the comet which we saw for three days before together, shines no more; and now it is likely that at his death there arose this horrible storm; for while they are alive all happiness attends both this and the adjacent islands, and a settled calm and serenity. At the death of every one of them, we commonly hear in the forest loud and mournful groans, and the whole land is infested with pestilence, earthquakes, inundations, and other calamities; the air with fogs and obscurity, and the sea with storms and hurricanes. What you tell us seems to me likely enough, said Pantagruel. For as a torch or candle, as long as it hath life enough and is lighted, shines round about, disperses its light, delights those that are near it, yields them its service and clearness, and never causes any pain or displeasure; but as soon as 'tis extinguished, its smoke and evaporation infects the air, offends the by-standers, and is noisome to all; so, as long as those noble and renowned souls inhabit their bodies, peace, profit, pleasure, and honour never leave the places where they abide; but as soon as they leave them, both the continent and adjacent islands are annoyed with great commotions; in the air fogs, darkness, thunder, hail; tremblings, pulsations, agitations of the earth; storms and hurricanes at sea; together with sad complaints amongst the people, broaching of religions, changes in governments, and ruins of commonwealths.

We had a sad instance of this lately, said Epistemon, at the death of that valiant and learned knight, William du Bellay; during whose life France enjoyed so much happiness, that all the rest of the world looked upon it with envy, sought friendship with it, and stood in awe of its power; but soon after his decease it hath for a considerable time been the scorn of the rest of the world.

Thus, said Pantagruel, Anchises being dead at Drepani in Sicily, Æneas was dreadfully tossed and endangered by a storm; and perhaps for the same reason Herod, that tyrant and cruel King of Judæa, finding himself near the pangs of a horrid kind of death—for he died of a phthiriasis, devoured by vermin and lice; as before him died L. Sylla, Pherecydes the Syrian, the preceptor of Pythagoras, the Greek poet Alcmæon, and others—and foreseeing that the Jews would make bonfires at his death, caused all the nobles and magistrates to be summoned to his seraglio out of all the cities, towns, and castles of Judæa, fraudulently pretending that he had some things of moment to impart to them. They made their personal appearance; whereupon he caused them all to be shut in the hippodrome of the seraglio; then said to his sister Salome and Alexander her husband: I am certain that the Jews will rejoice at my death; but if you will observe and perform what I tell you, my funeral shall be honourable, and there will be a general mourning. As soon as you see me dead, let my guards, to whom I have already given strict commission to that purpose, kill all the noblemen and magistrates that are secured in the hippodrome. By these means all Jewry shall, in spite of themselves, be obliged to mourn and lament, and foreigners will imagine it to be for my death, as if some heroic soul had left her body. A desperate tyrant wished as much when he said, When I die, let earth and fire be mixed together; which was as good as to say, let the whole world perish. Which saying the tyrant Nero altered, saying, While I live, as Suetonius affirms it. This detestable saying of which Cicero, lib. *De Finib.*, and Seneca, lib. 2, *De Clementia*, make mention, is ascribed to the Emperor Tiberius by Dion Nicæus and Suidas.

CHAPTER 15

PANTAGRUEL'S DISCOURSE OF THE DECEASE OF HEROIC SOULS; AND OF THE DREADFUL PRODIGIES THAT HAPPENED BEFORE THE DEATH OF THE LATE LORD DE LANGEY

I WOULD not, continued Pantagruel, have missed the storm that hath thus disordered us, were I also to have missed the relation of these things told us by this good Macrobius. Neither am I unwilling to believe what he said of a comet that appears in the sky some days before such a decease. For some of those souls are so noble, so precious, and so heroic that heaven gives us notice of their departing some days before it happens. And as a prudent physician, seeing by some symptoms that his patient draws towards his end, some days before gives notice of it to his wife, children, kindred, and friends, that, in that little time he hath yet to live, they may admonish him to settle all things in his family, to tutor and instruct his children as much as he can, recommend his relict to his friends in her widowhood, and declare what he knows to be necessary about a provision for the orphans; that he may not be surprised by death without making his will, and may take care of his soul and family; in the same manner the heavens, as it were joyful for the approaching reception of those blessed souls, seem to make bonfires by those comets and blazing meteors, which they at the same time kindly design should prognosticate to us here that in a few days one of those venerable souls is to leave her body and this terrestrial globe. Not altogether unlike this was what was formerly done at Athens by the judges of the Areopagus. For when they gave their verdict to cast or clear the culprits that were tried before them, they used certain notes according to the substance of the sentences; by Th, signifying condemnation to death; by T, absolution; by A, ampliation or a demur, when the case was not sufficiently examined. Thus having publicly set up those letters, they eased the relations and friends of the prisoners, and such others as desired to know their doom, of their doubts. Likewise by these comets, as in ethereal characters, the heavens silently say to us, Make haste, mortals, if you would know or learn of the blessed souls anything concerning the public good or your private interest; for their catastrophe is near, which being past, you will vainly wish for them afterwards.

The good-natured heavens still do more; and that mankind may be declared unworthy of the enjoyment of those renowned souls, they fright and astonish us with prodigies, monsters, and other foreboding signs that thwart the order of nature.

Of this we had an instance several days before the decease of the heroic soul of the learned and valiant Chevalier de Langey, of whom you have already spoken. I remember it, said Epistemon; and my heart still trembles within me when I think on the many dreadful prodigies that we saw five or six days before he died. For the Lords D'Assier, Chemant, one-eyed Mailly, St. Ayl, Villeneufe-la-Guyart, Master Gabriel, physician of Savillan, Rabelais, Cohuau, Massuau, Majorici, Bullou, Cercu, alias Bourgmaistre, Francis Proust, Ferron, Charles Girard, Francis Bourré, and many other friends and servants to the deceased, all dismayed, gazed on each other without uttering one word; yet not without foreseeing that France would in a short time be deprived of a knight so accomplished and necessary for its glory and protection, and that heaven claimed him again as its due. By the tufted tip of my cowl, cried Friar John, I am e'en resolved to become a scholar before I die. I have a pretty good headpiece of my own, you must own. Now pray give me leave to ask you a civil question. Can these same heroes or demigods you talk of die? May I never be damned if I was not so much a lobcock as to believe they had been immortal, like so many fine angels. Heaven forgive me! but this most reverend father, Macroby, tells us they die at last. Not all, returned Pantagruel.

The Stoics held them all to be mortal, except one, who alone is immortal, impassible, invisible. Pindar plainly saith that there is no more thread, that is to say, no more life, spun from the distaff and flax of the hard-hearted Fates for the goddesses Hamadryades than there is for those trees that are preserved by them, which are good, sturdy, downright oaks; whence they derived their original, according to the opinion of Callimachus and Pausanias in Phoci. With whom concurs Martianus Capella. As for the demigods, fauns, satyrs, sylvans, hobgoblins, ægipanes, nymphs, heroes, and demons, several men have, from the total sum, which is the result of the divers ages calculated by Hesiod, reckoned their life to be 9720 years; that sum consisting of four special numbers orderly arising from one, the same added together and multiplied by four every way amounts to forty;

these forties, being reduced into triangles by five times, make up the total of the aforesaid number. See Plutarch, in his book about the Cessation of Oracles.

This, said Friar John, is not matter of breviary; I may believe as little or as much of it as you and I please. I believe, said Pantagruel, that all intellectual souls are exempted from Atropos's scissors. They are all immortal, whether they be of angels, of demons, or human; yet I will tell you a story concerning this that is very strange, but is written and affirmed by several learned historians.

CHAPTER 16

HOW PANTAGRUEL RELATED A VERY SAD STORY OF THE DEATH OF THE HEROES

EPITHERSES, the father of Æmilian the rhetorician, sailing from Greece to Italy in a ship freighted with divers goods and passengers, at night the wind failed 'em near the Echinades, some islands that lie between the Morea and Tunis, and the vessel was driven near Paxos. When they were got thither, some of the passengers being asleep, others awake, the rest eating and drinking, a voice was heard that called aloud, Thamous! which cry surprised them all. This same Thamous was their pilot, an Egyptian by birth, but known by name only to some few travellers. The voice was heard a second time calling Thamous, in a frightful tone; and none making answer, but trembling and remaining silent, the voice was heard a third time, more dreadful than before.

This caused Thamous to answer: Here am I; what dost thou call me for? What wilt thou have me do? Then the voices, louder than before, bid him publish when he should come to Palodes, that the great god Pan was dead.

Epitherses related that all the mariners and passengers,

having heard this, were extremely amazed and frighted; and that, consulting among themselves whether they had best conceal or divulge what the voice had enjoined, Thamous said his advice was that if they happened to have a fair wind they should proceed without mentioning a word on't, but if they chanced to be becalmed he would publish what he had heard. Now when they were near Palodes they had no wind, neither were they in any current. Thamous then getting up on the top of the ship's forecastle, and casting his eyes on the shore, said that he had been commanded to proclaim that the great god Pan was dead. The words were hardly out of his mouth, when deep groans, great lamentations, and doleful shrieks, not of one person, but of many together, were heard from the land.

The news of this—many being present then—was soon spread at Rome; insomuch that Tiberius, who was then emperor, sent for this Thamous, and having heard him gave credit to his words. And inquiring of the learned in his court and at Rome who was that Pan, he found by their relation that he was the son of Mercury and Penelope, as Herodotus and Cicero in his third book of the Nature of the Gods had written before.

For my part, I understand it of that great Saviour of the faithful who was shamefully put to death at Jerusalem by the envy and wickedness of the doctors, priests, and monks of the Mosaic law. And methinks my interpretation is not improper; for he may lawfully be said in the Greek tongue to be *Pan,* since he is our *all.* For all that we are, all that we live, all that we have, all that we hope, is him, by him, from him, and in him. He is the good Pan, the great shepherd, who, as the loving shepherd Corydon affirms, hath not only a tender love and affection for his sheep, but also for their shepherds. At his death, complaints, sighs, fears, and

lamentations were spread through the whole fabric of the
universe, whether heavens, land, sea, or hell.

The time also concurs with this interpretation of mine;
for this most good, most mighty Pan, our only Saviour, died
near Jerusalem during the reign of Tiberius Cæsar.

Pantagruel, having ended this discourse, remained silent
and full of contemplation. A little while after we saw the
tears flow out of his eyes as big as ostrich's eggs. God take
me presently if I tell you one single syllable of a lie in the
matter.

CHAPTER 17

HOW PANTAGRUEL SAILED BY THE SNEAKING ISLAND, WHERE SHROVETIDE REIGNED

THE jovial fleet being refitted and repaired, new stores
taken in, the Macreons over and above satisfied and pleased
with the money spent there by Pantagruel, our men in better
humour than they used to be, if possible, we merrily put to
sea the next day, near sunset, with a delicious fresh gale.

Xenomanes showed us afar off the Sneaking Island, where
reigned Shrovetide, of whom Pantagruel had heard much
talk formerly; for that reason he would gladly have seen
him in person, had not Xenomanes advised him to the contrary; first, because this would have been much out of our
way, and then for the lean cheer which he told us was to be
found at that prince's court, and indeed all over the island.

You can see nothing there for your money, said he, but
a huge greedy-guts, a tall woundy swallower of hot wardens
and mussels; a long-shanked mole-catcher; an overgrown
bottler of hay; a mossy-chinned demi-giant, with a double-
shaven crown, of lantern breed; a very great loitering, noddy-
peaked youngster, banner-bearer to the fish-eating tribe,
dictator of mustard-land, flogger of little children, calciner of

ashes, father and foster-father to physicians, swarming with pardons, indulgences, and stations; a very honest man; a good catholic, and as brimful of devotion as ever he can hold.

He weeps the three-fourth parts of the day, and never assists at any weddings; but, give the devil his due, he is the most industrious larding-stick and skewer-maker in forty kingdoms.

About six years ago, as I passed by Sneaking-land, I brought home a large skewer from thence, and made a present of it to the butchers of Quande, who set a great value upon them, and that for a cause. Some time or other, if ever we live to come back to our own country, I will show you two of them fastened on the great church porch. His usual food is pickled coats of mail, salt helmets and head-pieces, and salt salads; which sometimes makes him piss pins and needles. As for his clothing, 'tis comical enough o' conscience, both for make and colour; for he wears grey and cold, nothing before, and naught behind, with the sleeves of the same.

You will do me a kindness, said Pantagruel, if, as you have described his clothes, food, actions, and pastimes, you will also give me an account of his shape and disposition in all his parts. Prithee do, dear cod, said Friar John, for I have found him in my breviary, and then follow the movable holy days. With all my heart, answered Xenomanes; we may chance to hear more of him as we touch at the Wild Island, the dominions of the squab Chitterlings, his enemies, against whom he is eternally at odds; and were it not for the help of the noble Carnival, their protector and good neighbour, this meagre-looked lozelly Shrovetide would long before this have made sad work among them, and rooted them out of their habitation. Are these same Chitterlings, said Friar John, male or female, angels or mortals, women or maids?

They are, replied Xenomanes, females in sex, mortal in kind, some of them maids, others not. The devil have me, said Friar John, if I ben't for them. What a shameful disorder in nature, is it not, to make war against women? Let's go back and hack the villain to pieces. What! meddle with Shrovetide? cried Panurge, in the name of Beelzebub, I am not yet so weary of my life. No, I'm not yet so mad as that comes to. *Quid juris?* Suppose we should find ourselves pent up between the Chitterlings and Shrovetide? between the anvil and the hammers? Shankers and buboes! stand off! god-zooks, let us make the best of our way. I bid you good night, sweet Mr. Shrovetide; I recommend to you the Chitterlings, and pray don't forget the puddings.

CHAPTER 18

HOW SHROVETIDE IS ANATOMIZED AND DESCRIBED BY XENOMANES

As for the inward parts of Shrovetide, said Xenomanes; his brain is (at least, it was in my time) in bigness, colours, substance, and strength, much like the left cod of a he hand-worm.

The ventricles of his said brain, like an auger.

The worm-like excrescence, like a Christmas-box.

The membranes, like a monk's cowl.

The funnel, like a mason's chisel.

The fornix, like a casket.

The grandula pinealis, like a bag-pipe.

The stomach, like a belt.

The pylorus, like a pitch-fork.

The windpipe, like an oy-ster-knife.

The throat, like a pin-cushion stuffed with oak-um.

The lungs, like a prebend's fur-gown.

The heart, like a cope.

The rete mirable, like a gutter.

The dug-like processus, like a patch.

The tympanums, like a whirligig.

The rocky bones, like a goosewing.

The nape of the neck, like a paper lantern.

The nerves, like a pipkin.

The uvula, like a sackbut.

The palate, like a mitten.

The spittle, like a shuttle.

The almonds, like a telescope.

The bridge of his nose, like a wheelbarrow.

The head of the larynx, like a vintage-basket.

The kidneys, like a towel.

The lions, like a padlock.

The ureters, like a pothook.

The emulgent veins, like two gilliflowers.

The spermatic vessels, like a cully-mully-puff.

The parastata, like an inkpot.

The bladder, like a stonebow.

The neck, like a mill-clapper.

The mediastine, like an earthen cup.

The pleura, like a crow's bill.

The arteries, like a watch-coat.

The midriff, like a montero-cap.

The liver, like a double-tongued-mattock.

The veins, like a sash-window.

The spleen, like a catcall.

The guts, like a trammel.

The gall, like a cooper's adze.

The entrails, like a gauntlet.

The mesentery, like an abbot's mitre.

The hungry gut, like a button.

The blind gut, like a breastplate.

The colon, like a bridle.

The arse-gut, like a monk's leathern bottle.

The ligaments, like a tinker's budget.

The bones, like three-cornered cheesecakes.

The cartilages, like a field-tortoise, alias a mole.

The mirach, or lower parts of the belly, like a high-crowned hat.

The siphach, or its inner rind, like a wooden cuff.

The muscles, like a pair of bellows.

The tendons, like a hawking-glove.

The marrow, like a wallet.

The glandules in the mouth, like a pruning knife.

The animal spirits, like swingeing fisticuffs.

The blood-fermenting, like a multiplication of flirts on the nose.

The urine, like a figpecker.

The sperm, like a hundred ten-penny nails.

And his nurse told me, that being married to Mid-lent, he only begot a good number of local adverbs and certain double fasts.

His memory he had like a scarf.

His common sense, like a buzzing of bees.

His imagination, like the chime of a set of bells.

His conscience, like the un-nestling of a parcel of young herons.

His thoughts, like a flight of starlings.

His deliberations, like a set of organs.

His repentance, like the carriage of a double cannon.

His reason, like a cricket.

His undertakings, like the ballast of a galleon.

His understanding, like a torn breviary.

His notions, like snails crawling out of straw-berries.

His will, like three filberts in a porringer.

His desire, like six trusses of hay.

His judgment, like a shoeing-horn.

His discretion, like the truckle of a pulley.

CHAPTER 19

SHROVETIDE'S OUTWARD PARTS ANATOMIZED

SHROVETIDE, continued Xenomanes, is somewhat better proportioned in his outward parts, excepting the seven ribs which he had over and above the common shape of men.

His toes were like a virginal on an organ.

His nails, like a gimlet.

His feet, like a guitar.

His heels, like a club.

The soles of his feet, like a crucible.

His legs, like a hawk's lure.

His knees, like a joint-stool.

His thighs, like a steel cap.

His hips, like a wimble.

His belly as big as a tun, buttoned after the old fashion, with a girdle riding over the middle of his bosom.

His navel, like a cymbal.

His groan, like a minced pie.

His member, like a slipper.

His purse, like an oil cruet.

His genitals, like a joiner's planer.

Their erecting muscles, like a racket.

The perineum, like a flageolet.

The peritoneum, or caul wherein his bowels were wrapped, like a billiard-table.

His back, like an overgrown rack-bent cross-bow.

The vertebræ, or joints of his backbone, like a bagpipe.

His ribs, like a spinning-wheel.

His brisket, like a canopy.

His shoulder-blades, like a mortar.

His breast, like a game at nine-pins.

His paps, like a hornpipe.

His shoulders, like a hand-barrow.

His fingers, like a brotherhood's andirons.

The fibulæ, or lesser bones of his legs, like a pair of stilts.

His shin-bones, like sickles.

His elbows, like a mouse-trap.

His arse-hole, like a crystal looking-glass.

His bum, like a harrow.

His loins, like a butter-pot.

The knob in his throat, like a barrel, where hanged two brazen wens, very fine and harmonious, in the shape of an hour-glass.

His beard, like a lantern.

His chin, like a mushroom.

His ears, like a pair of gloves.

His nose, like a buskin.

His nostrils, like a forehead cloth.

His eyebrows, like a dripping pan.

On his left brow was a mark of the shape and bigness of an urinal.

His eyelids, like a fiddle.

His eyes, like a comb-box.

His optic nerves, like a tinder-box.

His forehead, like a false-cup.

His temples, like the cock of a cistern.

His cheeks, like a pair of wooden shoes.

His armpits, like a chequer.

His arms like a riding-hood.

His hands, like a curry-comb.

His neck, like a talboy.

His throat, like a felt to distil hippocras.

His jaws, like a caudle cup.

His teeth, like a hunter's staff.

Of such colt's teeth as his, you will find one at Colonges les Royaux in Poitou, and two at La Brosse in Xaintonge, on the cellar door.

His tongue, like a jew's-harp.

His mouth, like a horse-cloth.

His face embroidered like a mule's pack-saddle.

His head contrived like a still.

His skull, like a pouch.

The suturæ, or seams of his skull, like the annulus piscatoris. or the fisher's signet.

His skin, like a gabardine.

His epidermis, or outward skin, like a bolting-cloth.

His hair, like a scrubbing-brush.

His fur, such as above said.

CHAPTER 20

A CONTINUATION OF SHROVETIDE'S COUNTENANCE

'TIS a wonderful thing, continued Xenomanes, to hear and see the state of Shrovetide.

If he chanced to spit, it was whole basketsful of gold-finches.

If he blowed his nose, it was pickled grigs.

When he wept, it was ducks with onion sauce.

When he trembled, it was large venison pasties.

When he did sweat, it was old ling with butter sauce.

When he belched, it was bushels of oysters.

When he sneezed, it was whole tubsful of mustard.

When he coughed, it was boxes of marmalade.

When he sobbed, it was water-cresses.

When he yawned, it was potsful of pickled peas.

When he sighed, it was dried neats' tongues.

When he whistled, it was a whole scuttleful of green apes.

When he frowned, it was soused hogs' feet.

When he spoke, it was coarse brown russet cloth; so little it was like crimson silk, with which Parisatis desired that the words of such as spoke to her son Cyrus, King of Persia, should be interwoven.

When he blowed, it was indulgence money-boxes.

When he winked, it was buttered buns.

When he grumbled, it was March cats.

When he nodded, it was iron-bound wagons.

When he made mouths, it was broken staves.

When he muttered, it was lawyers' revels.

When he hopped about, it was letters of licence and protections.

When he was hoarse, it was

When he snored, it was a whole panful of fried beans.

When he stepped back, it was sea cockle-shells.

When he slabbered, it was common ovens.

When he scratched himself, it was new proclamations.

When he puffed, it was cabbages with oil, alias caules amb'olif.

When he sung, it was peas in cods.

an entry of morrice-dancers.

When he talked, it was the last year's snow.

When he dreamt, it was of a cock and a bull.

When he gave nothing, so much for the bearer.

If he thought to himself, it was whimsies and maggots.

If he dozed, it was leases of lands.

What is yet more strange, he used to work doing nothing, and did nothing though he worked; caroused sleeping, and slept carousing, with his eyes open, like the hares in our country, for fear of being taken napping by the Chitterlings, his inveterate enemies; biting he laughed, and laughing bit; eat nothing fasting, and fasted eating nothing; mumbled upon suspicion, drank by imagination, swam on the tops of high steeples, dried his clothes in ponds and rivers, fished in the air and there used to catch decumane lobsters; hunted at the bottom of the herring pond, and caught there ibexes, stamboucs, chamois, and other wild goats; used to put out the eyes of all the crows which he took sneakingly; feared nothing but his own shadow and the cries of fat kids; used to gad abroad some days, like a truant schoolboy; played with the ropes of bells on festival days of saints; made a mallet of his fists, and writ on hairy parchment prognostications and almanacks with his huge pin-case.

Is that the gentleman? said Friar John. He is my man;

this is the very fellow I looked for. I will send him a challenge immediately. This is, said Pantagruel, a strange and monstrous sort of man, if I may call him a man. You put me in mind of the form and looks of Amodunt and Dissonance. How were they made? said Friar John. May I be peeled like a raw onion if ever I heard a word of them. I'll tell you what I read of them in some ancient apologues, replied Pantagruel.

Physis—that is to say, Nature—at her first burthen begat Beauty and Harmony without carnal copulation being of herself very fruitful and prolific. Antiphysis, who ever was the counter part of Nature, immediately out of a malicious spite against her for her beautiful and honourable productions, in opposition begat Amodunt and Dissonance by copulation with Tellumon. Their heads were round like a football, and not gently flatted on both sides, like the common shape of men. Their ears stood pricked up like those of asses; their eyes, as hard as those of crabs, and without brows, stared out of their heads, fixed on bones like those of our heels; their feet were round like tennis-balls; their arms and hands turned backwards towards their shoulders; and they walked on their heads, continually turning round like a ball, topsy-turvy, heels over head.

Yet—as you know that apes esteem their young the handsomest in the world—Antiphysis extolled her offspring, and strove to prove that their shape was handsomer and neater than that of the children of Physis, saying that thus to have spherical heads and feet, and walk in a circular manner, wheeling round, had something in it of the perfection of the divine power, which makes all beings eternally turn in that fashion; and that to have our feet uppermost, and the head below them, was to imitate the Creator of the universe; the hair being like the roots, and the legs like the branches of man; for trees are better planted by their roots than they could be by their branches. By this demonstration she implied that her children were much more to be praised for being like a standing tree, than those of Physis, that made a figure of a tree upside down. As for the arms and hands, she pretended to prove that they were more justly turned towards the shoulders, because that part of the body ought not to be without defence, while the fore-part is duly fenced with teeth, which a man cannot only use to chew, but also to defend himself against those things that offend him. Thus, by the testimony and astipulation of the brute beasts, she drew all the witless herd and mob of fools into her opinion, and was admired by all brainless and nonsensical people.

Since that, she begot the hypocritical tribes of eavesdropping dissemblers, superstitious pope-mongers, and priest-ridden bigots, the frantic Pistolets, [the demoniacal Calvins, impostors of Geneva,] the scrapers of benefices, apparitors with the devil in them, and other grinders and squeezers of livings, herb-stinking hermits, gulligutted dunces of the cowl, church vermin, false zealots, devourers of the substance of men, and many more other deformed and ill-favoured monsters, made in spite of nature.

CHAPTER 21

HOW PANTAGRUEL DISCOVERED A MONSTROUS PHYSETER, OR WHIRLPOOL, NEAR THE WILD ISLAND

ABOUT sunset, coming near the Wild Island, Pantagruel spied afar off a huge monstrous physeter (a sort of whale, which some call a whirlpool), that came right upon us, neighing, snorting, raised above the waves higher than our maintops, and spouting water all the way into the air before itself, like a large river falling from a mountain. Pantagruel showed it to the pilot and to Xenomanes.

By the pilot's advice the trumpets of the Thalamege were sounded to warn all the fleet to stand close and look to themselves. This alarm being given, all the ships, galleons, frigates, brigantines, according to their naval discipline, placed themselves in the order and figure of an Y (upsilon), the letter of Pythagoras, as cranes do in their flight, and like an acute angle, in whose cone and basis the Thalamege placed herself ready to fight smartly. Friar John with the grenadiers got on the forecastle.

Poor Panurge began to cry and howl worse than ever. Babillebabou, said he, shrugging up his shoulders, quivering all over with fear, there will be the devil upon dun. This is a worse business than that t'other day. Let us fly, let us fly; old Nick take me if it is not Leviathan, described by the noble prophet Moses in the life of patient Job. It will swallow us all, ships and men, shag, rag, and bobtail, like a dose of pills. Alas! it will make no more of us, and we shall hold no more room in its hellish jaws, than a sugarplum in an ass's throat. Look, look, 'tis upon us; let us wheel off, whip it away, and get ashore. I believe 'tis the very individual sea-monster that was formerly designed to devour Andromeda; we are all undone. Oh! for some valiant Perseus here now to kill the dog.

I'll do its business presently, said Pantagruel; fear nothing. Ods-belly, said Panurge, remove the cause of my fear then. When the devil would you have a man be afraid but when there is so much cause? If your destiny be such as Friar John was saying a while ago, replied Pantagruel, you ought to be afraid of Pyroeis, Eous, Æthon, and Phlegon, the sun's coach-horses, that breathe fire at the nostrils; and not of physeters, that spout nothing but water at the snout and mouth. Their water will not endanger your life; and that element will rather save and preserve than hurt or endanger you.

Ay, ay, trust to that, and hang me, quoth Panurge; yours is a very pretty fancy. Ods-fish! did I not give you a sufficient account of the elements' transmutation, and the blunders that are made of roast for boiled, and boiled for roast? Alas! here 'tis; I'll go hide myself below. We are dead men, every mother's son of us. I see upon our main-top that merciless hag Atropos, with her scissors new ground, ready to cut our threads all at one snip. Oh! how dreadful and abominable thou art; thou hast drowned a good many beside us, who never made their brags of it. Did it but spout good, brisk, dainty, delicious white wine, instead of this damned bitter salt water, one might better bear with it, and there would be some cause to be patient; like that English lord, who being doomed to die, and had leave to choose what kind of death he would, chose to be drowned in a butt of malmsey. Here it is. Oh, oh! devil! Sathanas! Leviathan! I cannot abide to look upon thee, thou art so abominably ugly. Go to the bar, go take the pettifoggers.

CHAPTER 22

HOW THE MONSTROUS PHYSETER WAS SLAIN BY PANTAGRUEL

THE physeter, coming between the ships and the galleons, threw water by whole tuns upon them, as if it had been the cataracts of the Nile in Ethiopia. On the other side, arrows, darts, gleaves, javelins, spears, harping-irons, and partizans, flew upon it like hail. Friar John did not spare himself in it. Panurge was half dead for fear. The artillery roared and thundered like mad, and seemed to gall it in good earnest, but did but little good; for the great iron and brass cannon-shot entering its skin seemed to melt like tiles in the sun.

Pantagruel then, considering the weight and exigency of the matter, stretched out his arms and showed what he could do. You tell us, and it is recorded, that Commodus, the Roman emperor, could shoot with a bow so dexterously that at a good distance he would let fly an arrow through a child's fingers and never touch them. You also tell us of an Indian archer, who lived when Alexander the Great conquered India, and was so skilful in drawing the bow, that at a considerable distance he would shoot his arrows through a ring, though they were three cubits long, and their iron so large and weighty that with them he used to pierce steel cutlasses, thick shields, steel breastplates, and generally what he did hit, how firm, resisting, hard, and strong soever it were. You also tell us wonders of the industry of the ancient Franks, who were preferred to all others in point of archery; and when they hunted either black or dun beasts, used to rub the head of their arrows with hellebore, because the flesh of the venison struck with such an arrow was more tender, dainty, wholesome, and delicious—paring off, nevertheless, the part that was touched round about. You also talk of the Parthians, who used to shoot backwards more dexterously than other nations forwards; and also celebrate the skill of the Scythians in that art, who sent once to Darius, King of Persia, an ambassador that made him a present of a bird, a frog, a mouse, and five arrows, without speaking one word; and being asked what those presents meant, and if he had commission to say anything, answered that he had not; which puzzled and gravelled Darius very much, till Gobrias, one of the seven captains that had killed the magi, explained it, saying, to Darius: By these gifts and offerings the Scythians silently tell you that except the Persians like birds fly up to heaven, or like mice hide themselves near the centre of the earth, or like frogs dive to the very bottom of ponds and lakes, they shall be destroyed by the power and arrows of the Scythians.

The noble Pantagruel was, without comparison, more admirable yet in the art of shooting and darting; for with his dreadful piles and darts, nearly resembling the huge beams that support the bridges of Nantes, Saumur, Bergerac, and at Paris the millers' and the changers' bridges, in length, size, weight, and iron-work, he at a mile's distance would open an oyster and never touch the edges; he would snuff a candle without putting it out; would shoot a magpie in the eye; take off a boot's under-sole, or a riding-hood's lining, without soiling them a bit; turn over every leaf of Friar John's breviary, one after another, and not tear one.

With such darts, of which there was good store in the ship, at the first blow he ran the physeter in at the forehead so furiously that he pierced both its jaws and tongue; so that from that time to this it no more opened its guttural trap-door, nor drew and spouted water. At the second blow he put out its right eye, and at the third its left; and we had all the pleasure to see the physeter bearing those three horns in its forehead, somewhat leaning forwards in an equilateral triangle.

Meanwhile it turned about to and fro, staggering and straying like one stunned, blinded, and taking his leave of the world. Pantagruel, not satisfied with this, let fly another dart, which took the monster under the tail likewise sloping; then with three other on the chine, in a perpendicular line, divided its flank from the tail to the snout at an equal distance. Then he larded it with fifty on one side, and after that, to make even work, he darted as many on its other side; so that the body of the physeter seemed like the hulk of a galleon with three masts, joined by a competent dimension of its beams, as if they had been the ribs and chain-wales of the keel; which was a pleasant sight. The physeter then giving up the ghost, turned itself upon its back, as all dead fishes do; and being thus overturned, with the beams and darts upside down in the sea, it seemed a scolopendra or centipede, as that servant is described by the ancient sage Nicander.

CHAPTER 23

HOW PANTAGRUEL WENT ON SHORE IN THE WILD ISLAND, THE ANCIENT ABODE OF THE CHITTERLINGS

THE boat's crew of the ship Lantern towed the physeter ashore on the neighbouring shore, which happened to be the Wild Island, to make an anatomical dissection of its body and save the fat of its kidneys, which, they said, was very useful and necessary for the cure of a certain distemper, which they called want of money. As for Pantagruel, he took no manner of notice of the monster; for he had seen many such, nay, bigger, in the Gallic ocean. Yet he condescended to land in the Wild Island, to dry and refresh some of his men (whom the physeter had wetted and bedaubed), at a small desert seaport towards the south, seated near a fine pleasant grove, out of which flowed a delicious brook of fresh, clear, and purling water. Here they pitched their tents and set up their kitchens; nor did they spare fuel.

Everyone having shifted as they thought fit, Friar John rang the bell, and the cloth was immediately laid, and supper brought in. Pantagruel eating cheerfully with his men, much about the second course perceived certain little sly Chitterlings clambering up a high tree near the pantry, as still as so many mice. Which made him ask Xenomanes what kind of creatures these were, taking them for squirrels, weasels, martins, or ermines. They are Chitterlings, replied Xenomanes. This is the Wild Island of which I spoke to you this morning; there hath been an irreconcilable war this long time between them and Shrovetide, their malicious and ancient enemy. I

believe that the noise of the guns which we fired at the physeter hath alarmed them, and made them fear their enemy
was come with his forces to surprise them, or lay the island
waste, as he hath often attempted to do; though he still
came off but bluely, by reason of the care and vigilance of
the Chitterlings, who (as Dido said to Æneas's companions
that would have landed at Carthage without her leave or
knowledge) were forced to watch and stand upon their guard,
considering the malice of their enemy and the neighbourhood
of his territories.

Pray, dear friend, said Pantagruel, if you find that by some
honest means we may bring this war to an end, and reconcile
them together, give me notice of it; I will use my endeavours
in it with all my heart, and spare nothing on my side to
moderate and accommodate the points in dispute between
both parties.

That's impossible at this time, answered Xenomanes.
About four years ago, passing incognito by this country, I
endeavoured to make a peace, or at least a long truce among
them; and I had certainly brought them to be good friends
and neighbours if both one and the other parties would have
yielded to one single article. Shrovetide would not include
in the treaty of peace the wild puddings nor the highland
sausages, their ancient gossips and confederates. The Chitterlings demanded that the fort of Cacques might be under
their government, as is the Castle of Sullouoir, and that a
parcel of I don't know what stinking villains, murderers, robbers, that held it then, should be expelled. But they could not
agree in this, and the terms that were offered seemed too
hard to either party. So the treaty broke off, and nothing was
done. Nevertheless they became less severe, and gentler
enemies than they were before; but since the denunciation of
the national Council of Chesil, whereby they were roughly

handled, hampered, and cited; whereby also Shrovetide was declared filthy, and bewrayed, in case he made any league or agreement with them; they are grown wonderfully inveterate, incensed, and obstinate against one another, and there is no way to remedy it. You might sooner reconcile cats and rats, or hounds and hares together.

CHAPTER 24

HOW THE WILD CHITTERLINGS LAID AN AMBUSCADO FOR PANTAGRUEL

WHILE Xenomanes was saying this, Friar John spied twenty or thirty young slender-shaped Chitterlings posting as fast as they could towards their town, citadel, castle, and fort of Chimney, and said to Pantagruel, I smell a rat; there will be here the devil upon two sticks, or I am much out. These worshipful Chitterlings may chance to mistake you for Shrovetide, though you are not a bit like him. Let us once in our lives leave our junketing for a while, and put ourselves in a posture to give 'em a bellyful of fighting, if they would be at that sport. There can be no false Latin in this, said Xenomanes; Chitterlings are still Chitterlings, always double-hearted and treacherous.

Pantagruel then arose from table to visit and scour the thicket, and returned presently; having discovered, on the left, an ambuscade of squab Chitterlings; and on the right, about half a league from thence, a large body of huge giant-like armed Chitterlings ranged in battalia along a little hill, and marching furiously towards us at the sound of bagpipes, sheep's paunches, and bladders, the merry fifes and drums, trumpets, and clarions, hoping to catch us as Moss caught his mare. By the conjecture of seventy-eight standards which we told, we guessed their number to be two and forty thousand, at a modest computation.

Their order, proud gait, and resolute looks made us judge that they were none of your raw, paltry links, but old warlike Chitterlings and Sausages. From the foremost ranks to the colours they were all armed cap-à-pie with small arms, as we reckoned them at a distance, yet very sharp and case-hardened. Their right and left wings were lined with a great number of forest puddings, heavy pattipans, and horse sausages, all of them tall and proper islanders, banditti, and wild.

Pantagruel was very much daunted, and not without cause; though Epistemon told him that it might be the use and custom of the Chitterlingonians to welcome and receive thus in arms their foreign friends, as the noble kings of France are received and saluted at their first coming into the chief cities of the kingdom after their advancement to the crown. Perhaps, said he, it may be the usual guard of the queen of the place, who, having notice given her by the junior Chitterlings of the forlorn hope whom you saw on the tree, of the arrival of your fine and pompous fleet, hath judged that it was without doubt some rich and potent prince, and is come to visit you in person.

Pantagruel, little trusting to this, called a council, to have their advice at large in this doubtful case. He briefly showed them how this way of reception with arms had often, under colour of compliment and friendship, been fatal. Thus, said he, the Emperor Antonius Caracalla at one time destroyed the citizens of Alexandria, and at another time cut off the attendants of Artabanus, King of Persia, under colour of marrying his daughter; which, by the way, did not pass unpunished, for a while after this cost him his life.

Thus Jacob's children destroyed the Sichemites, to revenge the rape of their sister Dinah. By such another hypocritical trick Gallienus, the Roman emperor, put to death the military men in Constantinople. Thus, under colour of friendship, Antonius enticed Artavasdes, King of Armenia; then, having caused him to be bound in heavy chains and shackled, at last put him to death.

We find a thousand such instances in history; and King Charles VI. is just commended for his prudence to this day, in that, coming back victorious over the Ghenters and other Flemings to his good city of Paris, and when he came to Bourget, a league from thence, hearing that the citizens with their mallets—whence they got the name of Maillotins—were marched out of town in battalia, twenty thousand strong, he would not go into the town till they had laid down their arms and retired to their respective homes; though they protested to him that they had taken arms with no other design than to receive him with the greater demonstration of honour and respect.

CHAPTER 25

HOW FRIAR JOHN JOINED WITH THE COOKS TO FIGHT THE CHITTERLINGS

FRIAR JOHN seeing these furious Chitterlings thus boldly march up, said to Pantagruel, Here will be a rare battle of hobby-horses, a pretty kind of puppet-show fight, for aught I see. Oh! what mighty honour and wonderful glory will attend our victory! I would have you only be a bare spectator of this fight, and for anything else leave me and my men to deal with them. What men? said Pantagruel. Matter of breviary, replied Friar John. How came Potiphar, who was head-cook of Pharaoh's kitchens, he that bought Joseph, and whom the said Joseph might have made a cuckold if he had not been a Joseph; how came he, I say, to be made general of all the horse in the kingdom of Egypt? Why was Nabuzardan, King

Nebuchadnezzar's head-cook, chosen to the exclusion of all other captains to besiege and destroy Jerusalem? I hear you, replied Pantagruel. By St. Christopher's whiskers, said Friar John, I dare lay a wager that it was because they had formerly engaged Chitterlings, or men as little valued; whom to rout, conquer, and destroy, cooks are without comparison more fit than cuirassiers and gendarmes armed at all points, or all the horse and foot in the world.

You put me in mind, said Pantagruel, of what is written amongst the facetious and merry sayings of Cicero. During the more than civil wars between Cæsar and Pompey, though he was much courted by the first, he naturally leaned more to the side of the latter. Now one day hearing that the Pompeians in a certain rencontre had lost a great many men, he took a fancy to visit their camp. There he perceived little strength, less courage, but much disorder. From that time, foreseeing that things would go ill with them, as it since happened, he began to banter now one and then another, and be very free of his cutting jests; so some of Pompey's captains, playing the good fellows to show their assurance, told him, Do you see how many eagles we have yet? (They were then the device of the Romans in war.) They might be of use to you, replied Cicero, if you had to do with magpies.

Thus, seeing we are to fight Chitterlings, pursued Pantagruel, you infer thence that it is a culinary war, and have a mind to join with the cooks. Well, do as you please, I'll stay here in the meantime, and wait for the event of the rumpus.

Friar John went that very moment among the sutlers, into the cooks' tents, and told them in a pleasing manner: I must see you crowned with honour and triumph this day, my lads; to your arms are reserved such achievements as never yet were performed within the memory of man. Ods-belly, do they make nothing of the valiant cooks? Let us go fight yonder fornicating Chitterlings! I'll be your captain. But first let's drink, boys. Come on! let us be of good cheer. Noble captain, returned the kitchen tribe, this was spoken like yourself; bravely offered. Huzza! we are all at your excellency's command, and we live and die by you. Live, live, said Friar John, a-God's name; but die by no means. That is the Chitterlings' lot; they shall have their bellyful of it. Come on then, let us put ourselves in order; Nabuzardan's the word.

CHAPTER 26

HOW FRIAR JOHN FITTED UP THE SOW; AND OF THE VALIANT COOKS THAT WENT INTO IT

THEN, by Friar John's order, the engineers and their workmen fitted up the great sow that was in the ship Leathern Bottle. It was a wonderful machine, so contrived that, by means of large engines that were round about it in rows, it throw'd forked iron bars and four-squared steel bolts; and in its hold two hundred men at least could easily fight, and be sheltered. It was made after the model of the sow of Riole, by the means of which Bergerac was retaken from the English in the reign of Charles the Sixth.

Here are the names of the noble and valiant cooks who went into the sow, as the Greeks did into the Trojan horse:

Sour-sauce.	Crisp-pig.	Carbonado.
Sweet-meat.	Greasy-slouch.	Sop-in-pan.
Greedy-gut.	Fat-gut.	Pick-fowl.
Liquorice-chops.	Bray-mortar.	Mustard-pot.
Soused-pork.	Lick-sauce.	Hog's-haslet.
Slap-sauce.	Hog's-foot.	Chopped-phiz.
Cock-broth.	Hodge-podge.	Gallimaufry.
Slipslop.		

All these noble cooks in their coat-of-arms did bear, in a field gules, a larding-pin vert, charged with a chevron argent.

Lard, hog's-lard.	Pinch-lard.	Snatch-lard.
Nibble-lard.	Top-lard.	Gnaw-lard.
Filch-lard.	Pick-lard.	Scrape-lard.
Fat-lard.	Save-lard.	Chew-lard.

Gaillard (by syncope) born near Rambouillet. The said culinary doctor's name was Gaillardlard, in the same manner as you use to say idolatrous for idololatrous.

Stiff-lard.	Cut-lard.	Waste-lard.
Watch-lard.	Mince-lard.	Ogle-lard.
Sweet-lard.	Dainty-lard.	Weigh-lard.
Eat-lard.	Fresh-lard.	Gulch-lard.
Snap-lard.	Rusty-lard.	Eye-lard.
Catch-lard.		

Names unknown among the Marranes and Jews.

Pick-sallat.	Thirsty.	Porridge-pot.
Broil-rasher.	Kitchen-stuff.	Lick-dish.
Coney-skin.	Verjuice.	Salt-gullet.
Dainty-chops.	Save-dripping.	Snail-dresser.
Pie-wright.	Watercress.	Soup-monger.
Pudding-pan.	Scrape-turnip.	Brewis-belly.
Toss-pot.	Trivet.	Chine-picker.
Mustard-sauce.	Monsieur Ragout.	Suck-gravy.
Claret-sauce.	Crack-pipkin.	Macaroon.
Swill-broth.	Scrape-pot.	Skewer-maker.

Smell-smock. He was afterwards taken from the kitchen and removed to chamber-practice, for the service of the noble Cardinal Hunt-venison.

Rot-roast.	Hog's gullet.	Fox-tail.
Dish-clout.	Sirloin.	Fly-flap.
Save-suet.	Spit-mutton.	Old Grizzle.
Fire-fumbler.	Fritter-frier.	Ruff-belly.
Pillicock.	Flesh-smith.	Saffron-sauce.
Long-tool.	Cram-gut.	Strutting-tom.
Prick-pride.	Tuzzy-mussy.	Slashed-snout.
Prick-madam.	Jacket-liner.	Smutty-face.
Pricket.	Guzzle-drink.	

Mondam, that first invented madam's sauce, and for that discovery was thus called in the Scotch-French dialect.

Loblolly.	Sloven.	Trencher-man.
Slabber-chops.	Swallow-pitcher.	Goodman Goosecap.
Scum-pot.	Wafer-monger.	Munch-turnip.
Gully-guts.	Snap-gobbet.	Pudding-bag.
Rinse-pot.	Scurvy-phiz.	Pig-sticker.
Drink-spiller.		

Robert. He invented Robert's sauce, so good and necessary for roasted coneys, ducks, fresh pork, poached eggs, salt fish, and a thousand other such dishes.

Cold-eel.	Frying-pan.	Big-snout.
Thornback.	Man of dough.	Lick-finger.
Gurnard.	Sauce-doctor.	Tit-bit.
Grumbling-gut.	Waste-butter.	Sauce-box.
Alms-scrip.	Shitbreech.	All-fours.
Taste-all.	Thick-brawn.	Whimwham.
Scrap-merchant.	Tom T—d.	Baste-roast.
Belly-timberman.	Mouldy-crust.	Gaping-hoyden.
Hashee.	Hasty.	Calf's-pluck.
Frig-palate.	Red-herring.	Leather-breeches.
Powdering-tub.	Cheese-cake.	

All these noble cooks went into the sow, merry, cheery, hale, brisk, old dogs at mischief, and ready to fight stoutly. Friar John ever and anon waving his huge scimitar, brought up the rear, and double-locked the doors on the inside.

CHAPTER 27

HOW PANTAGRUEL BROKE THE CHITTERLINGS AT THE KNEES

THE Chitterlings advanced so near that Pantagruel perceived that they stretched their arms and already began to charge their lances, which caused him to send Gymnast to know what they meant, and why they thus, without the least provocation, came to fall upon their old trusty friends, who had neither said nor done the least ill thing to them. Gymnast being advanced near their front, bowed very low, and said to them as loud as ever he could: We are friends, we are friends; all, all of us your friends, yours, and at your command; we are for Carnival, your old confederate. Some have since told me that he mistook, and said cavernal instead of carnival.

Whatever it was, the word was no sooner out of his mouth but a huge little squab Sausage, starting out of the front of their main body, would have gripped him by the collar. By the helmet of Mars, said Gymnast, I will swallow thee; but thou shalt only come in in chips and slices; for, big as thou art, thou couldst never come in whole. This spoke, he lugs out his trusty sword, Kiss-mine-arse (so he called it) with both his fists, and cut the Sausage in twain. Bless me, how fat the foul thief was! it puts me in mind of the huge bull of Berne, that was slain at Marignan when the drunken Swiss were so mauled there. Believe me, it had little less than four inches lard on its paunch.

The Sausage's job being done, a crowd of others flew upon

Gymnast, and had most scurvily dragged him down when Pantagruel with his men came up to his relief. Then began the martial fray, higgledypiggledy. Maul-chitterling did maul chitterlings; Cut-pudding did cut pudding; Pantagruel did break the Chitterlings at the knees; Friar John played at least in sight within his sow, viewing and observing all things; when the Pattipans that lay in ambuscade most furiously sallied out upon Pantagruel.

Friar John, who lay snug all this while, by that time perceiving the rout and hurlyburly, set open the doors of his sow and sallied out with his merry Greeks, some of them armed with iron spits, others with andirons, racks, fire-shovels, frying-pans, kettles, gridirons, oven forks, tongs, dripping pans, brooms, iron pots, mortars, pestles, all in battle array, like so many housebreakers, hallooing and roaring out all together most frightfully, Nabuzardan, Nabuzardan, Nabuzardan. Thus shouting and hooting they fought like dragons, and charged through the Pattipans and Sausages. The Chitterlings perceiving this fresh reinforcement, and that the others would be too hard for 'em, betook themselves to their heels, scampering off with full speed, as if the devil had come for them. Friar John, with an iron crow, knocked them down as fast as hops; his men, too, were not sparing on their side. Oh, what a woeful sight it was! the field was all over strewed with heaps of dead or wounded Chitterlings; and history relates that had not heaven had a hand in it, the Chitterling tribe had been totally routed out of the world by the culinary champions. But there happened a wonderful thing, you may believe as little or as much of it as you please.

From the north flew towards us a huge, fat, thick, grizzly swine, with long and large wings, like those of a windmill; its plumes red crimson, like those of a phenicoptere (which in Languedoc they call flaman); its eyes were red, and flaming like a carbuncle; its ears green, like a Prasin emerald; its teeth like a topaz; its tail long and black, like jet; its feet white, diaphanous and transparent like a diamond, somewhat broad, and of the splay kind, like those of geese, and as Queen Dick's used to be at Toulouse in the days of yore. About its neck it wore a gold collar, round which were some Ionian characters, whereof I could pick out but two words, SUS ATHENAN, hog-teaching Minerva.

The sky was clear before; but at that monster's appearance it changed so mightily for the worse that we were all amazed at it. As soon as the Chitterlings perceived the flying hog, down they all threw their weapons and fell on their knees, lifting up their hands joined together, without speaking one word, in a posture of adoration. Friar John and his party kept on mincing, felling, braining, mangling, and spitting the Chitterlings like mad; but Pantagruel sounded a retreat, and all hostility ceased.

The monster having several times hovered backwards and forwards between the two armies, with a tail-shot voided above twenty-seven butts of mustard on the ground; then flew away through the air, crying all the while, Carnival, Carnival, Carnival.

CHAPTER 28

HOW PANTAGRUEL HELD A TREATY WITH NIPHLESETH, QUEEN OF THE CHITTERLINGS

THE monster being out of sight, and the two armies remaining silent, Pantagruel demanded a parley with the lady Niphleseth, Queen of the Chitterlings, who was in her chariot by the standards; and it was easily granted. The queen alighted, courteously received Pantagruel, and was glad to see him. Pantagruel complained to her of this breach of peace; but she civilly made her excuse, telling him that a false information had caused all this mischief; her spies having brought her word that Shrovetide, their mortal foe, was landed, and spent his time in examining the urine of physeters.

She therefore entreated him to pardon them their offence, telling him that sir-reverence was sooner found in Chitterlings than gall; and offering, for herself and all her successors, to hold of him and his the whole island and country; to obey him in all his commands, be friends to his friends, and foes to his foes; and also to send every year, as an acknowledgment of their homage, a tribute of seventy-eight thousand royal Chitterlings, to serve him at his first course at table six months in the year; which was punctually performed. For the next day she sent the aforesaid quantity of royal Chitterlings to the good Gargantua, under the conduct of young Niphleseth, infanta of the island.

The good Gargantua made a present of them to the great King of Paris. But by change of air, and for want of mustard (the natural balsam and restorer of Chitterlings), most of them died. By the great king's particular grant they were buried in heaps in a part of Paris to this day called *La Rue pavee d'Andouilles*, the street paved with Chitterlings. At the request of the ladies at his court young Niphleseth was preserved, honourably used, and since that married to heart's content; and was the mother of many children, for which heaven be praised.

Pantagruel civilly thanked the queen, forgave all offences, refused the offer she had made of her country, and gave her a pretty little knife. After that he asked several nice questions concerning the apparition of that flying hog. She answered that it was the idea of Carnival, their tutelary god in time of war, first founder and original of all the Chitterling race; for which reason he resembled a hog, for Chitterlings drew their extraction from hogs.

Pantagruel asking to what purpose and curative indication he had voided so much mustard on the earth, the queen replied that mustard was their sanc-greal and celestial balsam, of which, laying but a little in the wounds of the fallen Chitterlings, in a very short time the wounded were healed and the dead restored to life. Pantagruel held no further discourse with the queen, but retired a-shipboard. The like did all the boon companions, with their implements of destruction and their huge sow.

CHAPTER 29

HOW PANTAGRUEL WENT ASHORE AT THE DWELLING OF GASTER, THE FIRST MASTER OF ARTS IN THE WORLD

THAT day Pantagruel went ashore in an island which, for situation and governor, may be said not to have its fellow. When you just come into it, you find it rugged, craggy, and barren, unpleasant to the eye, painful to the feet, and almost as inaccessible as the mountain of Dauphiné, which is somewhat like a toadstool, and was never climbed as any can remember by any but Doyac, who had the charge of King Charles the Eighth's train of artillery.

This same Doyac with strange tools and engines gained that mountain's top, and there he found an old ram. It puzzled many a wise head to guess how it got thither. Some said that some eagle or great horncoot, having carried it thither while it was yet a lambkin, it had got away and saved itself among the bushes.

As for us, having with much toil and sweat overcome the difficult ways at the entrance, we found the top of the mountain so fertile, healthful, and pleasant, that I thought I was then in the true garden of Eden, or earthly paradise, about whose situation our good theologues are in such a quandary and keep such a pother.

As for Pantagruel, he said that here was the seat of Areté —that is as much as to say, virtue—described by Hesiod. This, however, with submission to better judgments. The ruler of this place was one Master Gaster, the first master of arts in this world. For, if you believe that fire is the great master of arts, as Tully writes, you very much wrong him and yourself; alas! Tully never believed this. On the other side, if you fancy Mercury to be the first inventor of arts, as our ancient Druids believed of old, you are mightily beside the mark. The satirist's sentence, that affirms Master Gaster to be the master of all arts, is true. With him peacefully resided old goody Penia, alias Poverty, the mother of the ninety-nine Muses, on whom Porus, the lord of Plenty, formerly begot Love, that noble child, the mediator of heaven and earth, as Plato affirms *in Symposio*.

We were all obliged to pay our homage and swear allegiance to that mighty sovereign; for he is imperious, severe, blunt, hard, uneasy, inflexible; you cannot make him believe, represent to him, or persuade him anything.

He does not hear; and as the Egyptians said that Harpocrates, the god of silence, named Sigalion in Greek, was astomé, that is, without a mouth, so Gaster was created without ears, even like the image of Jupiter in Candia.

He only speaks by signs; but those signs are more readily obeyed by everyone than the statutes of senates or commands of monarchs. Neither will he admit the least let or delay in his summons. You say that when a lion roars all the beasts at a considerable distance round about, as far as his roar can be heard, are seized with a shivering. This is written, it is true; I have seen it. I assure you that at Master Gaster's command the very heavens tremble, and all the earth shakes. His command is called, Do this or die. Needs must when the devil drives; there's no gainsaying of it.

The pilot was telling us how, on a certain time, after the manner of the members that mutinied against the belly, as Æsop describes it, the whole kingdom of the Somates went off into a direct faction against Gaster, resolving to throw off his yoke; but they soon found their mistake, and most humbly submitted, for otherwise they had all been famished.

What company soever he is in, none dispute with him for precedence or superiority; he still goes first, though kings, emperors, or even the pope, were there. So he held the first place at the council of Basle; though some will tell you that the council was tumultuous by the contention and ambition of many for priority.

Everyone is busied and labours to serve him, and indeed, to make amends for this, he does this good to mankind, as to invent for them all arts, machines, trades, engines, and crafts; he even instructs brutes in arts which are against their nature, making poets of ravens, jackdaws, chattering jays, parrots, and starlings, and poetesses of magpies, teaching them to utter human language, speak, and sing; and all for the gut. He reclaims and tames eagles, gerfalcons, falcons gentle, sakers, lanners, goshawks, sparrowhawks, merlins, haggards, passengers, wild rapacious birds; so that, setting them free in the air whenever he thinks fit, as high as long as he pleases, he keeps them suspended, straying, flying, hovering, and courting him above the clouds. Then on a sudden he makes them stoop, and come down amain from heaven next to the ground; and all for the gut.

Elephants, lions, rhinoceroses, bears, horses, mares, and dogs, he teaches to dance, prance, vault, fight, swim, hide themselves, fetch and carry what he pleases; and all for the gut.

Salt and fresh-water fish, whales, and the monsters of the main, he brings them up from the bottom of the deep; wolves he forces out of the woods, bears out of the rocks, foxes out of their holes, and serpents out of the ground; and all for the gut.

In short, he is so unruly, that in his rage he devours all men and beasts; as was seen among the Vascons, when Q. Metellus besieged them in the Sertorian wars; among the Sagutines besieged by Hannibal; among the Jews besieged by the Romans, and six hundred more; and all for the gut. When his regent Penia takes a progress, wherever she moves all senates are shut up, all statutes repealed, all orders and proclamations vain; she knows, obeys, and has no law. All shun her, in every place choosing rather to expose themselves to shipwreck at sea, and venture through fire, rocks, caves, and precipices, than be seized by that most dreadful tormentor.

CHAPTER 30

HOW, AT THE COURT OF THE MASTER OF INGENUITY, PANTAGRUEL DETESTED THE ENGASTRIMYTHES AND THE GASTROLATERS

At the court of that great master of ingenuity, Pantagruel observed two sorts of troublesome and too officious apparitors, whom he very much detested. The first were called Engastrimythes; the others, Gastrolaters.

The first pretended to be descended of the ancient race of Eurycles, and for this brought the authority of Aristophanes in his comedy called the Wasps; whence of old they were called Euryclians, as Plato writes, and Plutarch in his book of the Cessation of Oracles. In the holy decrees, 26, qu. 3, they are styled Ventriloqui; and the same name is given them in Ionian by Hippocrates, in his fifth book of *Epid.*, as men who speak from the belly. Sophocles calls them Sternomantes. These were soothsayers, enchanters, cheats, who gulled the mob, and seemed not to speak and give answers from the mouth, but from the belly.

Such a one, about the year of our Lord 1513, was Jacoba Rodogina, an Italian woman of mean extract; from whose belly we, as well as an infinite number of others at Ferrara and elsewhere, have often heard the voice of the evil spirit speak, low, feeble, and small, indeed, but yet very distinct, articulate, and intelligible, when she was sent for out of curiosity by the lords and princes of the Cisalpine Gaul. To remove all manner of doubt, and be assured that this was not a trick, they used to have her stripped stark naked, and caused her mouth and nose to be stopped. This evil spirit would be called Curled-pate, or Cincinnatulo, seeming pleased when any called him by that name, at which he was always ready to answer. If any spoke to him of things past or present, he gave pertinent answers, sometimes to the amazement of the hearers; but if of things to come, then the devil was gravelled, and used to lie as fast as a dog can trot. Nay, sometimes he seemed to own his ignorance, instead of an answer letting out a rousing fart, or muttering some words with barbarous and uncouth inflexions, and not to be understood.

As for the Gastrolaters, they stuck close to one another in knots and gangs. Some of them merry, wanton, and soft as so many milk-sops; others louring, grim, dogged, demure, and crabbed; all idle, mortal foes to business, spending half their time in sleeping and the rest in doing nothing, a rent-charge and dead unnecessary weight on the earth, as Hesiod saith; afraid, as we judged, of offending or lessening their paunch. Others were masked, disguised, and so oddly dressed that it would have done you good to have seen them.

There's a saying, and several ancient sages write, that the skill of nature appears wonderful in the pleasure which she seems to have taken in the configuration of sea-shells, so great is their variety in figures, colours, streaks, and inimitable shapes. I protest the variety we perceived in the dresses of the gastrolatrous coquillons was not less. They all owned Gaster for their supreme god, adored him as a god, offered him sacrifices as to their omnipotent deity, owned no other god, served, loved, and honoured him above all things.

You would have thought that the holy apostle spoke of those when he said (Phil. chap. 3), Many walk, of whom I have told you often, and now tell you even weeping, that they are enemies of the cross of Christ: whose end is destruction, whose God is their belly. Pantagruel compared them to the Cyclops Polyphemus, whom Euripides brings in speaking thus: I only sacrifice to myself—not to the gods—and to this belly of mine, the greatest of all the gods.

CHAPTER 31

OF THE RIDICULOUS STATUE MANDUCE; AND HOW AND WHAT THE GASTROLATERS SACRIFICE TO THEIR VENTRIPOTENT GOD

WHILE we fed our eyes with the sight of the phizzes and actions of these lounging gulli-gutted Gastrolaters, we on a sudden heard the sound of a musical instrument called a bell; at which all of them placed themselves in rank and file for some mighty battle, everyone according to his office, degree, and seniority.

In this order they moved towards Master Gaster, after a plump, young, lusty, gorbellied fellow, who on a long staff fairly gilt, carried a wooden statue, grossly carved, and as scurvily daubed over with paint; such a one as Plautus, Juvenal, and Pomp. Festus describe it. At Lyons during the Carnival it is called Maschecroute or Gnawcrust; they call'd this Manduce.

It was a monstrous, ridiculous, hideous figure, fit to fright little children; its eyes were bigger than its belly, and its head larger than all the rest of its body; well mouth-cloven however, having a good pair of wide, broad jaws, lined with two rows of teeth, upper tier and under tier, which, by the magic of a small twine hid in the hollow part of the golden staff, were made to clash, clatter, and rattle dreadfully one against another; as they do at Metz with St. Clement's dragon.

Coming near the Gastrolaters I saw they were followed by a great number of fat waiters and tenders, laden with baskets, dossers, hampers, dishes, wallets, pots, and kettles. Then, under the conduct of Manduce, and singing I do not know what dithyrambics, crepalocomes, and epenons, opening their baskets and pots, they offered their god:

White hippocras, with dry toasts.
White bread.
Brown bread.
Carbonadoes, six sorts.
Brawn.
Sweetbreads.
Fricassees, nine sorts.
Monastical brewis.
Gravy soup.
Hotch-pots.

Soft bread.
Household bread.
Capirotadoes.
Cold loins of veal, with spice.
Zinziberine.
Beatille pies.
Brewis.
Marrow-bones, toast, and cabbage.
Hashes.

Eternal drink intermixed. Brisk delicate white wine led the van; claret and champagne followed, cool, nay, as cold as the very ice, I say, filled and offered in large silver cups. Then they offered:

Chitterlings, garnished with mustard.	Puddings.
Sausages.	Cervelats.
Neats' tongues.	Bologna sausages.
Hung beef.	Hams.
Chines and peas.	Brawn heads.
Hogs' haslets.	Powdered venison, with turnips.
Scotch collops.	Pickled olives.

All this associated with sempiternal liquor. Then they housed within his muzzle:

Legs of mutton, with shallots.	Pigeon pies.
Olias.	Kid pasties.
Lumber pies, with hot sauce.	Capon pies.
Ribs of pork, with onion sauce.	Bacon pies.
	Soused hogs' feet.
Roast capons, basted with their own dripping.	Fried pasty-crust.
	Forced capons.
Caponets.	Parmesan cheese.
Caviare and toast.	Red and pale hippocras.
Fawns, deer.	Gold-peaches.
Hares, leverets.	Artichokes.
Partridges and young partridges.	Dry and wet sweetmeats, seventy-eight sorts.
Plovers.	Boiled hens, and fat capons marinated.
Dwarf-herons.	Pullets, with eggs.
Teals.	Chickens.
	Rabbits, and sucking rabbits.

Duckers.

Bitterns.

Shovellers.

Curlews.

Wood-hens.

Coots, with leeks.

Fat kids.

Shoulders of mutton, with capers.

Sirloins of beef.

Breasts of veal.

Pheasants and pheasant poots.

Peacocks.

Storks.

Woodcocks.

Snipes.

Ortolans.

Turkey cocks, hen turkeys, and turkey poots.

Stock-doves, and wood-culvers.

Pigs, with wine sauce.

Blackbirds, ousels, and rails.

Moorhens.

Bustards, and bustard poots.

Fig-peckers.

Young Guinea hens.

Flamingoes.

Cygnets.

A reinforcement of vinegar intermixed.

Venison pasties.

Quails, and young quails.

Herons, and young herons.

Pigeons, squabs, and squeakers.

Fieldfares.

Olives.

Thrushes.

Young sea-ravens.

Geese, goslings.

Queests.

Widgeons.

Mavises.

Grouses.

Turtles.

Doe-coneys.

Hedgehogs.

Snites.

Then large puffs.

Thistle-finches.

Whore's farts.

Fritters.

Cakes, sixteen sorts.

Crisp wafers.

Quince tarts.

Curds and cream.

Whipped cream.

Preserved mirabolans.

Jellies.

Welsh barrapyclids.

Macaroons.

Tarts, twenty sorts.

Lemon cream, raspberry cream, &c.

Lark pies.
Dormice pies.
Cabretto pasties.
Roebuck pasties.

Comfits, one hundred colours.
Cream wafers.
Cream cheese.

Vinegar brought up the rear to wash the mouth, and for fear of the squinsy; also toasts to scour the grinders.

CHAPTER 32

WHAT THE GASTROLATERS SACRIFICED TO THEIR GOD ON INTERLARDED FISH-DAYS

PANTAGRUEL did not like this pack of rascally scoundrels with their manifold kitchen sacrifices, and would have been gone had not Epistemon prevailed with him to stay and see the end of the farce. He then asked the skipper what the idle lobcocks used to sacrifice to their gorbellied god on interlarded fish-days. For his first course, said the skipper, they gave him:

Caviare.
Botargoes.
Fresh butter.
Pease soup.
Spinach.
Fresh herring, full roed.
Salads, a hundred varieties of cresses, sodden hop-tops, bishop's-cods, celery, chives, rampions, jew's-ears (a sort of mushrooms that sprout out of old elders), sparagus, woodbind, and a world of others.
Red herrings.
Pilchards
Anchovies.
Fry of tunny.
Cauliflowers.
Beans.
Salt salmon.
Pickled grigs.
Oysters in the shell.

Then he must drink, or the devil would gripe him at the throat; this, therefore, they take care to prevent, and nothing is wanting. Which being done, they give him lampreys with hippocras sauce:

Gurnards.
Salmon trouts.
Barbels, great and small.
Roaches.
Cockerels.
Minnows.
Thornbacks.
Sleeves.
Sturgeons.
Sheath-fish.
Mackerels.
Maids.
Plaice.
Fried Oysters.
Cockles.
Prawns.
Smelts.
Rock-fish.
Gracious lords.
Sword-fish.
Skate-fish.
Lamprels.
Jegs.
Pickerels.
Golden carps.
Burbates.
Salmons.
Salmon-peels.

Sharplings.
Tunnies.
Silver-eels.
Chevins.
Crayfish.
Pallours.
Shrimps.
Congers.
Porpoises.
Bases.
Shads.
Murenes, a sort of lampreys.
Graylings.
Smys.
Turbots.
Trout, not above a foot long.
Salmons.
Meagers.
Sea-breams.
Halibuts.
Soles.
Dog's tongue, or kind fool.
Mussels.
Lobsters.
Great prawns.
Dace.
Bleaks.
Tenches.

Dolphins.

Barn trouts.

Miller's-thumbs.

Precks.

Bret-fish.

Flounders.

Sea-nettles.

Mullets.

Gudgeons.

Dabs and sandings.

Haddocks.

Carps.

Pikes.

Bottitoes.

Rochets.

Sea-bears.

Ombres.

Fresh cods.

Dried melwels.

Darefish.

Fausens, and grigs.

Eel-pouts.

Tortoises.

Serpents, *i. e.* wood-eels.

Dories.

Moor-game.

Perches.

Loaches.

Crab-fish.

Snails and whelks.

Frogs.

If, when he had crammed all this down his guttural trap-door, he did not immediately make the fish swim again in his paunch, death would pack him off in a trice. Special care is taken to antidote his godship with vine-tree syrup. Then is sacrificed to him haberdines, poor-jack, minglemangled, mismashed, &c.

Eggs, fried, beaten, buttered, poached, hardened, boiled, broiled, stewed, sliced, roasted in the embers, tossed in the chimney, &c.

Stock-fish.

Green-fish.

Sea-batts.

Cod's sounds.

Sea-pikes.

Which to concoct and digest the more easily, vinegar is multiplied. For the latter part of their sacrifices they offer:

Rice milk, and hasty pudding.

Figs.

Almond butter.

Buttered, wheat, and flummery.

Water-gruel, and milk porridge.

Frumenty and bonny clamber.

Stewed prunes, and baked bullace.

Pistachios, or fistic nuts.

Skirred root.

White-pot.

Raisins.

Dates.

Chestnuts and walnuts.

Filberts.

Parsnips.

Artichokes.

Perpetuity of soaking with the whole.

It was none of their fault, I will assure you, if this same god of theirs was not publicly, preciously, and plentifully served in the sacrifices, better yet than Heliogabalus's idol; nay, more than Bel and the Dragon in Babylon, under King Belshazzar. Yet Gaster had the manners to own that he was no god, but a poor, vile, wretched creature. And as King Antigonus, first of the name, when one Hermodotus (as poets will flatter, especially princes) in some of his fustian dubbed him a god, and made the sun adopt him for his son, said to him: My lasanophore (or, in plain English, my groom of the close-stool) can give thee the lie; so Master Gaster very civilly used to send back his bigoted worshippers to his close-stool, to see, smell, taste, philosophize, and examine what kind of divinity they could pick out of his sir-reverence.

CHAPTER 33

HOW GASTER INVENTED MEANS TO GET AND PRESERVE CORN

THOSE gastrolatrous hobgoblins being withdrawn, Pantagruel carefully minded the famous master of arts, Gaster. You know that, by the institution of nature, bread has been assigned him for provision and food; and that, as an addition to this blessing, he should never want the means to get bread.

Accordingly, from the beginning he invented the smith's art, and husbandry to manure the ground, that it might yield him corn; he invented arms and the art of war to defend corn; physic and astronomy, with other parts of mathematics which might be useful to keep corn a great number of years in safety from the injuries of the air, beasts, robbers, and purloiners; he invented water, wind, and hand-mills, and a thousand other engines to grind corn and to turn it into meal; leaven to make the dough ferment, and the use of salt to give it a savour; for he knew that nothing bred more diseases than heavy, unleavened, unsavory bread.

He found a way to get fire to bake it; hour-glasses, dials and clocks to mark the time of its baking; and as some countries wanted corn, he contrived means to convey some out of one country into another.

He had the wit to pimp for asses and mares, animals of different species, that they might copulate for the generation of a third, which we call mules, more strong and fit for hard service than the other two. He invented carts and waggons to draw him along with greater ease; and as seas and rivers hindered his progress, he devised boats, galleys, and ships (to the astonishment of the elements) to waft him over to barbarous, unknown, and far distant nations, thence to bring or thither to carry corn.

Besides, seeing that when he had tilled the ground, some years the corn perished in it for want of rain in due season, in others rotted or was drowned by its excess, sometimes spoiled by hail, eat by worms in the ear, or beaten down by storms, and so his stock was destroyed on the ground, we were told that ever since the days of yore he has found out a way to conjure the rain down from heaven only with cutting certain grass, common enough in the field, yet know

to very few, some of which was then shown us. I took it to
be the same as the plant, one of whose boughs being dipped
by Jove's priest in the Agrian fountain on the Lycian mountain in Arcadia, in time of drought raised vapours which
gathered into clouds, and then dissolved into rain that kindly
moistened the whole country.

Our master of arts was also said to have found a way to
keep the rain up in the air, and make it to fall into the sea;
also to annihilate the hail, suppress the winds, and remove
storms as the Methanensians of Trœzene used to do. And
as in the fields thieves and plunderers sometimes stole and
took by force the corn and bread which others had toiled to
get, he invented the art of building towns, forts, and castles,
to hoard and secure that staff of life. On the other hand,
finding none in the fields, and hearing that it was hoarded
up and secured in towns, forts, and castles, and watched
with more care than ever were the golden pippins of the
Hesperides, he turned engineer, and found ways to beat,
storm, and demolish forts and castles with machines and
warlike thunderbolts, battering-rams, ballists, and catapults,
whose shapes were shown to us, not over-well understood by
our engineers, architects, and other disciples of Vitruvius;
as Master Philibert de l'Orme, King Megistus's principal
architect, has owned to us.

CHAPTER 34

HOW PANTAGRUEL PASSED THE TIME WITH HIS SERVANTS

In what hierarchy of such venomous creatures do you
place Panurge's future spouse? asked Friar John. Art thou
speaking ill of women, cried Panurge, thou mangy scoundrel,
thou sorry, noddy-peaked shaveling monk? By the cenomanic
paunch and gixy, said Epistemon, Euripides has written, and

makes Andromache say it, that by industry, and the help of the gods, men had found remedies against all poisonous creatures; but none was yet found against a bad wife.

This flaunting Euripides, cried Panurge, was gabbling against women every foot, and therefore was devoured by dogs, as a judgment from above; as Aristophanes observes. Let's go on. Let him speak that is next. I can leak now like any stone-horse, said then Epistemon. I am, said Xenomanes, full as an egg and round as a hoop; my ship's hold can hold no more, and will now make shift to bear a steady sail. Said Carpalin, A truce with thirst, a truce with hunger; they are strong, but wine and meat are stronger. I'm no more in the dumps, cried Panurge; my heart's a pound lighter. I'm in the right cue now, as brisk as a body-louse, and as merry as a beggar. For my part, I know what I do when I drink; and it is a true thing (though 'tis in your Euripides) that is said by that jolly toper Silenus of blessed memory, that—

> The man's emphatically mad,
> Who drinks the best, yet can be sad.

We must not fail to return our humble and hearty thanks to the Being who, with this good bread, this cool delicious wine, these good meats and rare dainties, removes from our bodies and minds these pains and perturbations, and at the same time fills us with pleasure and with food.

But methinks, sir, you did not give an answer to Friar John's question; which, as I take it, was how to raise good weather. Since you ask no more than this easy question, Pantagruel, I'll strive to give you satisfaction; and some other time we'll talk of the rest of the problems, if you will.

Well then, Friar John asked how good weather might be raised. Have we not raised it? Look up and see our full topsails. Hark how the wind whistles through the shrouds, what a stiff gale it blows. Observe the rattling of the tacklings, and see the sheets that fasten the mainsail behind; the force of the wind puts them upon the stretch. While we passed our time merrily, the dull weather also passed away; and while we raised the glasses to our mouths, we also raised the wind by a secret sympathy in nature.

Thus Atlas and Hercules clubbed to raise and underprop the falling sky, if you'll believe the wise mythologists, but they raised it some half an inch too high, Atlas, to entertain his guest Hercules more pleasantly, and Hercules to make himself amends for the thirst which some time before had tormented him in the deserts of Africa. Your good father, said Friar John, interrupting him, takes care to free many people from such an inconveniency; for I have been told by many venerable doctors that his chief-butler, Turelupin, saves above eighteen hundred pipes of wine yearly to make servants, and all comers and goers, drink before they are a-dry. As the camels and dromedaries of a caravan, continued Pantagruel, use to drink for the thirst that's past, for the present, and for that to come, so did Hercules; and being thus excessively raised, this gave new motion to the sky, which is that of *titubation and trepidation*, about which our crackbrained astrologers make such a pother. This, said Panurge, makes the saying good:

> While jolly companions carouse it together,
> A fig for the storm, it gives way to good weather.

Nay, continued Pantagruel, some will tell you that we have not only shortened the time of the calm, but also much disburthened the ship; not like Æsop's basket, by easing it of the provision, but by breaking our fasts; and that a man

is more terrestrial and heavy when fasting than when he has
eaten and drank, even as they pretend that he weighs more
dead than living. However it is, you will grant they are in
the right who take their morning's draught and breakfast
before a long journey; then say that the horses will perform the better, and that a spur in the head is worth two
in the flank; or, in the same horse dialect—

> That a cup in the pate
> Is a mile in the gate.

Don't you know that formerly the Amycleans worshipped
the noble Bacchus above all other gods, and gave him the
name of Psila, which in the Doric dialect signifies wings; for,
the birds raise themselves by towering flight with their wings
above the clouds, so, with the help of soaring Bacchus, the
powerful juice of the grape, our spirits are exalted to a pitch
above themselves, our bodies are more sprightly, and their
earthly parts become soft and pliant.

CHAPTER 35

HOW, BY PANTAGRUEL'S ORDER, THE MUSES WERE SALUTED NEAR THE ISLE OF GANABIM

This fair wind and as fine talk brought us in sight of a
high land, which Pantagruel discovering afar off, showed it
Xenomanes, and asked him, Do you see yonder to the lee-
ward a high rock with two tops, much like Mount Parnassus
in Phocis? I do plainly, answered Xenomanes; 'tis the isle of
Ganabim. Have you a mind to go ashore there? No, returned
Pantagruel. You do well, indeed, said Xenomanes; for there
is nothing worth seeing in the place. The people are all
thieves; yet there is the finest fountain in the world, and a

ery large forest towards the right top of the mountain.
Your fleet may take in wood and water there.

He that spoke last, spoke well, quoth Panurge; let us
not by any means be so mad as to go among a parcel of
thieves and sharpers. You may take my word for't, this
place is just such another as, to my knowledge, formerly
were the islands of Sark and Herm, between the smaller and
greater Britain; such as was the Poneropolis of Philip in
Thrace; islands of thieves, banditti, picaroons, robbers, ruf-
fians, and murderers, worse than raw-head and bloody-
bones, and full as honest as the senior fellows of the college
of iniquity, the very outcasts of the county gaol's common-
side. As you love yourself, do not go among 'em. If you go
you'll come off but bluely, if you come off at all. If you will
not believe me, at least believe what the good and wise
Xenomanes tells you; for may I never stir if they are not
worse than the very cannibals; they would certainly eat us
alive. Do not go among 'em, I pray you; it were safer to
take a journey to hell. Hark! by Cod's body, I hear 'em
ringing the alarm-bell most dreadfully, as the Gascons about
Bordeaux used formerly to do against the commissaries and
officers for the tax on salt, or my ears tingle. Let's sheer off.

Believe me, sir, said Friar John, let's rather land; we will
rid the world of that vermin, and inn there for nothing. Old
Nick go with thee for me, quoth Panurge. This rash hard-
brained devil of a friar fears nothing, but ventures and runs
on like a mad devil as he is, and cares not a rush what becomes of others; as if everyone was a monk, like his friar-
ship. A pox on grinning honour, say I. Go to, returned the
friar, thou mangy noddy-peak! thou forlorn druggleheaded
sneaksby! and may a million of black devils anatomize thy
cockle brain. The hen-hearted rascal is so cowardly that he
bewrays himself for fear every day. If thou art so afraid,

dunghill, do not go; stay here and be hanged, or go and hide thy loggerhead under Madam Proserpine's petticoat.

Panurge hearing this, his breech began to make buttons; so he slunk in in an instant, and went to hide his head down in the bread-room among the musty biscuits and the orts and scraps of broken bread.

Pantagruel in the meantime said to the rest: I feel a pressing retraction in my soul, which like a voice admonishes me not to land there. Whenever I have felt such a motion within me I have found myself happy in avoiding what it directed me to shun, or in undertaking what it prompted me to do; and I never had occasion to repent following its dictates.

As much, said Epistemon, is related of the dæmon of Socrates, so celebrated among the Academics. Well then, sir, said Friar John, while the ship's crew water have you a mind to have good sport? Panurge is got down somewhere in the hold, where he is crept into some corner, and lurks like a mouse in a cranny. Let 'em give the word for the gunner to fire yon gun over the round-house on the poop; this will serve to salute the Muses of this Anti-parnassus; besides, the powder does but decay in it. You are in the right, said Pantagruel; here, give the word for the gunner.

The gunner immediately came, and was ordered by Pantagruel to fire that gun, and then charge it with fresh powder, which was soon done. The gunners of the other ships, frigates, galleons, and galleys of the fleet, hearing us fire, gave every one a gun to the island; which made such a horrid noise that you would have sworn heaven had been tumbling about our ears.

The Fourth Book of

RABELAIS

Treating of the Heroic Deeds and Sayings
of the Good Pantagruel

CHAPTER I

PURSUING our voyage, we sailed three days without discovering anything; on the fourth we made land. Our pilot told us that it was the Ringing Island, and indeed we heard a kind of a confused and often repeated noise, that seemed to us at a great distance not unlike the sound of great, middle-sized, and little bells rung all at once, as 'tis customary at Paris, Tours, Gergeau, Nantes, and elsewhere on high holidays; and the nearer we came to the land the louder we heard that jangling.

Some of us doubted that it was the Dodonian kettle, or the portico called Heptaphone in Olympia, or the eternal humming of the colossus raised on Memnon's tomb in Thebes of Egypt, or the horrid din that used formerly to be heard about a tomb at Lipara, one of the Æolian islands. But this did not square with chorography.

I do not know, said Pantagruel, but that some swarms of bees hereabouts may be taking a ramble in the air, and so the neighbourhood make this dingle-dangle with pans, kettles, and basins, the corybantine cymbals of Cybele, grandmother of the gods, to call them back. Let's hearken. When we were nearer, among the everlasting ringing of these indefatigable bells we heard the singing, as we thought, of some men. For this reason, before we offered to land on the Ringing Island, Pantagruel was of opinion that we should go in the pinnace to a small rock, near which we discovered an

437

hermitage and a little garden. There we found a diminutive old hermit, whose name was Braguibus, born at Glenay. He gave us a full account of all the jangling, and regaled us after a strange sort of fashion—four livelong days did he make us fast, assuring us that we should not be admitted into the Ringing Island otherwise, because it was then one of the four fasting, or ember weeks. As I love my belly, quoth Panurge, I by no means understand this riddle. Methinks this should rather be one of the fourwindy weeks; for while we fast we are only puffed up with wind. Pray now, good father hermit, have not you here some other pastime besides fasting? Methinks it is somewhat of the leanest; we might well enough be without so many palace holidays and those fasting times of yours. In my Donatus, quoth Friar John, I could find yet but three times or tenses, the preterit, the present, and the future; doubtless here the fourth ought to be a work of supererogation. That time or tense, said Epistemon, is aorist, derived from the preter-imperfect tense of the Greeks, admitted in war [?] and odd cases. Patience perforce is a remedy for a mad dog. Saith the hermit: It is, as I told you, fatal to go against this; whosoever does it is a rank heretic, and wants nothing but fire and faggot, that's certain. To deal plainly with you, my dear pater, cried Panurge, being at sea, I much more fear being wet than being warm, and being drowned than being burned.

Well, however, let us fast, a-God's name; yet I have fasted so long that it has quite undermined my flesh, and I fear at last that the bastions of this bodily fort of mine will fall to ruin. Besides, I am much more afraid of vexing you in this same trade of fasting; for the devil a bit I understand anything in it, and it becomes me very scurvily, as several people have told me, and I am apt to believe them. For my part, I have no great stomach to fasting;

for alas! it is as easy as pissing a-bed, and a trade of which anybody may set up; there needs no tools. I am much more inclined not to fast for the future; for to do so there is some stock required, and some tools are set a-work. No matter, since you are so steadfast, and would have us fast, let us fast as fast as we can, and then breakfast in the name of famine. Now we are come to these esurial idle days. I vow I had quite put them out of my head long ago. If we must fast, said Pantagruel, I see no other remedy but to get rid of it as soon as we can, as we would out of a bad way. I'll in that space of time somewhat look over my papers, and examine whether the marine study be as good as ours at land. For Plato, to describe a silly, raw, ignorant fellow, compares him to those that are bred on shipboard, as we would do one bred up in a barrel, who never saw anything but through the bunghole.

To tell you the short and the long of the matter, our fasting was most hideous and terrible; for the first day we fasted at fisticuffs, the second at cudgels, the third at sharps, and the fourth at blood and wounds: such was the order of the fairies.

CHAPTER 2

HOW THE RINGING ISLAND HAD BEEN INHABITED BY THE SITICINES, WHO WERE BECOME BIRDS

HAVING fasted as aforesaid, the hermit gave us a letter for one whom he called Albian Camar, Master Ædituus of the Ringing Island; but Panurge greeting him called him Master Antitus. He was a little queer old fellow, bald-pated, with a snout whereat you might easily have lighted a card-match, and a phiz as red as a cardinal's cap. He made us all very welcome, upon the hermit's recommendation, hearing that we had fasted, as I have told you.

When we had well stuffed our puddings, he gave us an account of what was remarkable in the island, affirming that it had been at first inhabited by the Siticines; but that, according to the course of nature—as all things, you know, are subject to change—they were become birds.

There I had a full account of all that Atteius Capito, Paulus, Marcellus, A. Gellius, Athenæus, Suidas, Ammonius, and others had writ of the Siticines and Sicinnists; and then we thought we might as easily believe the transmutations of Nectymene, Progne, Itys, Alcyone, Antigone, Tereus, and other birds. Nor did we think it more reasonable to doubt of the transmogrification of the Macrobian children into swans, or that of the men of Pallene in Thrace into birds, as soon as they had bathed themselves in the Tritonic lake. After this the devil a word could we get out of him but of birds and cages.

The cages were spacious, costly, magnificent, and of an admirable architecture. The birds were large, fine, and neat accordingly, looking as like the men in my country as one pea does like another; for they ate and drank like men, muted like men, endued or digested like men, farted like men, but stunk like devils; slept, billed, and trod their females like men, but somewhat oftener: in short, had you seen and examined them from top to toe, you would have laid your head to a turnip that they had been mere men. However, they were nothing less, as Master Ædituus told us; assuring us, at the same time, that they were neither secular nor laic; and the truth is, the diversity of their feathers and plumes did not a little puzzle us.

Some of them were all over as white as swans, other as black as crows, many as grey as owls, others black and white like magpies, some all red like red-birds, and others purple and white like some pigeons. He called the males clerg-hawks, monk-hawks, priest-hawks, abbot-hawks, bish-hawks, cardin-hawks, and one pope-hawk, who is a species by himself. He called the females clerg-kites, nun-kites, priest-kites, abbess-kites, bish-kites, cardin-kites, and pope-kites.

However, said he, as hornets and drones will get among the bees, and there do nothing but buzz, eat, and spoil everything; so, for these last three hundred years, a vast swarm of bigottelloes flocked, I do not know how, among these goodly birds every fifth full moon, and have bemuted, bewrayed, and conskited the whole island. They are so hard-favoured and monstrous that none can abide them. For their wry necks make a figure like a crooked billet; their paws are hairy, like those of rough-footed pigeons; their claws and pounces belly and breech, like those of the Stymphalid harpies. Nor is it possible to root them out, for if you get rid of one, straight four-and-twenty new ones fly thither.

There had been need of another monster-hunter such as was Hercules; for Friar John had like to have run distracted about it, so much he was nettled and puzzled in the matter. As for the good Pantagruel, he was even served as was Messer Priapus, contemplating the sacrifices of Ceres, for want of skin.

CHAPTER 3

HOW THERE IS BUT ONE POPE-HAWK IN THE RINGING ISLAND

WE then asked Master Ædituus why there was but one pope-hawk among such venerable birds multiplied in all their species. He answered that such was the first institution and fatal destiny of the stars that the clerg-hawks begot the priest-hawks and monk-hawks without carnal copulation, as some bees are born of a young bull; the priest-hawks begat the bish-hawks, the bish-hawks the stately cardin-hawks, and the stately cardin-hawks, if they live long enough, at last come to be pope-hawk.

Of this last kind there never is more than one at a time as in a beehive there is but one king, and in the world is but one sun.

When the pope-hawk dies, another arises in his stead out of the whole brood of cardin-hawks; that is, as you must understand it all along, without carnal copulation. So that there is in that species an individual unity, with a perpetuity of succession, neither more or less than in the Arabian phœnix.

'Tis true that, about two thousand seven hundred and sixty moons ago, two pope-hawks were seen upon the face of the earth; but then you never saw in your lives such a woeful rout and hurly-burly as was all over this island. For all these same birds did so peck, clapper-claw, and maul one another all that time, that there was the devil and all to do, and the island was in a fair way of being left without inhabitants. Some stood up for this pope-hawk, some for t'other. Some, struck with a dumbness, were as mute as so many fishes; the devil a note was to be got out of them; part of the merry bells here, were as silent as if they had lost their tongues, I mean their clappers.

During these troublesome times they called to their assistance the emperors, kings, dukes, earls, barons, and commonwealths of the world that live on t'other side the water; nor was this schism and sedition at an end till one of them died, and the plurality was reduced to a unity.

We then asked what moved those birds to be thus continually chanting and singing. He answered that it was the bells that hung on the top of their cages. Then he said to us, Will you have me make these monk-hawks whom you see bardocuculated with a bag such as you use to still brandy, sing like any woodlarks? Pray do, said we. He then gave half a dozen pulls to a little rope, which caused a diminutive bell to give so many ting-tangs; and presently a parcel of monk-hawks ran to him as if the devil had drove 'em, and fell a-singing like mad.

Pray, master, cried Panurge, if I also rang this bell could I make those other birds yonder, with red-herring-coloured feathers, sing? Ay, marry would you, returned Ædituus. With this Panurge hanged himself (by the hands, I mean) at the bell-rope's end, and no sooner made it speak but those smoked birds hied them thither and began to lift up their voices and made a sort of untowardly hoarse noise, which I grudge to call singing. Ædituus indeed told us that they fed on nothing but fish, like the herns and cormorants of the world, and that they were a fifth kind of cucullati newly stamped.

He added that he had been told by Robert Valbringue, who lately passed that way in his return from Africa, that a sixth kind was to fly hither out of hand, which he called capus-hawks, more grum, vinegar-faced, brain-sick, froward, and loathsome than any kind whatsoever in the whole island. Africa, said Pantagruel, still uses to produce some new and monstrous thing.

CHAPTER 4

HOW THE BIRDS OF THE RINGING ISLAND WERE ALL PASSENGERS

SINCE you have told us, said Pantagruel, how the pope-hawk is begot by the cardin-hawks, the cardin-hawks by the bish-hawks, and the bish-hawks by the priest-hawks, and the priest-hawks by the clerg-hawks, I would gladly know whence you have these same clerg-hawks. They are all of them passengers, or travelling birds, returned Ædituus, and come hither from t'other world; part out of a vast country called Want-o'-bread, the rest out of another toward the west, which they style Too-many-of-'em. From these two countries flock hither, every year, whole legions of these clerg-hawks, leaving their fathers, mothers, friends, and relations.

This happens when there are too many children, whether male or female, in some good family of the latter country; insomuch that the house would come to nothing if the paternal estate were shared among them all (as reason requires, nature directs, and God commands). For this cause parents use to rid themselves of that inconveniency by packing off the younger fry, and forcing them to seek their fortune in this isle Bossart (Crooked Island). I suppose he means L'Isle Bouchart, near Chinon, cried Panurge. No, replied t'other, I mean Bossart (Crooked), for there is not one in ten among them but is either crooked, crippled, blinking, limping, ill-favoured, deformed, or an unprofitable load to the earth.

'Twas quite otherwise among the heathens, said Pantagruel, when they used to receive a maiden among the number of vestals; for Leo Antistius affirms that it was absolutely forbidden to admit a virgin into that order if she had any vice in her soul or defect in her body, though it were but the smallest spot on any part of it. I can hardly believe, continued Ædituus, that their dams on t'other side the water go nine months with them; for they cannot endure them nine years, nay, scarce seven sometimes, in the house, but by putting only a shirt over the other clothes of the young urchins, and lopping off I don't well know how many hairs from their crowns, mumbling certain apostrophized and expiatory words, they visibly, openly, and plainly, by a Pythagorical metempsychosis, without the least hurt, transmogrify them into such birds as you now see; much after the fashion of the Egyptian heathens, who used to constitute their isiacs by shaving them and making them put on certain linostoles, or surplices. However, I don't know, my good friends, but that these she-things, whether clerg-kites, monk-kites, and abbess-kites, instead of singing pleasant verses and charisteres, such as used to be sung to Oromasis by Zoroaster's institution, may be bellowing out such cataracts and scythropys (cursed lamentable and wretched imprecations) as were usually offered to the Arimanian demon; being thus in devotion for their kind friends and relations that transformed them into birds, whether when they were maids, or thornbacks, in their prime, or at their last prayers.

But the greatest numbers of our birds came out of Want-o'-bread, which, though a barren country, where the days are of a most tedious lingering length, overstocks this whole island with the lower class of birds. For hither fly the asapheis that inhabit that land, either when they are in danger of passing their time scurvily for want of belly-timber, being unable, or, what's more likely, unwilling to take heart of grace and follow some honest lawful calling, or too proud-hearted and lazy to go to service in some sober family. The same is done by your frantic inamoradoes, who, when crossed in their wild desires, grow stark staring mad, and choose this life suggested to them by their despair, too cowardly to make them swing, like their brother Iphis of doleful memory. There is another sort, that is, your gaol-birds, who, having done some rogue's trick or other heinous villainy, and being sought up and down to be trussed up and made to ride the two or three-legged mare that groans for them, warily scour off and come here to save their bacon; because all these sorts of birds are here provided for, and grow in an instant as fat as hogs, though they came as lean as rakes; for having the benefit of the clergy, they are as safe as thieves in a mill within this sanctuary.

But, asked Pantagruel, do these birds never return to the world where they were hatched? Some do, answered Ædituus; formerly very few, very seldom, very late, and very unwillingly; however, since some certain eclipses, by the virtue of the celestial constellations, a great crowd of them fled back to the world. Nor do we fret or vex ourselves a jot about it; for those that stay wisely sing, The fewer the better cheer; and all those that fly away, first cast off their feathers here among these nettles and briars.

Accordingly we found some thrown by there; and as we looked up and down, we chanced to light on what some people will hardly thank us for having discovered; and thereby hangs a tale.

CHAPTER 5

OF THE DUMB KNIGHT-HAWKS OF THE RINGING ISLAND

THESE words were scarce out of his mouth when some five-and-twenty or thirty birds flew towards us; they were of a hue and feather like which we had not seen anything in the whole island. Their plumes were as changeable as the skin of the chameleon, and the flower of tripolion, or teucrion. They had all under the left wing a mark like two diameters dividing a circle into equal parts, or, if you had rather have it, so like a perpendicular line falling on a right line. The marks which each of them bore were much of the same shape, but of different colours; for some were white, others green, some red, others purple, and some blue. Who are those? asked Panurge; and how do you call them? They are mongrels, quoth Ædituus.

We call them knight-hawks, and they have a great number of rich commanderies (fat livings) in your world. Good your worship, said I, make them give us a song, an't please you, that we may know how they sing. They scorn your words, cried Ædituus; they are none of your singing-birds; but, to make amends, they feed as much as the best two of them all. Pray where are their hens? where are their females? said I. They have none, answered Ædituus. How comes it to pass then, asked Panurge, that they are thus bescabbed, bescurfed, all embroidered o'er the phiz with carbuncles, pushes, and pock-royals, some of which undermine the handles of their faces? This same fashionable and illustrious disease, quoth Ædituus, is common among that kind of birds, because they are pretty apt to be tossed on the salt deep.

He then acquainted us with the occasion of their coming. This next to us, said he, looks so wistfully upon you to see whether he may not find among your company a stately gaudy kind of huge dreadful birds of prey, which yet are so untoward that they ne'er could be brought to the lure nor to perch on the glove. They tell us that there are such in your world, and that some of them have goodly garters below the knee with an inscription about them which condemns him (*qui mal y pense*) who shall think ill of it to be bewrayed and conskited. Others are said to wear the devil in a string before their paunches; and others a ram's skin. All that's true enough, good Master Ædituus, quoth Panurge; but we have not the honour to be acquainted with their knightships.

Come on, cried Ædituus in a merry mood, we have had chat enough o' conscience! let's e'en go drink. And eat, quoth Panurge. Eat, replied Ædituus, and drink bravely, old boy; twist like plough-jobbers and swill like tinkers. Pull away and save time, for nothing is so dear and precious as time; therefore we will be sure to put it to a good use.

He would fain have carried us first to bathe in the bagnios of the cardin-hawks, which are goodly delicious places, and have us licked over with precious ointments by the alyptes, alias rubbers, as soon as we should come out of the bath. But Pantagruel told him that he could drink but too much without that. He then led us into a spacious delicate refectory, or fratery-room, and told us: Braguibus the hermit made you fast four days together; now, contrariwise, I'll make you eat and drink of the best four days through stitch before you budge from this place. But hark ye me, cried Panurge, may not we take a nap in the meantime? Ay, ay, answered Ædituus; that is as you shall think good; for he that sleeps, drinks. Good Lord! how we lived! what good bub! what dainty cheer! O what an honest cod was this same Ædituus.

CHAPTER 6

HOW THE BIRDS ARE CRAMMED IN THE RINGLAND ISLAND

PANTAGRUEL looked I don't know howish, and seemed not very well pleased with the four days' junketing which Ædituus enjoined us. Ædituus who soon found it out, said to him, You know, sir, that seven days before winter, and seven days after, there is no storm at sea; for then the elements are still out of respect for the halcyons, or kingfishers, birds sacred to Thetis, which then lay their eggs and hatch their young near the shore. Now here the sea makes itself amends for this long calm; and whenever any foreigners come hither it grows boisterous and stormy for four days together. We can give no other reason for it but that it is a piece of its civility, that those who come among us may stay whether they will or no, and be copiously

feasted all the while with the incomes of the ringing. Therefore pray don't think your time lost; for, willing, nilling,
you'll be forced to stay, unless you are resolved to encounter
Juno, Neptune, Doris, Æolus, and his fluster-blusters, and,
in short all the pack of ill-natured left-handed godlings and
vejoves. Do but resolve to be cheery, and fall-to briskly.

After we had pretty well stayed our stomachs with some
tight snatches, Friar John said, Ædituus, For aught I see,
you have none but a parcel of birds and cages in this island
of yours, and the devil a bit of one of them all that sets his
hand to the plough, or tills the land whose fat he devours;
their whole business is to be frolic, to chirp it, to whistle it,
to warble it, tossing it, and roar it merrily night and day.
Pray then, if I may be so bold, whence comes this plenty
and overflowing of all dainty bits and good things which
we see among you? From all the other world, returned
Ædituus, if you except some part of the northern regions,
who of late years have stirred up the jakes. Mum! they may
chance ere long to rue the day they did so; their cows shall
have porridge, and their dogs oats; there will be work made
among them, that there will. Come, a fig for't, let's drink.
But pray what countryman are you? Touraine is our country, answered Panurge. Cod so, cried Ædituus, you were not
then hatched of an ill bird, I will say that for you, since the
blessed Touraine is your mother; for from thence there
comes hither every year such a vast store of good things,
that we were told by some folks of the place that happened
to touch at this island, that your Duke of Touraine's income
will not afford him to eat his bellyful of beans and bacon
(a good dish spoiled between Moses and Pythagoras) because his predecessors have been more than liberal to these
most holy birds of ours, that we might here munch it, twist
it, cram it, gorge it, craw it, riot it, junket it, and tickle it

off, stuffing our puddings with dainty pheasants, partridges, pullets with eggs, fat capons of Loudunois, and all sorts of venison and wild fowl. Come, box it about; tope on, my friends. Pray do you see yon jolly birds that are perched together, how fat, how plump, and in good case they look, with the income that Touraine yields us! And in faith they sing rarely for their good founders, that is the truth on't. You never saw any Arcadian birds mumble more fairly than they do over a dish when they see these two gilt batons, or when I ring for them those great bells that you see above their cages. Drink on, sirs, whip it away. Verily, friends, 'tis very fine drinking to-day, and so 'tis every day o' the week; then drink on, toss it about, here's to you with all my soul. You are most heartily welcome; never spare it, I pray you; fear not we should ever want good bub and belly-timber; for, look here, though the sky were of brass, and the earth of iron, we should not want wherewithal to stuff the gut, though they were to continue so seven or eight years longer than the famine in Egypt. Let us then, with brotherly love and charity, refresh ourselves here with the creature.

Woons, man, cried Panurge, what a rare time you have on't in this world! Psha, returned Ædituus, this is nothing to what we shall have in t'other; the Elysian fields will be the least that can fall to our lot. Come, in the meantime let us drink here; come, here's to thee, old fuddlecap.

Your first Siticines, said I, were superlatively wise in devising thus a means for you to compass whatever all men naturally covet so much, and so few, or, to speak more properly, none can enjoy together—I mean, a paradise in this life, and another in the next. Sure you were born wrapt in your mother's smickets! O happy creatures! O more than men! Would I had the luck to fare like you! *

* Motteux inserts Chapter XVI after Chapter VI.

CHAPTER 7

HOW WITH MUCH ADO WE GOT A SIGHT OF THE POPE-HAWK

OUR junketting and banquetting held on at the same rate
the third day as the two former. Pantagruel then earnestly
desired to see the pope-hawk; but Ædituus told him it was
not such an easy matter to get a sight of him. How, asked
Pantagruel, has he Plato's helmet on his crown, Gyges's
ring on his pounces, or a chameleon on his breast, to make
him invisible when he pleases? No, sir, returned Ædituus;
but he is naturally of pretty difficult access. However, I'll
see and take care that you may see him, if possible. With
this he left us piddling; then within a quarter of an hour
came back, and told us the pope-hawk is now to be seen. So
he led us, without the least noise, directly to the cage
wherein he sat drooping, with his feathers staring about him,
attended by a brace of little cardin-hawks and six lusty fusty
bish-hawks.

Panurge stared at him like a dead pig, examining exactly
his figure, size, and emotions. Then with a loud voice he
said, A curse light on the hatcher of the ill bird; o' my
word, this is a filthy whoop-hooper. Tush, speak softly, said
Ædituus; by G—, he has a pair of ears, as formerly Michael
de Matiscones remarked. What then? returned Panurge; so
hath a whoopcat. So, said Ædituus; if he but hear you speak
such another blasphemous word, you had as good be damned.
Do you see that basin yonder in his cage? Out of it shall
sally thunderbolts and lightnings, storms, bulls, and the
devil and all, that will sink you down to Peg Trantum's, an
hundred fathom under ground. It was better to drink and
be merry, quoth Friar John.

Panurge was still feeding his eyes with the sight of the
pope-hawk and his attendants, when somewhere under his

cage he perceived a madge-howlet. With this he cried out,
By the devil's maker, master, there's roguery in the case;
they put tricks upon travellers here more than anywhere
else. What damned cozening, gulling, and coney-catching
have we here! Do you see this madge-howlet? Odsoons,
said Ædituus, speak softly, I tell you. It is no madge-howlet,
no she-thing on my honest word; but a male and a noble
bird.

May we not hear the pope-hawk sing? asked Pantagruel. I dare not promise that, returned Ædituus; for he
only sings and eats at his own hours. So don't I, quoth Panurge; poor pilgarlic is fain to make everybody's time his own;
if they have time, I find time. Come, then, let us go drink,
if you will. Now this is something like a tansy, said Ædituus;
you begin to talk somewhat like; still speak in that fashion,
and I'll secure you from being thought a heretic. Come on,
I am of your mind.

As we went back to have t'other fuddling bout, we spied
an old green-headed bish-hawk, who sat moping with his
mate and three jolly bittern attendants, all snoring under
an arbour. Near the old cuff stood a buxom abbess-kite that
sung like any linnet; and we were so mightily tickled with
her singing that I vow and swear we could have wished
all our members but one turned into ears, to have had more
of the melody. Quoth Panurge, This pretty cherubim of
cherubims is here breaking her head with chanting to this
huge, fat ugly face, who lies grunting all the while like a
hog as he is. I will make him change his note presently, in
the devil's name. With this he rang a bell that hung over
the bish-hawk's head; but though he rang and rang again,
the devil a bit bish-hawk would hear; the louder the sound,
the louder his snoring. There was no making him sing. By
G—, quoth Panurge, you old buzzard, if you won't sing by

fair means, you shall by foul. Having said this, he took up
one of St. Stephen's loaves, alias a stone, and was going to
hit him with it about the middle. But Ædituus cried to him,
Hold, hold, honest friend! strike, wound, poison, kill, and
murder all the kings and princes in the world, by treachery
or how thou wilt, and as soon as thou wouldst unnestle the
angels from their cockloft. Pope-hawk will pardon thee all
this. But never be so mad as to meddle with these sacred
birds, as much as thou lovest the profit, welfare, and life
not only of thyself, and thy friends and relations alive or
dead, but also of those that may be born hereafter to the
thousandth generation; for so long thou wouldst entail
misery upon them. Do but look upon that basin. Catso! let
us rather drink, then, quoth Panurge. He that spoke last,
spoke well, Mr. Antitus, quoth Friar John; while we are
looking on these devilish birds we do nothing but blaspheme;
and while we are taking a cup we do nothing but praise
God. Come on, then, let's go drink; how well that word
sounds!

The third day (after we had drank, as you must understand) Ædituus dismissed us. We made him a present of a
pretty little Perguois knife, which he took more kindly than
Artaxerxes did the cup of cold water that was given him by
a clown. He most courteously thanked us, and sent all sorts
of provisions aboard our ships, wished us a prosperous voyage
and success in our undertakings, and made us promise and
swear by Jupiter of stone to come back to his territories.
Finally he said to us, Friends, pray note that there are
many more stones in the world than men; take care you
don't forget it.

CHAPTER 8

HOW WE PASSED THROUGH THE WICKET INHABITED BY
GRIPE-MEN-ALL, ARCHDUKE OF THE FURRED LAW-CATS

FROM thence Condemnation was passed by us. 'Tis another
damned barren island, whereat none for the world cared to
touch. Then we went through the wicket; but Pantagruel
had no mind to bear us company, and 'twas well he did not,
for we were nabbed there, and clapped into lob's-pound by
order of Gripe-men-all, Archduke of the Furred Law-cats,
because one of our company would ha' put upon a sergeant
some hats of the Sharping Island.

The Furred Law-cats are most terrible and dreadful monsters, they devour little children, and trample over marble
stones. Pray tell me, noble topers, do they not deserve to
have their snouts slit! The hair of their hides doesn't lie
outward, but inwards, and every mother's son of 'em for his
device wears a gaping pouch, but not all in the same manner;
for some wear it tied to their neck scarfwise, others upon the
breech, some on the paunch, others on the side, and all for
a cause, with reason and mystery. They have claws so very
strong, long, and sharp that nothing can get from 'em that
is once fast between their clutches. Sometimes they cover
their heads with mortar-like caps, at other times with mortified caparisons.

As we entered their den, said a common mumper, to whom
we had given half a teston, Worshipful culprits, God send
you a good deliverance! Examine well, said he, the countenance of these stout props and pillars of this catch-coin
law and iniquity; and pray observe, that if you still live
but six olympiads, and the age of two dogs more, you'll see
these Furred Law-cats lords of all Europe, and in peaceful
possession of all the estates and dominions belonging to it;

unless, by divine providence, what's got over the devil's back is spent under his belly, or the goods which they unjustly get perish with their prodigal heirs. Take this from an honest beggar.

Among 'em reigns the sixth essence; by the means of which they gripe all, devour all, conskite all, burn all, draw all, hang all, quarter all, behead all, murder all, imprison all, waste all, and ruin all, without the least notice of right or wrong; for among them vice is called virtue; wickedness, piety; treason, loyalty; robbery, justice. Plunder is their motto, and when acted by them is approved by all men, except the heretics; and all this they do because they dare; their authority is sovereign and irrefragable. For a sign of the truth of what I tell you, you'll find that there the mangers are above the racks. Remember hereafter that a fool told you this; and if ever plague, famine, war, fire, earthquakes, inundations, or other judgments befall the world, do not attribute 'em to the aspects and conjunctions of the malevolent planets; to the abuses of the court of Romania, or the tyranny of secular kings and princes; to the impostures of the false zealots of the cowl, heretical bigots, false prophets, and broachers of sects; to the villainy of griping usurers, clippers, and coiners, or to the ignorance, impudence, and imprudence of physicians, surgeons, and apothecaries; nor to the lewdness of adultresses and destroyers of by-blows; but charge them all, wholly and solely, to the inexpressible, incredible, and inestimable wickedness and ruin which is continually hatched, brewed, and practised in the den or shop of those Furred Law-cats. Yet 'tis no more known in the world than the cabala of the Jews, the more's the pity; and therefore 'tis not detested, chastised, and punished as 'tis fit it should be. But should all their villainy be once displayed in its true colours and exposed to the people, there never was, is, nor will be any spokesman so sweet mouthed, whose fine colloguing tongue could save 'em; nor any law so rigorous and draconic that could punish 'em as they deserve; nor yet any magistrate so powerful as to hinder their being burnt alive in their coney-burrows without mercy. Even their own furred kittlings, friends, and relations would abominate 'em.

For this reason, as Hannibal was solemnly sworn by his father Amilcar to pursue the Romans with the utmost hatred as long as ever he lived, so my late father has enjoined me to remain here without, till God Almighty's thunder reduce them there within to ashes, like other presumptuous Titans, profane wretches, and opposers of God; since mankind is so inured to their oppressions that they either do not remember, foresee, or have a sense of the woes and miseries which they have caused; or, if they have, either will not, dare not, or cannot root 'em out.

How, said Panurge, say you so? Catch me there and hang me! Damme, let's march off! This noble beggar has scared me worse than thunder in autumn.* Upon this we are filing off; but, alas! we found ourselves trapped—the door was double-locked and barricadoed. Some messengers of ill news told us it was full as easy to get in there as into hell, and no less hard to get out. Ay, there indeed lay the difficulty, for there is no getting loose without a pass and discharge in due course from the bench. This for no other reason than because folks go easier out of a church than out of a sponging-house, and because they could not have our company when they would. The worst on't was when we got through the wicket; for we were carried, to get out our pass or discharge, before a more dreadful monster than ever was read of in the legends of knight-errantry. They called him

* Motteux gives "than the thunder would do them."

Gripe-men-all. I can't tell what to compare it to better than to a Chimæra, a Sphinx, a Cerberus; or to the image of Osiris, as the Egyptians represented him, with three heads, one of a roaring lion, t'other of a fawning cur, and the last of a howling, prowling wolf, twisted about with a dragon biting his tail, surrounded with fiery rays. His hands were full of gore, his talons like those of the harpies, his snout like a hawk's bill, his fangs or tusks like those of an overgrown brindled wild boar; his eyes were flaming like the jaws of hell, all covered with mortars interlaced with pestles, and nothing of his arms was to be seen but his clutches. His hutch, and that of the warren-cats his collaterals, was a long, spick-and-span new rack, a top of which (as the mumper told us) some large stately mangers were fixed in the reverse. Over the chief seat was the picture of an old woman holding the case of a scabbard of a sickle in her right hand, a pair of scales in her left, with spectacles on her nose; the cups or scales of the balance were a pair of velvet pouches, the one full of bullion, which overpoised t'other, empty and long, hoisted higher than the middle of the beam. I'm of opinion it was the true effigies of Justice Gripe-men-all; far different from the institution of the ancient Thebans, who set up the statues of their dicasts without hands, in marble, silver, or gold, according to their merit, even after their death.

When we made our personal appearance before him, a sort of I don't know what men, all clothed with I don't know what bags and pouches, with long scrolls in their clutches, made us sit down upon a cricket (such as criminals sit on when tried in France). Quoth Panurge to 'em, Good my lords, I'm very well as I am; I'd as lief stand, an't please you. Besides, this same stool is somewhat of the lowest for a man that has new breeches and a short doublet. Sit you

down, said Gripe-men-all again, and look that you don'
make the court bid you twice. Now, continued he, the earth
shall immediately open its jaws and swallow you up to quick
damnation if you don't answer as you should.

CHAPTER 9

HOW GRIPE-MEN-ALL PROPOUNDED A RIDDLE TO US

WHEN we were sat, Gripe-men-all, in the middle of his
furred cats, called to us in a hoarse dreadful voice, Well
come on, give me presently—an answer. Well, come on, muttered Panurge between his teeth, give, give me presently—
a comforting dram. Hearken to the court, continued Gripe-
men-all.

AN ENIGMA

A young tight thing, as fair as may be,
Without a dad conceived a baby,
And brought him forth without the pother
In labour made by teeming mother.
Yet the cursed brat feared not to gripe her,
But gnawed, for haste, her sides like viper.
Then the black upstart boldly sallies,
And walks and flies o'er hills and valleys.
Many fantastic sons of wisdom,
Amazed, foresaw their own in his doom;
And thought like an old Grecian noddy,
A human spirit moved his body.

Give, give me out of hand—an answer to this riddle, quoth
Gripe-men-all. Give, give me—leave to tell you, good, good
my lord, answered Panurge, that if I had but a sphinx at
home, as Verres one of your precursors had, I might then

solve your enigma presently. But verily, good my lord, I was not there; and, as I hope to be saved, am as innocent in the matter as the child unborn. Foh, give me—a better answer, cried Gripe-men-all; or, by gold, this shall not serve your turn. I'll not be paid in such coin; if you have nothing better to offer, I'll let your rascalship know that it had been better for you to have fallen into Lucifer's own clutches than into ours. Dost thou see 'em here, sirrah? hah? and dost thou prate here of thy being innocent, as if thou couldst be delivered from our racks and tortures for being so? Give me —Patience! thou widgeon. Our laws are like cobwebs; your silly little flies are stopped, caught and destroyed therein, but your stronger ones break them, and force and carry them which way they please. Likewise, don't think we are so mad as to set up our nets to snap up your great robbers and tyrants. No, they are somewhat too hard for us, there's no meddling with them; for they would make no more of us than we make of the little ones. But you paltry, silly, innocent, wretches must make us amends; and, by gold, we will innocentize your fopship with a wannion, you never were so innocentized in your days; the devil shall sing mass among ye.

Friar John, hearing him run on at that mad rate, had no longer the power to remain silent, but cried to him, Heigh-dey! Prithee, Mr. Devil in a coif, wouldst thou have a man tell thee more than he knows? Hasn't the fellow told you he does not know a word of the business? His name is Twyford. A plague rot you! won't truth serve your turns? Why, how now, Mr. Prate-apace, cried Gripe-men-all, taking him short, marry come up, who made you so saucy as to open your lips before you were spoken to? Give me— Patience. By gold! this is the first time since I have reigned that anyone has had the impudence to speak before he was bidden. How came this mad fellow to break loose! (Villain, thou liest, said Friar John, without stirring his lips.) Sirrah, sirrah, continued Gripe-men-all, I doubt thou wilt have business enough on thy hands when it comes to thy turn to answer. (Damme, thou liest, said Friar John, silently.) Dost thou think, continued my lord, thou art in the wilderness of your foolish university, wrangling and bawling among the idle, wandering searchers and hunters after truth? By gold, we have here other fish to fry; we go another gate's way to work, that we do. By gold, people here must give categorical answers to what they don't know. By gold, they must confess they have done those things which they have not nor ought to have done. By gold, they must protest that they know what they never knew in their lives; and, after all, patience perforce must be their only remedy, as well as a mad dog's. Here silly geese are plucked, yet cackle not. Sirrah, give me—an account whether you had a letter of attorney, or whether you were feed or no, that you offered to bawl in another man's cause? I see you had no authority to speak, and I may chance to have you wed to something you won't like. Oh, you devils, cried Friar John, proto-devils, panto-devils, you would wed a monk, would you? Ho hu! ho hu! A heretic! a heretic! I'll give thee out for a rank heretic.

CHAPTER 10

HOW PANURGE SOLVED GRIPE-MEN-ALL'S RIDDLE

GRIPE-MEN-ALL, as if he had not heard what Friar John said, directed his discourse to Panurge, saying to him, Well, what have you to say for yourself, Mr. Rogue-enough, hah? Give, give me out of hand—an answer. Say? quoth Panurge; why, what would you have me say? I say that you give no heed at all to the equity of the plea, and the devil sings among you. Let this answer serve for all, I beseech you, and let us go out about our business; I am no longer able to hold out, as gad shall judge me.

Go to, go to, cried Gripe-men-all; when did you ever hear that for these three hundred years last past anybody ever got out of this weel without leaving something of his behind him? No, no; get out of the trap if you can without losing leather, life, or at least some hair, and you will have done more than ever was done yet. For why, this would bring the wisdom of the court into question, as if we had took you up for nothing, and dealt wrongfully by you. Well, by hook or by crook, we must have something out of you. Look ye, it is a folly to make a rout for a fart and ado; one word is as good as twenty. I have no more to say to thee, but that, as thou likest thy former entertainment, thou wilt tell me more of the next; for it will go ten times worse with thee unless, by gold, you give me—a solution to the riddle I propounded. Give, give—it, without any more ado.

By gold, quoth Panurge, 'tis a black mite or weevil which is born of a white bean, and sallies out at the hole which he makes gnawing it; the mite being turned into a kind of fly, sometimes walks and sometimes flies over hills and dales. Now Pythagoras, the philosopher, and his sect, besides many others, wondering at its birth in such a place (which makes some argue for equivocal generation), thought that by a metempsychosis the body of that insect was the lodging of a human soul. Now, were you men here, after your welcomed death, according to his opinion, your souls would most certainly enter into the body of mites or weevils; for in your present state of life you are good for nothing in the world but to gnaw, bite, eat, and devour all things, so in the next you'll e'en gnaw and devour your mother's very sides, as the vipers do. Now, by gold, I think I have fairly solved and resolved your riddle.

Panurge then, without any more ado, threw a large leathern purse stuffed with gold crowns (*ecus au soleil*) among them.

The Furred Law-cats no sooner heard the jingling of the chink but they all began to bestir their claws, like a parcel of fiddlers running a division; and then fell to't, squimble, squamble, catch that catch can. They all said aloud, These are the fees, these are the gloves now, this is somewhat like a tansy. Oh! 'twas a pretty trial, a sweet trial, a dainty trial. O' my word, they did not starve the cause. These are none of your snivelling *forma pauperis's;* no, they are noble clients, gentlemen, every inch of them. By gold, it is gold, quoth Panurge, good old gold, I'll assure you.

Saith Gripe-men-all, The court, upon a full hearing (of the gold, quoth Panurge), and weighty reasons given, finds the prisoners not guilty, and accordingly orders them to be discharged out of custody, paying their fees. Now, gentlemen, proceed, go forwards, said he to us; we have not so much of the devil in us as we have of his hue; though we are stout, we are merciful.

As we came out at the wicket, we were conducted to the port by a detachment of certain highland griffins, *scribere cum dashoes,* who advised us before we came to our ships not to offer to leave the place until we had made the usual presents, first to the Lady Gripe-men-all, then to all the Furred Law-pusses; otherwise we must return to the place from whence we came. Well, well, said Friar John, we'll fumble in our fobs, examine every one of us his concern, and e'en give the women their due; we'll ne'er boggle or stick out on that account; as we tickled the men in the palm, we'll tickle the women in the right place. Pray, gentlemen, added they, don't forget to leave somewhat behind you for us poor devils to drink your healths. O lawd! never fear, answered Friar John, I don't remember that I ever went anywhere yet where the poor devils are not remembered and encouraged.

CHAPTER 11

HOW THE FURRED LAW-CATS LIVE ON CORRUPTION

FRIAR JOHN had hardly said those words ere he perceived seventy-eight galleys and frigates just arriving at the port. So he hied him thither to learn some news; and as he asked what goods they had o' board, he soon found that their whole cargo was venison, hares, capons, turkeys, pigs, swine, bacon, kids, calves, hens, ducks, teals, geese, and other poultry and wild-fowl.

He also spied among these some pieces of velvet, satin, and damask. This made him ask the new-comers whither and to whom they were going to carry those dainty goods. They answered that they were for Gripe-men-all and the Furred Law-cats.

Pray, asked he, what is the true name of all these things in your country language? Corruption, they replied. If they live on corruption, said the friar, they will perish with their generation. May the devil be damned, I have it now: their fathers devoured the good gentlemen who, according to their state of life, used to go much a-hunting and hawking, to be the better inured to toil in time of war; for hunting is an image of a martial life, and Xenophon was much in the right of it when he affirmed that hunting had yielded a great number of excellent warriors, as well as the Trojan horse. For my part, I am no scholar; I have it but by hearsay, yet I believe it. Now the souls of those brave fellows, according to Gripe-men-all's riddle, after their decease enter into wild boars, stags, roebucks, herns, and such other creatures which they loved, and in quest of which they went while they were men; and these Furred Law-cats, having first destroyed and devoured their castles, lands, demesnes, possessions, rents, and revenues, are still seeking to have their blood and soul in another life. What an honest fellow was that same mumper who had forewarned us of all these things, and bid us take notice of the mangers above the racks!

But, said Panurge to the new-comers, how do you come by all this venison? Methinks the great king has issued out a proclamation strictly inhibiting the destroying of stags, does, wild boars, roebucks, or other royal game, on pain of death. All this is true enough, answered one for the rest, but the great king is so good and gracious, you must know, and these Furred Law-cats so curst and cruel, so mad, and thirsting after Christian blood, that we have less cause to fear in trespassing against that mighty sovereign's commands than reason to hope to live if we do not continually stop the mouths of these Furred Law-cats with such bribes and corruption. Besides, added he, to-morrow Gripe-men-all marries a furred law-puss of his to a high and mighty double-furred law-tybert. Formerly we used to call them chop-hay; but, alas! they are not such neat creatures now as to eat any, or chew the cud. We call them chop-hares, chop-partridges, chop-woodcocks, chop-pheasants, chop-pullets, chop-venison, chop-coneys, chop-pigs, for they scorn to feed on coarser meat. Next year we'll have 'em called chop-dung, chop-stront, chop-filth.

Would you take my advice? added he to the company. What is it? answered we. Let's do two things, returned he. First, let us secure all this venison and wild fowl—I mean, paying well for them; for my part, I am but too much tired already with our salt meat, it heats my flanks so horribly.

In the next place, let's go back to the wicket, and destroy all these devilish Furred Law-cats. For my part, quoth Panurge, I know better things; catch me there, and hang me. No, I am somewhat more inclined to be fearful than bold; I love to sleep in a whole skin.

CHAPTER 12

HOW FRIAR JOHN TALKS OF ROOTING OUT THE FURRED LAW-CATS

VIRTUE of the frock, quoth Friar John, what kind of voyage are we making? The devil of anything we do but fizzling, squattering, dozing, raving, and doing nothing. Ods-belly, 'tisn't in my nature to lie idle; I mortally hate it. Unless I am doing some heroic feat every foot, I can't sleep one wink o' nights. Damn it, did you then take me along with you for your chaplain, to sing mass and shrive you? By Maundy Thursday, the first of ye all that comes to me on such an account shall be fitted; for the only penance, I'll enjoin shall be, that he immediately throw himself headlong overboard into the sea like a base cowhearted son of ten fathers. This in deduction of the pains of purgatory.

What made Hercules such a famous fellow, d'ye think? Nothing but that while he travelled he still made it his business to rid the world of tyrannies, errors, dangers, and drudgeries; he still put to death all robbers, all monsters, all venomous serpents and hurtful creatures. Why then do we not follow his example, doing as he did in the countries through which we pass? He destroyed the Stymphalides, the Lernæan hydra, Cacus, Antheus, the Centaurs, and what not; I am no clericus, those that are such tell me so.

In imitation of that noble by-blow, let's destroy and root out these wicked Furred Law-cats, that are a kind of

ravenous devils; thus we shall remove all manner of tyranny
out of the land. Mawmet's tutor swallow me body and soul,
tripes and guts, if I would stay to ask your help or advice
in the matter were I but as strong as he was. Come, he that
would be thought a gentleman, let him storm a town; well,
then, shall we go? I dare swear we'll do their business for
them with a wet finger; they'll bear it, never fear; since
they could swallow down more foul language that came from
us than ten sows and their babies could swill hogwash. Damn
'em, they don't value all the ill words or dishonour in the
world at a rush, so they but get the coin into their purses,
though they were to have it in a shitten clout. Come, we
may chance to kill 'em all, as Hercules would have done
had they lived in his time. We only want to be set to work
by another Eurystheus, and nothing else for the present,
unless it be what I heartily wish them, that Jupiter may
give 'em a short visit, only some two or three hours long,
and walk among their lordships in the same equipage that
attended him when he came last to his Miss Semele, jolly
Bacchus's mother.

'Tis a very great mercy, quoth Panurge, that you have
got out of their clutches. For my part, I have no stomach
to go there again; I'm hardly come to myself yet, so scared
and appalled I was. My hair still stands up on end when I
think on't; and most damnably troubled I was there, for
three very weighty reasons. First, because I was troubled.
Secondly, because I was troubled. Thirdly and lastly, because I was troubled. Hearken to me a little on thy right
side, Friar John, my left cod, since thou'lt not hear at the
other. Whenever the maggot bites thee to take a trip down
to hell and visit the tribunal of Minos, Æacus, Rhadamanthus, [and Dis,] do but tell me, and I'll be sure to bear
thee company, and never leave thee as long as my name's

Panurge, but will wade over Acheron, Styx, and Cocytus, drink whole bumpers of Lethe's water—though I mortally hate that element—and even pay thy passage to that bawling, cross-grained ferryman Charon. But as for the damned wicket, if thou art so weary of thy life as to go thither again, thou mayst e'en look for somebody else to bear thee company, for I'll not move one step that way; e'en rest satisfied with this positive answer. By my good will I'll not stir a foot to go thither as long as I live, any more than Calpe will come over to Abyla.* Was Ulysses so mad as to go back into the Cyclop's cave to fetch his sword? No, marry was he not. Now I have left nothing behind me at the wicket through forgetfulness; why then should I think of going thither?

Well, quoth Friar John, as good sit still as rise up and fall; what cannot be cured must be endured. But, prithee, let's hear one another speak. Come, wert thou not a wise doctor to fling away a whole purse of gold on those mangy scoundrels? Ha! A squinsy choke thee! we were too rich, were we? Had it not been enough to have thrown the hellhounds a few cropped pieces of white cash?

How could I help it? returned Panurge. Did you not see how Gripe-men-all held his gaping velvet pouch, and every moment roared and bellowed, By gold, give me out of hand; by gold, give, give, give me presently? Now, thought I to myself, we shall never come off scot-free. I'll e'en stop their mouths with gold, that the wicket may be opened, and we may get out; the sooner the better. And I judged that lousy silver would not do the business; for, d'ye see, velvet pouches do not use to gape for little paltry clipt silver and small

---

* Here Motteux adds the following note: "Calpe is a mountain in Spain that faces another, called Abyla, in Mauritania, both said to have been severed by Hercules."

cash; no, they are made for gold, my friend John; that they are, my dainty cod. Ah! when thou hast been larded, basted, and roasted, as I was, thou wilt hardly talk at this rate, I doubt. But now what is to be done? We are enjoined by them to go forwards.

The scabby slabberdegullions still waited for us at the port, expecting to be greased in the fist as well as their masters. Now when they perceived that we were ready to put to sea, they came to Friar John and begged that we would not forget to gratify the apparitors before we went off, according to the assessment for the fees at our discharge. Hell and damnation! cried Friar John; are ye here still, ye bloodhounds, ye citing, scribbling imps of Satan? Rot you, am I not vexed enough already, but you must have the impudence to come and plague me, ye scurvy fly-catchers you? By cob's-body, I'll gratify your ruffianships as you deserve; I'll apparitorize you presently with a wannion, that I will. With this, he lugged out his slashing cutlass, and in a mighty heat came out of the ship to cut the cozening varlets into steaks, but they scampered away and got out of sight in a trice.

However, there was somewhat more to do, for some of our sailors, having got leave of Pantagruel to go ashore while we were had before Gripe-men-all, had been at a tavern near the haven to make much of themselves, and roar it, as seamen will do when they come into some port. Now I don't know whether they had paid their reckoning to the full or no, but, however it was, an old fat hostess, meeting Friar John on the quay, was making a woeful complaint before a sergeant, son-in-law to one of the furred law-cats, and a brace of bums, his assistants.

The friar, who did not much care to be tired with their impertinent prating, said to them, Harkee me, ye lubberly

gnat-snappers! do ye presume to say that our seamen are
not honest men? I'll maintain they are, ye dotterels, and
will prove it to your brazen faces, by justice—I mean, this
trusty piece of cold iron by my side. With this he lugged
it out and flourished with it. The forlorn lobcocks soon
showed him their backs, betaking themselves to their heels;
but the old fusty landlady kept her ground, swearing like any
butter-whore that the tarpaulins were very honest cods,
but that they only forgot to pay for the bed on which they
had lain after dinner, and she asked fivepence, French
money, for the said bed. May I never sup, said the friar, if
it be not dog-cheap; they are sorry guests and unkind
customers, that they are; they do not know when they have
a penny-worth, and will not always meet with such bargains.
Come, I myself will pay you the money, but I would willingly
see it first.

The hostess immediately took him home with her, and
showed him the bed, and having praised it for all its good
qualifications, said that she thought as times went she was
not out of the way in asking fivepence for it. Friar John
then gave her the fivepence; and she no sooner turned her
back but he presently began to rip up the ticking of the
feather-bed and bolster, and threw all the feathers out at
the window. In the meantime the old hag came down and
roared out for help, crying out murder to set all the neighbourhood in an uproar. Yet she also fell to gathering the
feathers that flew up and down in the air, being scattered
by the wind. Friar John let her bawl on, and, without any
further ado, marched off with the blanket, quilt, and both
the sheets, which he brought aboard undiscovered, for the
air was darkened with the feathers, as it uses sometimes
to be with snow. He gave them away to the sailors; then
said to Pantagruel that beds were much cheaper at that

place than in Chinnonois, though we have there the famous geese of Pautilé; for the old beldam had asked him but fivepence for a bed which in Chinnonois had been worth about twelve francs. *

CHAPTER 13

HOW OUR SHIPS WERE STRANDED, AND WE WERE RELIEVED BY SOME PEOPLE THAT WERE SUBJECT TO QUEEN WHIMS (QUI TENOIENT DE LA QUINTE)

WE weighed and set sail with a merry westerly gale. When about seven leagues off (twenty-two miles) some gusts or scuds of wind suddenly arose, and the wind veering and shifting from point to point, was, as they say, like an old woman's breech, at no certainty; so we first got our starboard tacks aboard, and hauled off our lee-sheets. Then the gusts increased, and by fits blowed all at once from several quarters, yet we neither settled nor braided up close our sails, but only let fly the sheets, not to go against the master of the ship's direction; and thus having let go amain, lest we should spend our topsails, or the ship's quick-side should lie in the water and she be overset, we lay by and run adrift; that is, in a landloper's phrase, we temporized it. For he assured us that, as these gusts and whirlwinds would not do us much good, so they could not do us much harm, considering their easiness and pleasant strife, as also the clearness of the sky and calmness of the current. So that we were to observe the philosopher's rule, bear and forbear; that is, trim, or go according to the time.

However, these whirlwinds and gusts lasted so long that we persuaded the master to let us go and lie at trie with

* Motteux omitted this passage altogether in the edition of 1694. It was restored by Ozell in the edition of 1738.

our main course; that is, to haul the tack aboard, the sheet close aft, the bowline set up, and the helm tied close aboard; so, after a stormy gale of wind, we broke through the whirlwind. But it was like falling into Scylla to avoid Charybdis (out of the frying pan into the fire). For we had not sailed a league ere our ships were stranded upon some sands such as are the flats of St. Maixent.

All our company seemed mightily disturbed except Friar John, who was not a jot daunted, and with sweet sugar-plum words comforted now one and then another, giving them hopes of speedy assistance from above, and telling them that he had seen Castor at the main yardarm. Oh! that I were but now ashore, cried Panurge, that is all I wish for myself at present, and that you who like the sea so well had each man of you two hundred thousand crowns. I would fairly let you set up shop on these sands, and would get a fat calf dressed and a hundred of faggots (*i. è.*, bottles of wine) cooled for you against you come ashore. I freely consent never to mount a wife, so you but set me ashore and mount me on a horse, that I may go home. No matter for a servant, I will be contented to serve myself; I am never better treated than when I am without a man. Faith, old Plautus was in the right on't when he said the more servants the more crosses; for such they are, even supposing they could want what they all have but too much of, a tongue, that most busy, dangerous, and pernicious member of servants. Accordingly, 'twas for their sakes alone that the racks and tortures for confession were invented, though some foreign civilians in our time have drawn alogical and unreasonable consequences from it.

That very moment we spied a sail that made towards us. When it was close by us, we soon knew what was the lading of the ship and who was aboard of her. She was full freighted with drums. I was acquainted with many of the passengers that came in her, who were most of 'em of good families; among the rest Harry Cotiral, an old toast, who had got a swinging ass's touch-tripe (*penis*) fastened to his waist, as the good women's beads are to their girdle. In his left hand he held an old overgrown greasy foul cap, such as your scald-pated fellows wear, and in the right a huge cabbage-stump.

As soon as he saw me he was overjoyed, and bawled out to me, What cheer, ho? How dost like me now? Behold the true Algamana (this he said showing me the ass's tickle-gizzard). This doctor's cap is my true elixir; and this (continued he, shaking the cabbage-stump in his fist) is *lunaria major*, you old noddy. I have 'em, old boy, I have 'em; we'll make 'em when thou'rt come back. But pray, father, said I, whence come you? Whither are you bound? What's your lading? Have you smelt the salt deep? To these four questions he answered, From Queen Whims; for Touraine; alchemy; to the very bottom.

Whom have you got o' board? said I. Said he, Astrologers, fortune-tellers, alchemists, rhymers, poets, painters, projectors, mathematicians, watchmakers, sing-songs, musicianers, and the devil and all of others that are subject to Queen Whims.* They have very fair legible patents to show for't, as anybody may see. Panurge had no sooner heard this but he was upon the high-rope, and began to rail at them like mad. What o' devil d'ye mean, cried he, to sit idly here like a pack of loitering sneaksbies, and see us stranded, while you may help us, and tow us off into the current? A plague o' your whims! you can make all things whatsoever, they say, so much as good weather and little children; ye won't

---

* Motteux gives the following footnote:—"*La Quinte.* This means a fantastic Humour, Maggots, or a foolish Giddiness of Brains; and also, a fifth, or the Proportion of Five in Music, &c."

make haste to fasten some hawsers and cables, and get us off. I was just coming to set you afloat, quoth Harry Cotiral; by Trismegistus, I'll clear you in a trice. With this he caused 7,532,810 huge drums to be unheaded on one side, and set that open side so that it faced the end of the stream- ers and pendants; and having fastened them to good tacklings and our ship's head to the stern of theirs, with cables fastened to the bits abaft the manger in the ship's loof, they towed us off ground at one pull so easily and pleasantly that you'd have wondered at it had you been there. For the dub-a-dub rattling of the drums, with the soft noise of the gravel which murmuring disputed us our way, and the merry cheers and huzzas of the sailors, made an harmony almost as good as that of the heavenly bodies when they roll and are whirled round their spheres, which rattling of the celestial wheels Plato said he heard some nights in his sleep.

We scorned to be behindhand with 'em in civility, and gratefully gave 'em store of our sausages and chitterlings, with which we filled their drums; and we were just a-hoisting two-and-sixty hogsheads of wine out of the hold when two huge whirlpools with great fury made towards their ship, spouting more water than is in the river Vienne (Vigenne) from Chinon to Saumur; to make short, all their drums, all their sails, their concerns, and themselves were soused, and their very hose were watered by the collar.

Panurge was so overjoyed, seeing this, and laughed so heartily, that he was forced to hold his sides, and it set him into a fit of the colic for two hours and more. I had a mind, quoth he, to make the dogs drink, and those honest whirlpools, egad, have saved me that labour and that cost. There's sauce for them; *wiston men udoz*. Water is good, saith a poet; let 'em Pindarize upon't. They never cared for fresh water but to wash their hands or their glasses. This good salt water will stand 'em in good stead for want of sal ammoniac and nitre in Geber's kitchen.

We could not hold any further discourse with 'em; for the former whirlwind hindered our ship from feeling the helm. The pilot advised us henceforwards to let her run adrift and follow the stream, not busying ourselves with anything, but making much of our carcasses. For our only way to arrive safe at the queendom of Whims was to trust to the whirlwind and be led by the current.

CHAPTER 14

HOW WE ARRIVED AT THE QUEENDOM OF WHIMS OR ENTELECHY

WE did as he directed us for about twelve hours and on the third day the sky seemed to us somewhat clearer, and we happily arrived at the port of Mateotechny, not far distant from Queen Whims, alias the Quintessence.

We met full butt on the quay a great number of guards and other military men that garrisoned the arsenal, and we were somewhat frighted at first because they made us all lay down our arms, and in a haughty manner asked us whence we came.

Cousin, quoth Panurge to him that asked the question, we are of Touraine, and come from France, being ambitious of paying our respects to the Lady Quintessence and visit this famous realm of Entelechy.

What do you say? cried they; do you call it Entelechy or Endelechy? Truly, truly, sweet cousins, quoth Panurge, we are a silly sort of grout-headed lobcocks, an't please you; be so kind as to forgive us if we chance to knock words out of joint. As for anything else, we are downright honest fellows and true hearts.

We have not asked you this question without a cause, said

they; for a great number of others who have passed this way from your country of Touraine seemed as mere jolt-headed doddipolls as ever were scored o'er the coxcomb, yet spoke as correct as other folks. But there has been here from other countries a pack of I know not what overweening self-conceited prigs, as moody as so many mules and as stout as any Scotch lairds, and nothing would serve these, forsooth, but they must wilfully wrangle and stand out against us at their coming; and much they got by it after all. Troth, we e'en fitted them and clawed 'em off with a vengeance, for all they looked so big and so grum.

Pray tell me, does your time lie so heavy upon you in your world that you do not know how to bestow it better than in thus impudently talking, disputing, and writing of our sovereign lady? There was much need that your Tully, the consul, should go and leave the care of his commonwealth to busy himself idly about her, and after him your Diogenes Laertius, the biographer, and your Theodorus Gaza, the philosopher, and your Argiropilus, the emperor, and your Bessario, the cardinal, and your Politian, the pedant, and your Budæus, the judge, and your Lascaris, the ambassador, and the devil and all of those you call lovers of wisdom; whose number, it seems, was not thought great enough already, but lately your Scaliger, Bigot, Chambrier, Francis Fleury, and I cannot tell how many such other junior sneaking fly-blows must take upon 'em to increase it.

A squinsy gripe the cod's-headed changelings at the swallow and eke at the cover-weasel; we shall make 'em—But the deuce take 'em! (They flatter the devil here, and smoothify his name, quoth Panurge, between his teeth.) You don't come here, continued the captain, to uphold 'em in their folly; you have no commission from 'em to this effect; well then, we will talk no more on't.

Aristotle, that first of men and peerless pattern of all philosophy, was our sovereign lady's godfather, and wisely and properly gave her the name of Entelechy. Her true name then is Entelechy, and no one dares call her by any other name; for whoever he is, he does her wrong, and is a very impudent person. You are heartily welcome, gentlemen. With this they colled and clipped us about the neck, which was no small comfort to us, I'll assure you.

Panurge then whispered me, Fellow-traveller, quoth he, hast thou not been somewhat afraid this bout? A little, said I. To tell you the truth of it, quoth he, never were the Ephraimites in a greater fear and quandary when the Gileadites killed and drowned them for saying sibboleth instead of shibboleth; and among friends, let me tell you that perhaps there is not a man in the whole country of Beauce but might easily have stopped my bunghole with a cartload of hay.

The captain afterwards took us to the queen's palace, leading us silently with great formality. Pantagruel would have said something to him, but the other, not being able to come up to his height, wished for a ladder or a very long pair of stilts; then said, Patience, if it were our sovereign lady's will, we would be as tall as you; well, we shall when she pleases.

In the first galleries we saw great numbers of sick persons, differently placed according to their maladies. The leprous were apart; those that were poisoned on one side; those that had got the plague on another; those that had the pox in the first rank, and the rest accordingly.

CHAPTER 15

HOW THE QUINTESSENCE CURED THE SICK WITH A SONG

THE captain showed us the queen, attended with her ladies and gentlemen, in the second gallery. She looked young, though she was at least eighteen hundred years old, and was handsome, slender, and as fine as a queen, that is, as hands could make her. He then said to us: It is not yet a fit time to speak to the queen; be you but mindful of her doings in the meanwhile.

You have kings in your world that fantastically pretend to cure some certain diseases, as, for example, scrofula or wens, swelled throats, nicknamed the king's evil, and quartan agues, only with a touch; now our queen cures all manner of diseases without so much as touching the sick, but barely with a song, according to the nature of the distemper. He then showed us a set of organs, and said that when it was touched by her those miraculous cures were performed. The organ was indeed the strangest that ever eyes beheld; for the pipes were of cassia fistula in the cod; the top and cornice of guiacum; the bellows of rhubarb; the pedas of turbith, and the clavier or keys of scammony.

While we were examining this wonderful new make of an organ, the leprous were brought in by her abstractors, spodizators, masticators, pregustics, tabachins, chachanins, neemanins, rabrebans, nercins, rozuins, nebidins, tearins, segamions, perarons, chasinins, sarins, soteins, aboth, enilins, archasdarpenins, mebins, chabbourins, and other officers, for whom I want names; so she played 'em I don't know what sort of a tune or song, and they were all immediately cured.

Then those who were poisoned were had in, and she had no sooner given them a song but they began to find a use for their legs, and up they got. Then came on the deaf, the blind, and the dumb, and they too were restored to their lost faculties and senses with the same remedy; which did so strangely amaze us (and not without reason, I think) that down we fell on our faces, remaining prostrate, like men ravished in ecstasy and were not able to utter one word through the excess of our admiration, till she came, and having touched Pantagruel with a fine fragrant nosegay of white roses which she held in her hand, thus made us recover our senses and get up. Then she made us the following speech in byssin words, such as Parisatis desired should be spoken to her son Cyrus, or at least of crimson alamode:

The probity that scintillizes in the superfices of your persons informs my ratiocinating faculty, in a most stupendous manner, of the radiant virtues latent within the precious caskets and ventricles of your minds. For, contemplating the mellifluous suavity of your thrice discreet reverences, it is impossible not to be persuaded with facility that neither your affections nor your intellects are vitiated with any defect or privation of liberal and exalted sciences. Far from it, all must judge that in you are lodged a cornucopia and encyclopædia, an unmeasurable profundity of knowledge in the most peregrine and sublime disciplines, so frequently the admiration, and so rarely the concomitants of the imperite vulgar. This gently compels me, who in preceding times indefatigably kept my private affections absolutely subjugated, to condescend to make my application to you in the trivial phrase of the plebeian world, and assure you that you are well, more than most heartily welcome.

I have no hand at making of speeches, quoth Panurge, to me privately; prithee, man, make answer to her for us, if thou canst. This would not work with me, however; neither did Pantagruel return a word. So that Queen Whims, or Queen Quintessence (which you please), perceiving that we stood as mute as fishes, said: Your taciturnity speaks you not only disciples of Pythagoras, from whom the venerable antiquity of my progenitors in successive propagation was emaned and derives its original, but also discovers, that through the revolution of many retrograde moons, you have in Egypt pressed the extremities of your fingers with the hard tenants of your mouths, and sculptized your heads with frequent applications of your unguicules. In the school of Pythagoras, taciturnity was the symbol of abstracted and superlative knowledge, and the silence of the Egyptians was agnited as an expressive manner of divine adoration; this caused the pontiffs of Hierapolis to sacrifice to the great deity in silence, impercussively, without any vociferous or obstreperous sound. My design is not to enter into a privation of gratitude towards you, but by a vivacious formality, though matter were to abstract itself from me, excentricate to you my cogitations.

Having spoken this, she only said to her officers, Tabachins, a panacea; and straight they desired us not to take it amiss if the queen did not invite us to dine with her; for she never ate anything at dinner but some categories, jecabots, emnins, dimions, abstractions, harborins, chelemins, second intentions, carradoths, antitheses, metempsychoses, transcendent prolepsies, and such other light food.

Then they took us into a little closet lined through with alarums, where we were treated God knows how. It is said that Jupiter writes whatever is transacted in the world on the dipthera or skin of the Amaltæan goat that suckled him in Crete, which pelt served him instead of a shield against the Titans, whence he was nicknamed Ægiochos. Now, as I hate to drink water, brother topers, I protest it would be impossible to make eighteen goatskins hold the description of all the good meat they brought before us, though it were written in characters as small as those in which were penned Homer's Iliads, which Tully tells us how he saw enclosed in a nutshell.

For my part, had I one hundred mouths, as many tongues, a voice of iron, a heart of oak, and lungs of leather, together with the mellifluous abundance of Plato, yet I never could give you a full account of a third part of a second of the whole.

Pantagruel was telling me that he believed the queen had given the symbolic word used among her subjects to denote sovereign good cheer, when she said to her tabachins, A panacea; just as Lucullus used to say, In Apollo, when he designed to give his friends a singular treat; though sometimes they took him at unawares, as, among the rest, Cicero and Hortensius sometimes used to do.

CHAPTER 16

HOW THE QUEEN PASSED HER TIME AFTER DINNER

When we had dined, a chachanin led us into the queen's hall, and there we saw how, after dinner, with the ladies and princes of her court, she used to sift, searce, bolt, range, and pass away time with a fine large white and blue silk sieve. We also perceived how they revived ancient sports, diverting themselves together at—

1. Cordax.*	6. Phrygia.	11. Monogas.
2. Emmelia.	7. Thracia.	12. Terminalia.
3. Sicinnia.	8. Calabrisme.	13. Floralia.
4. Jambics.	9. Molossia.	14. Pyrrhice.
5. Persica.	10. Cernophorum.	15. [Nicatism.]

And a thousand other dances.

* Motteux has the following footnote:—"1. A sort of country-dance. 2. A still tragic dance. 3. Dancing and singing used at funerals. 4. Cutting sarcasms and lampoons. 5. The Persian dance. 6. Tunes, whose measure inspired men with a kind of divine fury. 7. The Thracian movement. 8. Smutty verses. 9. A measure to which the Molossi of Epirus danced a certain morrice. 10. A dance with bowls or pots in their hands. 11. A song where one sings alone. 12. Sports at the holidays of the god of bounds. 13. Dancing naked at Floro's holidays. 14. The Trojan dance in armour."

Afterwards she gave orders that they should show us the apartments and curiosities in her palace. Accordingly we saw there such new, strange, and wonderful things, that I am still ravished in admiration every time I think of it. However, nothing surprised us more than what was done by the gentlemen of her household, abstractors, parazons, nebidins, spodizators, and others, who freely and without the least dissembling told us that the queen their mistress did all impossible things, and cured men of incurable diseases; and they, her officers, used to do the rest.

I saw there a young parazon cure many of the new consumption, I mean the pox, though they were never so peppered. Had it been the rankest Roan ague (Anglicé, the Covent-garden gout), 'twas all one to him; touching only their dentiform vertebræ thrice with a piece of a wooden shoe, he made them as wholesome as so many sucking-pigs.

Another did thoroughly cure folks of dropsies, tympanies, ascites, and hyposarcides, striking them on the belly nine times with a Tenedian hatchet, without any solution of the continuum.

Another cured all manner of fevers and agues on the spot, only with hanging a fox-tail on the left side of the patient's girdle.

One removed the toothache only with washing thrice the root of the aching tooth with elder-vinegar, and letting it dry half-an-hour in the sun.

Another the gout, whether hot or cold, natural or accidental, by barely making the gouty person shut his mouth and open his eyes.

I saw another ease nine gentlemen of St. Francis's distemper * in a very short space of time, having clapped a

* "A consumption in the pocket, or want of money; those of St. Francis's order must carry none about 'em."—MOTTEUX.

rope about their necks, at the end of which hung a box with ten thousand gold crowns in't.

One with a wonderful engine threw the houses out at the windows, by which means they were purged of all pestilential air.

Another cured all the three kinds of hectics, the tabid atrophes, and emaciated, without bathing, Tabian milk, dropax, alias depilatory, or other such medicaments, only turning the consumptives for three months into monks; and he assured me that if they did not grow fat and plump in a monastic way of living, they never would be fattened in this world, either by nature or by art.

I saw another surrounded with a crowd of two sorts of women. Some were young, quaint, clever, neat, pretty, juicy, tight, brisk, buxom, proper, kind-hearted, and as right as my leg, to any man's thinking. The rest were old, weather-beaten, over-ridden, toothless, blear-eyed, tough, wrinkled, shrivelled, tawny, mouldy, phthisicky, decrepit hags, beldams, and walking carcasses. We were told that his office was to cast anew those she-pieces of antiquity, and make them such as the pretty creatures whom we saw who had been made young again that day, recovering at once the beauty, shape, size, and disposition which they enjoyed at sixteen; except their heels, that were now much shorter than in their former youth.

This made them yet more apt to fall backwards whenever any man happened to touch 'em, than they had been before. As for their counterparts, the old mother scratch-tobies, they most devoutly waited for the blessed hour when the batch that was in the oven was to be drawn, that they might have their turns, and in a mighty haste they were pulling and hauling the man like mad, telling him that 'tis the most grievous and intolerable thing in nature for the tail to be on fire and the head to scare away those who should quench it.

The officer had his hands full, never wanting patients; neither did his place bring him his title, you may swear. Pantagruel asked him whether he could also make old men young again. He said he could not. But the way to make them new men was to get 'em to cohabit with a new-cast female; for thus they caught that fifth kind of crinckams, which some call pellade, in Greek, *ophiasis,* that makes them cast off their old hair and skin, just as the serpents do, and thus their youth is renewed like the Arabian phœnix's. This is the true fountain of youth, for there the old and discrepit become young, active, and lusty.

Just so, as Euripides tells us, Iolaus was transmogrified; and thus Phaon, for whom kind-hearted Sappho run wild, grew young again, for Venus's use; so Tithon by Aurora's means; so Æson by Medea, and Jason also, who, if you'll believe Pherecides and Simonides, was new-vamped and dyed by that witch; and so were the nurses of jolly Bacchus, and their husbands, as Æschylus relates.

CHAPTER 17

HOW QUEEN WHIMS' OFFICERS WERE EMPLOYED; AND HOW
THE SAID LADY RETAINED US AMONG HER ABSTRACTORS

I THEN saw a great number of the queen's officers, who made blackamoors white as fast as hops, just rubbing their bellies with the bottom of a pannier.

Others, with three couples of foxes in one yoke, ploughed a sandy shore, and did not lose their seed.

Others washed burnt tiles, and made them lose their colour.

Others extracted water out of pumice-stones, braying them a good while in a mortar, and changed their substance.

Others sheared asses, and thus got long fleece wool.

Others gathered barberries and figs off of thistles.

Others stroked he-goats by the dugs, and saved their milk in a sieve; and much they got by it.

[Others washed asses' heads without losing their soap.]

Others taught cows to dance, and did not lose their fiddling.

Others pitched nets to catch the wind, and took cocklobsters in them.

I saw a spodizator, who very artificially got farts out of a dead ass, and sold 'em for fivepence an ell.

Another did putrefy beetles. O the dainty food!

Poor Panurge fairly cast up his accounts, and gave up his halfpenny (*i. e.* vomited), seeing an archasdarpenin who laid a huge plenty of chamber lye to putrefy in horsedung, mishmashed with abundance of Christian sir-reverence. Pugh, fie upon him, nasty dog! However, he told us that with this sacred distillation he watered kings and princes, and made their sweet lives a fathom or two the longer.

Others built churches to jump over the steeples.

Others set carts before the horses, and began to flay eels at the tail; neither did the eels cry before they were hurt, like those of Melun.

Others out of nothing made great things, and made great things return to nothing.

Others cut fire into steaks with a knife, and drew water with a fish-net.

Others made chalk of cheese, and honey of a dog's t—d.

We saw a knot of others, about a baker's dozen in number, tippling under an arbour. They toped out of jolly bottomless cups four sorts of cool, sparkling, pure, delicious, vine-tree sirup, which went down like mother's milk; and healths and bumpers flew about like lightning. We were told that these true philosophers were fairly multiplying the stars by drinking till the seven were fourteen, as brawny Hercules did with Atlas.

Others made a virtue of necessity, and the best of a bad market, which seemed to me a very good piece of work.

Others made alchemy (*i. e.* sir-reverence) with their teeth, and clapping their hind retort to the recipient, made scurvy faces, and then squeezed.

Others, in a large grass plot, exactly measured how far the fleas could go at a hop, a step, and jump; and told us that this was exceedingly useful for the ruling of kingdoms, the conduct of armies, and the administration of commonwealths; and that Socrates, who first got philosophy out of heaven, and from idle and trifling made it profitable and of moment, used to spend half his philosophizing time in measuring the leaps of fleas, as Aristophanes the quintessential affirms.

I saw two gibroins by themselves keeping watch on the top of a tower, and we were told they guarded the moon from the wolves.

In a blind corner I met four more very hot at it, and ready to go to loggerheads. I asked what was the cause of the stir and ado, the mighty coil and pother they made. And I heard that for four livelong days those overwise roisters had been at it ding-dong, disputing on three high, more than metaphysical propositions, promising themselves mountains of gold by solving them. The first was concerning a he-ass's shadow; the second, of the smoke of a lantern; and the third of goat's hair, whether it were wool or no. We heard that they did not think it a bit strange that two contradictions in mode, form, figure, and time should be true; though I will warrant the sophists of Paris had rather be unchristened than own so much.

While we were admiring all those men's wonderful doings, the evening star already twinkling, the queen (God bless her!) appeared, attended with her court, and again amazed and dazzled us. She perceived it, and said to us:

What occasions the aberrations of human cogitations through the perplexing labyrinths and abysses of admiration, is not the source of the effects, which sagacious mortals visibly experience to be the consequential result of natural causes. 'Tis the novelty of the experiment which makes impressions on their conceptive, cogitative faculties; that do not previse the facility of the operation adequately, with a subact and sedate intellection, associated with diligent and congruous study. Consequently let all manner of perturbation abdicate the ventricles of your brains, if anyone has invaded them while they were contemplating what is transacted by my domestic ministers. Be spectators and auditors of every particular phenomenon and every individual proposition within the extent of my mansion; satiate yourselves with all that can fall here under the consideration of your visual or ausculating powers, and thus emancipate yourselves from the servitude of crassous ignorance. And that you may be induced to apprehend how sincerely I desire this in consideration of the studious cupidity that so demonstratively emicates at your external organs, from this present particle of time I retain you as my abstractors. Geber, my principal Tabachin, shall register and initiate you at your departing.

We humbly thanked her queenship without saying a word, accepting of the noble office she conferred on us.

CHAPTER 18

HOW THE QUEEN WAS SERVED AT DINNER, AND OF HER WAY
OF EATING

QUEEN WHIMS after this said to her gentlemen: The
orifice of the ventricle, that ordinary embassador for the
alimentation of all members, whether superior or inferior,
importunes us to restore, by the apposition of idoneous sustenance, what was dissipated by the internal calidity's action
on the radical humidity. Therefore spodizators, gesinins,
memains, and parazons, be not culpable of dilatory protrac-
tions in the opposition of every re-roborating species, but
rather let them pullulate and super-abound on the tables.
As for you, nobilissim præcustators, and my gentilissim masticators, your frequently experimented industry, internected
with perdiligent sedulity and sedulous perdiligence, continually adjuvates you to perficiate all things in so expeditious a
manner that there is no necessity of exciting in you a
cupidity to consummate them. Therefore I can only suggest
to you still to operate as you are assuefacted indefatigably to
operate.

Having made this fine speech, she retired for a while with
part of her women, and we were told that 'twas to bathe, as
the ancients did more commonly than we use nowadays to
wash our hands before we eat. The tables were soon placed,
the cloth spread, and then the queen sat down. She ate nothing but celestial ambrosia, and drank nothing but divine
nectar. As for the lords and ladies that were there, as well
as we, fared on as rare, costly, and dainty dishes as ever
Apicius wot or dreamed of in his life.

When we were as round as hoops, and as full as eggs, with
stuffing the gut, an olla podrida * was set before us to force

* "Some call it an *Olio*. Rabelais *Pot-pourry*."—MOTTEUX.

hunger to come to terms with us, in case it had not granted us a truce; and such a huge vast thing it was that the plate which Pythius Althius gave King Darius would hardly have covered it. The olla consisted of several sorts of pottages, salads, fricassees, saugrenees, cabirotadoes, roast and boiled meat, carbonadoes, swingeing pieces of powdered beef, good old hams, dainty somates, cakes, tarts, a world of curds after the Moorish way, fresh cheese, jellies, and fruit of all sorts.

All this seemed to me good and dainty; however, the sight of it made me sigh; for alas! I could not taste a bit on't, so full I had filled my puddings before, and a bellyful is a bellyful you know. Yet I must tell you what I saw that seemed to me odd enough o' conscience; 'twas some pasties in paste; and what should those pasties in paste be, d'ye think, but pasties in pots? At the bottom I perceived store of dice, cards, tarots,* luettes,† chessmen, and chequers, besides full bowls of gold crowns, for those who had a mind to have a game or two and try their chance. Under this I saw a jolly company of mules in stately trappings, with velvet foot-cloths, and a troop of ambling nags, some for men and some for women; besides I don't know how many litters all lined with velvet, and some coaches of Ferrara make; all this for those who had a mind to take the air.

This did not seem strange to me; but if anything did 'twas certainly the queen's way of eating, and truly 'twas very new, and very odd; for she chewed nothing, the good lady; not but that she had good sound teeth, and her meat required to be masticated, but such was her highness's custom. When her prægustators had tasted the meat, her masticators took it and chewed it most nobly; for their dainty chops and

---

* "Great cards on which many different things are figured."—Motteux.

† "Pieces of ivory to play withal."—Motteux.

gullets were lined through with crimson satin, with little
welts and gold purls, and their teeth were of delicate white
ivory. Thus, when they had chewed the meat ready for her
highness's maw, they poured it down her throat through
a funnel of fine gold, and so on to her craw. For that reason
they told us she never visited a close-stool but by proxy.

CHAPTER 19

HOW THERE WAS A BALL IN THE MANNER OF A TOURNAMENT, AT WHICH QUEEN WHIMS WAS PRESENT

AFTER supper there was a ball in the form of a tilt or a
tournament, not only worth seeing, but also never to be
forgotten. First, the floor of the hall was covered with a
large piece of velveted white and yellow chequered tapestry,
each chequer exactly square, and three full spans in breadth.

Then thirty-two young persons came into the hall; sixteen
of them arrayed in cloth of gold, and of these eight were
young nymphs such as the ancients described Diana's attendants; the other eight were a king, a queen, two wardens
of the castle, two knights, and two archers. Those of the
other band were clad in cloth of silver.

They posted themselves on the tapestry in the following
manner: the kings on the last line on the fourth square;
so that the golden king was on a white square, and the
silvered king on a yellow square, and each queen by her
king; the golden queen on a yellow square, and the silvered
queen on a white one; and on each side stood the archers
to guide their kings and queens; by the archers the knights,
and the wardens by them. In the next row before 'em stood
the eight nymphs; and between the two bands of nymphs
four rows of squares stood empty.

Each band had its musicians, eight on each side, dressed

in its livery; the one with orange-coloured damask, the other with white; and all played on different instruments most melodiously and harmoniously, still varying in time and measure as the figure of the dance required. This seemed to me an admirable thing, considering the numerous diversity of steps, back-steps, bounds, rebounds, jerks, paces, leaps, skips, turns, coupés, hops, leadings, risings, meetings, flights, ambuscadoes, moves, and removes.

I was also at a loss when I strove to comprehend how the dancers could so suddenly know what every different note meant; for they no sooner heard this or that sound but they placed themselves in the place which was denoted by the music, though their motions were all different. For the nymphs that stood in the first file, as if they designed to begin the fight, marched straight forwards to their enemies from square to square, unless it were the first step, at which they were free to move over two steps at once. They alone never fall back (which is not very natural to other nymphs), and if any of them is so lucky as to advance to the opposite king's row, she is immediately crowned queen of her king, and after that moves with the same state and in the same manner as the queen; but till that happens they never strike their enemies but forwards, and obliquely in a diagonal line. However, they make it not their chief business to take their foes; for if they did, they would leave their queen exposed to the adverse parties, who then might take her.

The kings move and take their enemies on all sides square-ways, and only step from a white square into a yellow one, and *vice versa,* except at their first step the rank should want other officers than the wardens; for then they can set 'em in their place, and retire by him.

The queens take a greater liberty than any of the rest; for they move backwards and forwards all manners of ways, in a straight line as far as they please, provided the place be not filled with one of her own party, and diagonally also, keeping to the colour on which she stands.

The archers move backwards or forwards, far and near, never changing the colour on which they stand. The knights move and take in a lineal manner, stepping over one square, though a friend or foe stand upon it, posting themselves on the second square to the right or left, from one colour to another, which is very unwelcome to the adverse party, and ought to be carefully observed, for they take at unawares.

The wardens move and take to the right or left, before or behind them, and like the kings, can advance as far as they find places empty; which liberty the kings take not.

The law which both sides observe, is, at the end of the fight, to besiege and enclose the king of either party, so that he may not be able to move; and being reduced to that extremity, the battle is over, and he loses the day.

Now, to avoid this, there is none of either sex of each party but is willing to sacrifice his or her life, and they begin to take one another on all sides in time, as soon as the music strikes up. When anyone takes a prisoner, he makes his honours, and striking him gently in the hand, puts him out of the field and combat, and encamps where he stood.

If one of the kings chance to stand were he might be taken, it is not lawful for any of his adversaries that had discovered him to lay hold on him; far from it, they are strictly enjoined humbly to pay him their respects, and give him notice, saying, God preserve you, sir! that his officers may relieve and cover him, or he may remove, if unhappily he could not be relieved. However, he is not to be taken, but greeted with a Good-morrow, the others bending the knee; and thus the tournament uses to end.

CHAPTER 20

HOW THE THIRTY-TWO PERSONS AT THE BALL FOUGHT

THE two companies having taken their stations, the music struck up, and with a martial sound, which had something of horrid in it, like a point of war, roused and alarmed both parties, who now began to shiver, and then soon were warmed with warlike rage; and having got in readiness to fight desperately impatient of delay stood waiting for the charge.

Then the music of the silvered band ceased playing, and the instruments of the golden side alone were heard, which denoted that the golden party attacked. Accordingly, a new movement was played for the onset, and we saw the nymph who stood before the queen turn to the left towards her king, as it were to ask leave to fight; and thus saluting her company at the same time, she moved two squares forwards, and saluted the adverse party.

Now the music of the golden brigade ceased playing, and their antagonists began again. I ought to have told you that the nymph who began by saluting her company, had by that formality also given them to understand that they were to fall on. She was saluted by them in the same manner, with a full turn to the left, except the queen, who went aside towards her king to the right; and the same manner of salutation was observed on both sides during the whole ball.

The silvered nymph that stood before her queen likewise moved as soon as the music of her party sounded a charge; her salutations, and those of her side, were to the right, and her queen's to the left. She moved in the second square forwards, and saluted her antagonists, facing the first golden nymph; so that there was not any distance between them, and you would have thought they two had been going to fight; but they only strike sideways.

Their comrades, whether silvered or golden, followed 'em in an intercalary figure, and seemed to skirmish a while, till the golden nymph who had first entered the lists, striking a silvered nymph in the hand on the right, put her out of the field, and set herself in her place. But soon the music playing a new measure, she was struck by a silvered archer, who after that was obliged himself to retire. A silvered knight then sallied out, and the golden queen posted herself before her king.

Then the silvered king, dreading the golden queen's fury, removed to the right, to the place where his warden stood, which seemed to him strong and well guarded.

The two knights on the left, whether golden or silvered, marched up, and on either side took up many nymphs who could not retreat; principally the golden knight, who made this his whole business; but the silvered knight had greater designs, dissembling all along, and even sometimes not taking a nymph when he could have done it, still moving on till he was come up to the main body of the enemies in such a manner that he saluted their king with a God save you, sir!

The whole golden brigade quaked for fear and anger, those words giving notice of their king's danger; not but that they could soon relieve him, but because their king being thus saluted they were to lose their warden on the right wing without any hopes of recovery. Then the golden king retired to the left, and the silvered knight took the golden warden, which was a mighty loss to that party. However, they resolved to be revenged, and surrounded the knight that he might not escape. He tried to get off, behaving himself with a great deal of gallantry, and his friends did what they could to save him; but at last he fell into the golden queen's hands, and was carried off.

Her forces, not yet satisfied, having lost one of her best men, with more fury than conduct moved about, and did much mischief among their enemies. The silvered party warily dissembled, watching their opportunity to be even with them, and presented one of their nymphs to the golden queen, having laid an ambuscado; so that the nymph being taken, a golden archer had like to have seized the silvered queen. Then the golden knight undertakes to take the silvered king and queen, and says, Good-morrow! Then the silvered archer salutes them, and was taken by a golden nymph, and she herself by a silvered one.

The fight was obstinate and sharp. The wardens left their posts, and advanced to relieve their friends. The battle was doubtful, and victory hovered over both armies. Now the silvered host charge and break through their enemy's ranks as far as the golden king's tent, and now they are beaten back. The golden queen distinguishes herself from the rest by her mighty achievements still more than by her garb and dignity; for at once she takes an archer, and, going sideways, seizes a silvered warden. Which thing the silvered queen perceiving, she came forwards, and, rushing on with equal bravery, takes the last golden warden and some nymphs. The two queens fought a long while hand to hand now striving to take each other by surprise, then to save themselves, and sometimes to guard their kings. Finally the golden queen took the silvered queen; but presently after she herself was taken by the silvered archer.

Then the silvered king had only three nymphs, an archer and a warden left, and the golden only three nymphs and the right knight, which made them fight more slowly and warily than before. The two kings seemed to mourn for the

ɔss of their loving queens, and only studied and endeavoured
ɔ get new ones out of all their nymphs to be raised to that
ignity, and thus be married to them. This made them excite
hose brave nymphs to strive to reach the farthest rank,
vhere stood the king of the contrary party, promising them
ertainly to have them crowned if they could do this. The
ɔolden nymphs were beforehand with the others, and out
f their number was created a queen, who was dressed in
ɔyal robes, and had a crown set on her head. You need not
ɔoubt the silvered nymphs made also what haste they could
ɔ be queens. One of them was within a step of the coronation
lace; but there the golden knight lay ready to intercept her,
ɔ that she could go no further.

The new golden queen, resolved to show herself valiant
nd worthy of her advancement to the crown, achieved great
eats of arms. But in the meantime the silvered knight takes
he golden warden who guarded the camp; and thus there
vas a new silvered queen, who, like the other, strove to
xcel in heroic deeds at the beginning of her reign. Thus
he fight grew hotter than before. A thousand stratagems,
harges, rallyings, retreats, and attacks were tried on both
ides; till at last the silvered queen, having by stealth ad-
anced as far as the golden king's tent, cried, God save you,
ir! Now none but his new queen could relieve him; so she
ravely came and exposed herself to the utmost extremity to
eliver him out of it. Then the silvered warden with his
ueen reduced the golden king to such a stress that, to save
imself, he was forced to lose his queen; but the golden
ing took him at last. However, the rest of the golden party
vere soon taken; and that king being left alone, the silvered
arty made him a low bow, crying, Good morrow, sir! which
enoted that the silvered king had got the day.

This being heard, the music of both parties loudly proclaimed the victory. And thus the first battle ended to the unspeakable joy of all the spectators.

After this the two brigades took their former stations, and began to tilt a second time, much as they had done before, only the music played somewhat faster than at the first battle, and the motions were altogether different. I saw the golden queen sally out one of the first, with an archer and a knight, as it were angry at the former defeat, and she had like to have fallen upon the silvered king in his tent among his officers; but having been baulked in her attempt she skirmished briskly, and overthrew so many silvered nymphs and officers that it was a most amazing sight. You would have sworn she had been another Penthesilea; for she behaved herself with as much bravery as that Amazonian queen did at Troy.

But this havoc did not last long; for the silvered party, exasperated by their loss, resolved to perish or stop her progress; and having posted an archer in ambuscado on a distant angle, together with a knight-errant, her highness fell into their hands and was carried out of the field. The rest was soon routed after the taking of their queen, who, without doubt, from that time resolved to be more wary and keep near her king, without venturing so far amidst her enemies unless with more force to defend her. Thus the silvered brigade once more got the victory.

This did not dishearten or deject the golden party; far from it. They soon appeared again in the field to face their enemies; and being posted as before, both the armies seemed more resolute and cheerful than ever. Now the martial concert began, and the music was above a hemiole the quicker, according to the warlike Phrygian mode, such as was invented by Marsyas.

Then our combatants began to wheel about, and charge

with such a swiftness that in an instant they made four
moves, besides the usual salutations. So they were continually
in action, flying, hovering, jumping, vaulting, curvetting,
with petauristical turns and motions, and often intermingled.

Seeing them then turn about on one foot after they had
made their honours, we compared them to your tops or
gigs, such as boys use to whip about, making them turn
round so swiftly that they sleep, as they call it, and motion
cannot be perceived, but resembles rest, its contrary; so
that if you make a point or mark on some part of one of
those gigs, 'twill be perceived not as a point, but a continual
line, in a most divine manner, as Cusanus has wisely observed.

While they were thus warmly engaged, we heard continually the claps and episemapsies which those of the two
bands reiterated at the taking of their enemies; and this,
joined to the variety of their motions and music, would have
forced smiles out of the most severe Cato, the never-laughing
Crassus, the Athenian manhater, Timon, nay, even whining
Heraclitus, though he abhorred laughing, the action that is
most peculiar to man. For who could have forborne? seeing
those young warriors, with their nymphs and queens, so
briskly and gracefully advance, retire, jump, leap, skip,
spring, fly, vault, caper, move to the right, to the left, every
way still in time, so swiftly, and yet so dexterously, that
they never touched one another but methodically.

As the number of the combatants lessened, the pleasure
of the spectators increased; for the stratagems and motions
of the remaining forces were more singular. I shall only add
that this pleasing entertainment charmed us to such a degree
that our minds were ravished with admiration and delight,
and the martial harmony moved our souls so powerfully that
we easily believed what is said of Ismenias's having excited

Alexander to rise from table and run to his arms, with such
a warlike melody. At last the golden king remained master
of the field; and while we were minding those dances, Queen
Whims vanished, so that we saw her no more from that
day to this.

Then Geber's michelots conducted us, and we were set
down among her abstractors, as her queenship had commanded. After that we returned to the port of Mateotechny,
and thence straight aboard our ships; for the wind was
fair; and had we not hoisted out of hand, we could hardly
have got off in three quarters of a moon in the wane.

CHAPTER 21

HOW WE CAME TO THE ISLAND OF SANDALS; AND OF THE
ORDER OF SEMIQUAVER FRIARS

THENCE we went to the island of Sandals, whose inhabitants live on nothing but ling-broth. However, we were
very kindly received and entertained by Benius the Third,
king of the island, who, after he had made us drink, took
us with him to show us a spick-and-span new monastery
which he had contrived for the Semiquaver Friars; so he
called the religious men whom he had there. For he said
that on t'other side the water lived friars who styled themselves her sweet ladyship's most humble servants. Item, the
goodly Friar-minors, who are semibreves of bulls; the
smoked-herring tribe of Minim Friars; then the Crochet
Friars. So that these diminutives could be no more than
Semiquavers. By the statutes, bulls, and patents of Queen
Whims, they were all dressed like so many house-burners,
except that, as in Anjou your bricklayers use to quilt their
knees when they tile houses, so these holy friars had usually
quilted bellies, and thick quilted paunches were among them

n much repute. Their codpieces were cut slipper-fashion,
nd every monk among them wore two—one sewed before
nd another behind—reporting that some certain dreadful
nysteries were duly represented by this duplicity of cod-
ieces.

They wore shoes as round as basins, in imitation of those
vho inhabit the sandy sea. Their chins were close-shaved,
nd their feet iron-shod; and to show they did not value
ortune, Benius made them shave and poll the hind part
f their polls as bare as a bird's arse, from the crown to
he shoulder-blades; but they had leave to let their hair grow
efore, from the two triangular bones in the upper part
f the skull.

At noon, as soon the clock struck, they used to awake.
ou must know that their clock-bell, church-bells, and
efectory-bells were all made according to the pontial device,
hat is, quilted with the finest down, and their clappers of
ox-tails.

Having then made shift to get up at noon, they pulled
ff their boots, and those that wanted to speak with a maid,
lias piss, pissed; those that wanted to scumber, scumbered;
nd those that wanted to sneeze, sneezed. But all, whether
hey would or no (poor gentlemen), were obliged largely and
lentifully to yawn; and this was their first breakfast (O
igorous statute!). Methought 'twas very comical to observe
heir transactions; for, having laid their boots and spurs on
. rack, they went into the cloisters. There they curiously
vashed their hands and mouths; then sat them down on
. long bench, and picked their teeth till the provost gave
he signal, whistling through his fingers; then every he
tretched out his jaws as much as he could, and they gaped
nd yawned for about half-an-hour, sometimes more, some-

times less, according as the prior judged the breakfast to
be suitable to the day.

After that they went in procession, two banners being
carried before them, in one of which was the picture of
Virtue, and that of Fortune in the other. The last went before, carried by a semiquavering friar, at whose heels was
another, with the shadow or image of Virtue in one hand
and an holy-water sprinkle in the other—I mean of that holy
mercurial water which Ovid describes in his Fasti. And as
the preceding Semiquaver rang a handbell, this shaked the
sprinkle with his fist. With that says Pantagruel, This order
contradicts the rule which Tully and the academics prescribed, that Virtue ought to go before, and Fortune follow.
But they told us they did as they ought, seeing their design
was to breech, lash, and bethwack Fortune.

After the procession they went sluggingly into the fratery-
room, by the way of walk and healthful exercise, and there
kneeled under the tables, leaning their breasts on lanterns.
While they were in that posture, in came a huge Sandal,
with a pitchfork in his hand, who used to baste, rib-roast,
swaddle, and swinge them well-favouredly, as they said, and
in truth treated them after a fashion. They began their
meal as you end yours, with cheese, and ended it with mustard and lettuce, as Martial tells us the ancients did. Afterwards a platterful of mustard was brought before every
one of them, and thus they made good the proverb, After
meat comes mustard.

Their diet was this:

O' Sundays they stuffed their puddings with puddings,
chitterlings, links, Bologna sausages, forced-meats, liverings,
hogs' haslets, young quails, and teals. You must also always
add cheese for the first course and mustard for the last.

O' Mondays they were crammed with peas and pork, *cum commento*, and interlineary glosses.

O' Tuesdays they used to twist store of holy-bread, cakes, buns, puffs, lenten loaves, jumbles, and biscuits.

O' Wednesdays my gentlemen had fine sheep's heads, calves' heads, and brocks' heads, of which there's no want in that country.

O' Thursdays they guzzled down seven sorts of porridge, not forgetting mustard.

O' Fridays they munched nothing but services or sorb-apples; neither were these full ripe, as I guessed by their complexion.

O' Saturdays they gnawed bones; not that they were poor or needy, for every mother's son of them had a very good fat belly-benefice.

As for their drink, 'twas an antifortunal; thus they called I don't know what sort of a liquor of the place.

When they wanted to eat or drink, they turned down the back-points or flaps of their cowls forwards below their chins, and that served 'em instead of gorgets or slabbering-bibs.

Such was their diet when they resided in the convent, and if the prior of the monk-house sent any of them abroad, then they were strictly enjoined neither to touch nor eat any manner of fish as long as they were on sea or rivers, and to abstain from all manner of flesh whenever they were at land, that everyone might be convinced that, while they enjoyed the object, they denied themselves the power, and even the desire, and were no more moved with it than the Marpesian rock.

All this was done with proper antiphones, still sung and chanted by ear, as we have already observed.

When the sun went to bed, they fairly booted and spurred

each other as before, and having clapped on their barnacles e'en jogged to bed too. At midnight the Sandal came to them, and up they got, and having well whetted and set their razors, and been a-processioning, they clapped the tables over themselves, and like wiredrawers under their work fell to it as aforesaid.

Friar John des Entoumeures, having shrewdly observed these jolly Semiquaver Friars, and had a full account of their statutes, lost all patience, and cried out aloud: Bounce tail, and God ha' mercy guts; if every fool should wear a bauble, fuel would be dear. A plague rot it, we must know how many farts go to an ounce. Would Priapus were here, as he used to be at the nocturnal festivals in Crete, that I might see him play backwards, and wriggle and shake to the purpose. Ay, ay, this is the world, and t'other is the country; may I never piss if this be not an antichthonian land, and our very antipodes. In German they pull down monasteries and unfrockify the monks; here they go quite kam, and act clean contrary to others, setting new ones up, against the hair.

CHAPTER 22

HOW PANURGE ASKED A SEMIQUAVER FRIAR MANY QUESTIONS, AND WAS ONLY ANSWERED IN MONOSYLLABLES

PANURGE, who had since been wholly taken up with staring at these royal Semiquavers, at last pulled one of them by the sleeve, who was as lean as a rake, and asked him,—

Hearkee me, Friar Quaver, Semiquaver, Demisemiquavering quaver.

PAN. What wood d'ye burn in your chambers? FRI. Pine. PAN. And of what other trees? FRI. Lime.

PAN. Hearkee me; as for the buttocks, I'll go your halves. Pray, how do you feed 'em?   FRI. Well.

PAN. First, what do they eat?   FRI. Bread.

PAN. Of what complexion?   FRI. White.

PAN. And what else?   FRI. Meat.

PAN. How do they love it dressed?   FRI. Roast.

PAN. What sort of porridge?   FRI. None.

PAN. Are they for pies and tarts?   FRI. Much.

PAN. Then I'm their man. Will fish go down with them?   FRI. Well.

PAN. And what else?   FRI. Eggs.

PAN. How do they like 'em?   FRI. Boiled.

PAN. How must they be done?   FRI. Hard.

PAN. Is this all they have?   FRI. No.

PAN. What have they besides, then?   FRI. Beef.

PAN. And what else?   FRI. Pork.

PAN. And what more?   FRI. Geese.

PAN. What then?   FRI. Ducks.

PAN. And what besides?   FRI. Cocks.

PAN. What do they season their meat with?   FRI. Salt.

PAN. What sauce are they most dainty for?   FRI. Must.

PAN. What's their last course?   FRI. Rice.

PAN. And what else?   FRI. Milk.

PAN. What besides?   FRI. Peas.

PAN. What sort?   FRI. Green.

PAN. What do they boil with 'em?   FRI. Pork.

PAN. What fruit do they eat?   FRI. Good.

PAN. How?   FRI. Raw.

PAN. What do they end with?   FRI. Nuts.

PAN. How do they drink?   FRI. Neat.

PAN. What liquor?   FRI. Wine.

PAN. What sort?   FRI. White.

PAN. In winter?   FRI. Strong.

PAN. In the spring? FRI. Brisk.

PAN. In summer? FRI. Cool.

PAN. In autumn? FRI. New.

Buttock of a monk! cried Friar John; how plump these plaguy trulls, these arch Semiquavering strumpets, must be! That damned cattle are so high fed that they must needs be high-mettled, and ready to wince and give two ups for one go-down when anyone offers to ride them below the crupper.

Prithee, Friar John, quoth Panurge, hold thy prating tongue; stay till I have done.

Till what time do the doxies sit up? FRI. Night.

PAN. When do they get up? FRI. Late.

PAN. May I ride on a horse that was foaled of an acorn, if this be not as honest a cod as ever the ground went upon, and as grave as an old gate-post into the bargain. Would to the blessed St. Semiquaver, and the blessed worthy virgin St. Semiquavera, he were lord chief president (justice) of Paris! Ods-bodkins, how he'd despatch! With what expedition would he bring disputes to an upshot! What an abbreviator and clawer off of lawsuits, reconciler of differences, examiner and fumbler of bags, peruser of bills, scribbler of rough drafts, and engrosser of deeds would he not make! Well, friar, spare your breath to cool your porridge. Come, let's now talk with deliberation, fairly and softly, as lawyers go to heaven. Let's know how you victual the venereal camp. How is the snatch-blatch? FRI. Rough.

PAN. How is the gateway? FRI. Free.

PAN. And how is it within? FRI. Deep.

PAN. I mean, what weather is it there? FRI. Hot.

PAN. What shadows the brooks? FRI. Groves.

PAN. Of what's the colour of the twigs? FRI. Red.

PAN. And that of the old? FRI. Grey.

PAN. How are you when you shake? FRI. Brisk.

Pan. How is their motion? Fri. Quick.

Pan. Would you have them vault or wriggle more? Fri. Less.

Pan. What kind of tools are yours? Fri. Big.

Pan. And in their helves? Fri. Round.

Pan. Of what colour is the tip? Fri. Red.

Pan. When they've been used, how are they? Fri. Shrunk.

Pan. How much weighs each bag of tools? Fri. Pounds.

Pan. How hang your pouches? Fri. Tight.

Pan. How are they when you've done? Fri. Lank.

Pan. Now, by the oath you have taken, tell me, when you have a mind to cohabit, how you throw 'em? Fri. Down.

Pan. And what do they say then? Fri. Fie.

Pan. However, like maids, they say nay, and take it; and speak the less, but think the more, minding the work in hand; do they not? Fri. True.

Pan. Do they get you bairns? Fri. None.

Pan. How do you pig together? Fri. Bare.

Pan. Remember you're upon your oath, and tell me justly and *bona fide* how many times a day you monk it? Fri. Six.

Pan. How many bouts a-nights? Fri. Ten.

Pan. Pray, Friar Shakewell, does your whole fraternity quaver and shake at that rate? Fri. All.

Pan. Who of them is the best cock o' the game? Fri. I.

Pan. Do you never commit dry-bobs or flashes in the pan? Fri. None.

Pan. I blush like any black dog, and could be as testy as an old cook when I think on all this; it passes my understanding. But, pray, when you have been pumped dry one day, what have you got the next? Fri. More.

PAN. By Priapus, they have the Indian herb of which Theophrastus spoke, or I'm much out. But hearkee me, thou man of brevity, should some impediment, honestly or otherwise, impair your talents and cause your benevolence to lessen, how would it fare with you, then? FRI. Ill.

PAN. What would the wenches do? FRI. Rail.

PAN. What if you skipped, and let 'em fast a whole day? FRI. Worse.

PAN. What do you give 'em then? FRI. Thwacks.

PAN. What do they say to this? FRI. Bawl.

PAN. And what else? FRI. Curse.

PAN. How do you correct 'em? FRI. Hard.

PAN. What do you get out of 'em then? FRI. Blood.

PAN. How's their complexion then? FRI. Odd.

PAN. What do they mend it with? FRI. Paint.

PAN. Then what do they do? FRI. Fawn.

PAN. By the oath you have taken, tell me truly what time of the year do you do it least in? FRI. Now.*

PAN. What season do you do it best in? FRI. March.

PAN. How is your performance the rest of the year? FRI. Brisk.

Then quoth Panurge, sneering, Of all, and of all, commend me to Ball; this is the friar of the world for my money. You've heard how short, concise, and compendious he is in his answers. Nothing is to be got out of him but monosyllables. By jingo, I believe he would make three bites of a cherry.

Damn him, cried Friar John, that's as true as I am his uncle. The dog yelps at another gate's rate when he is among his bitches; there he is polysyllable enough, my life for yours. You talk of making three bites of a cherry! God send fools more wit and us more money! May I be doomed to

* August.

fast a whole day if I don't verily believe he would not make above two bites of a shoulder of mutton and one swoop of a whole bottle of wine. Zoons, do but see how down o' the mouth the cur looks! He's nothing but skin and bones; he has pissed his tallow.

Truly, truly, quoth Epistemon, this rascally monastical vermin all over the world mind nothing but their gut, and are as ravenous as any kites, and then, forsooth, they tell us they've nothing but food and raiment in this world. 'Sdeath, what more have kings and princes?

CHAPTER 23

HOW WE ARRIVED AT THE ORACLE OF THE BOTTLE

OUR glorious lantern lighting and directing us to heart's content, we at last arrived at the desired island where was the Oracle of the Bottle. As soon as friend Panurge landed, he nimbly cut a caper with one leg for joy, and cried to Pantagruel, Now we are where we have wished ourselves long ago. This is the place we've been seeking with such toil and labour. He then made a compliment to our lantern, who desired us to be of good cheer, and not be daunted or dismayed whatever we might chance to see.

To come to the Temple of the Holy Bottle we were to go through a large vineyard, in which were all sorts of vines, as the Falernian, Malvoisian, the Muscadine, those of Taige, Beaune, Mirevaux, Orleans, Picardent, Arbois, Coussi, Anjou, Grave, Corsica, Vierron, Nerac, and others. This vineyard was formerly planted by the good Bacchus, with so great a blessing that it yields leaves, flowers, and fruit all the year round, like the orange trees at Suraine.

Our magnificent lantern ordered every one of us to eat

three grapes, to put some vine-leaves in his shoes, and take a vine-branch in his left hand.

At the end of the close we went under an arch built after the manner of those of the ancients. The trophies of a toper were curiously carved on it.

First, on one side was to be seen a long train of flagons, leathern bottles, flasks, cans, glass bottles, barrels, nipperkins, pint pots, quart pots, pottles, gallons, and old-fashioned semaises (swingeing wooden pots, such as those out of which the Germans fill their glasses); these hung on a shady arbour.

On another side was store of garlic, onions, shallots, hams, botargos, caviare, biscuits, neats' tongues, old cheese, and such like comfits, very artificially interwoven, and packed together with vine-stocks.

On another were a hundred sorts of drinking glasses, cups, cisterns, ewers, false cups, tumblers, bowls, mazers, mugs, jugs, goblets, talboys, and such other Bacchic artillery.

On the frontispiece of the triumphal arch, under the zoophore, was the following couplet:

> You who presume to move this way,
> Get a good lantern, lest you stray.

We took special care of that, cried Pantagruel when he had read them; for there is not a better or a more divine lantern than ours in all Lantern-land.

This arch ended at a fine large round alley covered over with the interlaid branches of vines, loaded and adorned with clusters of five hundred different colours, and of as many various shapes, not natural, but due to the skill of agriculture; some were golden, others bluish, tawny, azure, white, black, green, purple, streaked with many colours, long, round, triangular, cod-like, hairy, great-headed, and grassy. That pleasant alley ended at three old ivy-trees, verdant, and all loaden with rings. Our enlightened lantern directed us to make ourselves hats with some of their leaves, and cover our heads wholly with them, which was immediately done.

Jupiter's priestess, said Pantagruel, in former days would not like us have walked under this arbour. There was a mystical reason, answered our most perspicuous lantern, that would have hindered her; for had she gone under it, the wine, or the grapes of which 'tis made, that's the same thing, had been over her head, and then she would have seemed overtopped and mastered by wine. Which implies that priests, and all persons who devote themselves to the contemplation of divine things, ought to keep their minds sedate and calm, and avoid whatever might disturb and discompose their tranquillity, which nothing is more apt to do than drunkenness.

You also, continued our lantern, could not come into the Holy Bottle's presence, after you have gone through this arch, did not that noble priestess Bacbuc first see your shoes full of vine-leaves; which action is diametrically opposite to the other, and signifies that you despise wine, and having mastered it, as it were, tread it under foot.

I am no scholar, quoth Friar John, for which I'm heartily sorry, yet I find by my breviary that in the Revelation a woman was seen with the moon under her feet, which was a most wonderful sight. Now, as Bigot explained to me, this was to signify that she was not of the nature of other women; for they have all the moon at their heads, and consequently their brains are always troubled with a lunacy. This makes me willing to believe what you said, dear Madam Lantern.

CHAPTER 24

HOW WE WENT UNDERGROUND TO COME TO THE TEMPLE OF
THE HOLY BOTTLE, AND HOW CHINON IS THE OLDEST
CITY IN THE WORLD

WE went underground through a plastered vault on which
was coarsely painted a dance, of women and satyrs waiting
on old Silenus, who was grinning o' horseback on his ass.
This made me say to Pantagruel, that this entry put me in
mind of the painted cellar in the oldest city in the world,
where such paintings are to be seen, and in as cool a place.

Which is the oldest city in the world? asked Pantagruel.
'Tis Chinon, sir, or Cainon in Touraine, said I. I know, returned Pantagruel, where Chinon lies, and the painted cellar
also, having myself drunk there many a glass of cool wine;
neither do I doubt but that Chinon is an ancient town—witness its blazon. I own 'tis said twice or thrice:

> Chinon,
> Little town
> Great renown,
> On old stone
> Long has stood;
> There's the Vienne, if you look down;
> If you look up, there's the wood.

But how, continued he, can you make it out that 'tis the
oldest city in the world? Where did you find this written?
I have found it in the sacred writ, said I, that Cain was the
first that built a town; we may then reasonably conjecture
that from his name he gave it that of Cainon. Thus, after
his example, most other founders of towns have given them
their names: Athena, that's Minerva in Greek, to Athens;

Alexander to Alexandria; Constantine to Constantinople; Pompey to Pompeiopolis in Cilicia; Adrian to Adrianople; Canaan to the Canaanites; Saba, to the Sabæans; Assur, to the Assyrians; and so Ptolemais, Cæsarea, Tiberias, and Herodium in Judæa got their names.

While we were thus talking, there came to us the great flash whom our lantern called the philosopher, her holiness the Bottle's governor. He was attended with a troop of the temple-guards, all French bottles in wicker armour; and seeing us with our javelins wrapped with ivy, with our illustrious lantern, whom he knew, he desired us to come in with all manner of safety, and ordered we should be immediately conducted to the Princess Bacbuc, the Bottle's lady of honour, and priestess of all the mysteries; which was done.

CHAPTER 25

HOW WE WENT DOWN THE TETRADIC STEPS, AND OF PANURGE'S FEAR

WE went down one marble step under ground where there was a resting, or, as our workmen call it, a landing-place; then, turning to the left, we went down two other steps, where there was another resting-place; after that we came to three other steps, turning about, and met a third; and the like at four steps which we met afterwards. There quoth Panurge, Is it here? How many steps have you told? asked our magnificent lantern. One, two, three, four, answered Pantagruel. How much is that? asked she. Ten, returned he. Multiply that, said she, according to the same Pythagorical tetrad. That is, ten, twenty, thirty, forty, cried Pantagruel. How much is the whole? said she. One hundred, answered Pantagruel. Add, continued she, the first cube—

that's eight. At the end of that fatal number you'll find the temple gate; and pray observe, this is the true psychogony of Plato, so celebrated by the Academics, yet so little understood; one moiety of which consists of the unity of the two first numbers full of two square and two cubic numbers. We then went down those numerical stairs, all under ground, and I can assure you, in the first place, that our legs stood us in good stead; for had it not been for 'em, we had rolled just like so many hogsheads into a vault. Secondly, our radiant lantern gave us just so much light as is in St. Patrick's hole in Ireland or Trophonius's pit in Bœotia; which caused Panurge to say to her, after we had got down some seventy-eight steps:

Dear madam, with a sorrowful, aching heart, I most humbly beseech your lanternship to lead us back. May I be led to hell if I be not half dead with fear; my heart is sunk down into my hose; I am afraid I shall make buttered eggs in my breeches. I freely consent never to marry. You have given yourself too much trouble on my account. The Lord shall reward you in his great rewarder; neither will I be ungrateful when I come out of this cave of Troglodytes. Let's go back, I pray you. I'm very much afraid this is Tænarus, the low way to hell, and methinks I already hear Cerberus bark. Hark! I hear the cur, or my ears tingle. I have no manner of kindness for the dog, for there never is a greater toothache than when dogs bite us by the shins. And if this be only Trophonius's pit, the lemures, hob-thrushes, and goblins will certainly swallow us alive, just as they devoured formerly one of Demetrius's halberdiers for want of bridles. Art thou here, Friar John? Prithee, dear, dear cod, stay by me; I'm almost dead with fear. Hast thou got thy bilbo? Alas! poor pilgarlic's defenceless. I'm a naked man, thou knowest; let's go back. Zoons, fear nothing, cried Friar John;

I'm by thee, and have thee fast by the collar; eighteen
devils' shan't get thee out of my clutches, though I were unarmed. Never did a man yet want weapons who had a good
arm with as stout a heart. Heaven would sooner send down
a shower of them; even as in Provence, in the fields of La
Crau, near Mariannes, there rained stones (they are there
to this day) to help Hercules, who otherwise wanted wherewithal to fight Neptune's two bastards. But whither are we
bound? Are we a-going to the little children's limbo? By
Pluto, they'll bepaw and conskite us all. Or are we going to
hell for orders? By cob's body, I'll hamper, bethwack, and
belabour all the devils, now I have some vine-leaves in my
shoes. Thou shalt see me lay about me like mad, old boy.
Which way? where the devil are they? I fear nothing but
their damned horns; but cuckoldy Panurge's bull-feather
will altogether secure me from 'em. Lo! in a prophetic spirit
I already see him, like another Actæon, horned, horny, hornified. Prithee, quoth Panurge, take heed thyself, dear frater,
lest, till monks have leave to marry, thou weddest something
thou dostn't like, as some cat-o'-nine tails or the quartan
ague; if thou dost, may I never come safe and sound out of
this hypogeum, this subterranean cave, if I don't tup and
ram that disease merely for the sake of making thee a cornuted, corniferous property; otherwise I fancy the quartan
ague is but an indifferent bedfellow. I remember Gripe-men-
all threatened to wed thee to some such thing; for which thou
calledst him heretic.

Here our splendid lantern interrupted them, letting us
know this was the place where we were to have a taste of
the creature, and be silent; bidding us not despair of having
the word of the Bottle before we went back, since we had
lined our shoes with vine-leaves.

Come on then, cried Panurge, let's charge through and

through all the devils of hell; we can but perish, and that's soon done. However, I thought to have reserved my life for some mighty battle. Move, move, move forwards; I am as stout as Hercules, my breeches are full of courage; my heart trembles a little, I own, but that's only an effect of the coldness and dampness of this vault; 'tis neither fear nor ague. Come on, move on, piss, pish, push on. My name's William Dreadnought.

CHAPTER 26

HOW THE TEMPLE GATES IN A WONDERFUL MANNER OPENED OF THEMSELVES

AFTER we were got down the steps, we came to a portal of fine jasper, of Doric order, on whose front we read this sentence in the finest gold 'EN 'OINZ 'ALGHEIA—that is, In wine truth. The gates were of Corinthian-like brass, massy, wrought with little vine-branches, finely embossed and engraven, and were equally joined and closed together in their mortise without padlock, key-chain, or tie whatsoever. Where they joined, there hanged an Indian loadstone as big as an Egyptian bean, set in gold, having two points, hexagonal, in a right line; and on each side, towards the wall, hung a handful of scordium (garlic germander).

There our noble lantern desired us not to take it amiss that she went no farther with us, leaving us wholly to the conduct of the priestess Bacbuc; for she herself was not allowed to go in, for certain causes rather to be concealed than revealed to mortals. However, she advised us to be resolute and secure, and to trust to her for the return. She then pulled the loadstone that hung at the folding of the gates, and threw it into a silver box fixed for that purpose; which done, from the threshold of each gate she drew a twine of crimson silk about nine feet long, by which the scordium hung, and having fastened it to two gold buckles that hung at the sides, she withdrew.

Immediately the gates flew open without being touched, not with a creaking or loud harsh noise like that made by heavy brazen gates, but with a soft pleasing murmur that resounded through the arches of the temple.

Pantagruel soon knew the cause of it, having discovered a small cylinder or roller that joined the gates over the threshold, and, turning like them towards the wall on a hard well-polished ophites stone, with rubbing and rolling caused that harmonious murmur.

I wondered how the gates thus opened of themselves to the right and left, and after we were all got in, I cast my eye between the gates and the wall to endeavour to know how this happened; for one would have thought our kind lantern had put between the gates the herb æthiopis, which they say opens some things that are shut. But I perceived that the parts of the gates that joined on the inside were covered with steel, and just where the said gates touched when they were opened I saw two square Indian loadstones of a bluish hue, well polished, and half a span broad, mortised in the temple wall. Now, by the hidden and admirable power of the loadstones, the steel plates were put into motion, and consequently the gates were slowly drawn, however, not always, but when the said loadstone on the outside was removed, after which the steel was freed from its power, the two bunches of scordium being at the same time put at some distance, because it deadens the *magnes* and robs it of its attractive virtue.

On the loadstone that was placed on the right side the following iambic verse was curiously engraven in ancient Roman characters:

Ducunt volentem fata, nolentem trahunt.
Fate leads the will, and th' unwilling draws.

The following sentence was neatly cut in the loadstone that was on the left:

ALL THINGS TEND TO THEIR END.

CHAPTER 27

OF THE TEMPLE'S ADMIRABLE PAVEMENT

WHEN I had read those inscriptions, I admired the beauty of the temple, and particularly the disposition of its pavement, with which no work that is now, or has been under the cope of heaven, can justly be compared; not that of the Temple of Fortune at Præneste in Sylla's time, or the pavement of the Greeks, called asarotum, laid by Sosistratus at Pergamus. For this here was wholly in compartments of precious stones, all in their natural colours: one of red jasper, most charmingly spotted; another of ophites; a third of porphyry; a fourth of lycophthalmy, a stone of four different colours, powdered with sparks of gold as small as atoms; a fifth of agate, streaked here and there with small milk-coloured waves; a sixth of costly chalcedony or onyx-stone; and another of green jasper, with certain red and yellowish veins. And all these were disposed in a diagonal line.

At the portico some small stones were inlaid and evenly joined on the floor, all in their native colours, to embellish the design of the figures; and they were ordered in such a manner that you would have thought some vine-leaves and branches had been carelessly strewed on the pavement; for in some places they were thick, and thin in others. That inlaying was very wonderful everywhere. Here were seen, as it were in the shade, some snails crawling on the grapes; there, little lizards running on the branches. On this side were grapes that seemed yet greenish; on another, some clusters that seemed full ripe, so like the true that they could as easily have deceived starlings and other birds as those which Zeuxis drew.

Nay, we ourselves were deceived; for where the artist seemed to have strewed the vine-branches thickest, we could not forbear walking with great strides lest we should entangle our feet, just as people go over an unequal stony place.

I then cast my eyes on the roof and walls of the temple, that were all pargetted with porphyry and mosaic work, which from the left side at the coming in most admirably represented the battle in which the good Bacchus overthrew the Indians; as followeth.

CHAPTER 28

HOW WE SAW BACCHUS'S ARMY DRAWN UP IN BATTALIA IN MOSAIC WORK

At the beginning, divers towns, hamlets, castles, fortresses, and forests were seen in flames; and several mad and loose women, who furiously ripped up and tore live calves, sheep, and lambs limb from limb, and devoured their flesh. There we learned how Bacchus, at his coming into India, destroyed all things with fire and sword.

Notwithstanding this, he was so despised by the Indians that they did not think it worth their while to stop his progress, having been certainly informed by their spies that his camp was destitute of warriors, and that he had only with him a crew of drunken females, a low-built, old, effeminate, sottish fellow, continually addled, and as drunk as a wheelbarrow, with a pack of young clownish doddipolls, stark naked, always skipping and frisking up and down, with tails and horns like those of young kids.

For this reason the Indians had resolved to let them go through their country without the least opposition, esteeming a victory over such enemies more dishonourable than glorious.

In the meantime Bacchus marched on, burning everything; for, as you know, fire and thunder are his paternal arms, Jupiter having saluted his mother Semele with his thunder, so that his maternal house was ruined by fire. Bacchus also caused a great deal of blood to be spilt; which, when he is roused and angered, principally in war, is as natural to him as to make some in time of peace.

Thus the plains of the island of Samos are called Panema, which signifies bloody, because Bacchus there overtook the Amazons, who fled from the country of Ephesus, and there let 'em blood, so that they all died of phlebotomy. This may give you a better insight into the meaning of an ancient proverb than Aristotle has done in his problems, viz., Why 'twas formerly said, Neither eat nor sow any mint in time of war. The reason is, that blows are given then without any distinction of parts or persons, and if a man that's wounded has that day handled or eaten any mint, 'tis impossible, or at least very hard, to stanch his blood.

After this, Bacchus was seen marching in battalia, riding in a stately chariot drawn by six young leopards. He looked as young as a child, to show that all good topers never grow old. He was as red as a cherry, or a cherub, which you please, and had no more hair on his chin than there's in the inside of my hand. His forehead was graced with pointed horns, above which he wore a fine crown or garland of vine-leaves and grapes, and a mitre of crimson velvet, having also gilt buskins on.

He had not one man with him that looked like a man; his guards and all his forces consisted wholly of Bassarides, Evantes, Euhyades, Edonides, Trietherides, Ogygiæ, Mimallonides, Mænades, Thyades, and Bacchæ, frantic, raving, raging, furious, mad women, begirt with live snakes and serpents instead of girdles, dishevelled, their hair flowing about their shoulders, with garlands of vine-branches instead of forehead-cloths, clad with stag's or goat's skins, and armed with torches, javelins, spears, and halberds whose ends were like pineapples. Besides, they had certain small light bucklers that gave a loud sound if you touched 'em never so little and these served them instead of drums. They were just seventy-nine thousand two hundred and twenty-seven.

Silenus, who led the van, was one on whom Bacchus relied very much, having formerly had many proofs of his valour and conduct. He was a diminutive, stooping, palsied, plump, gorbellied old fellow, with a swingeing pair of stiff-standing lugs of his own, a sharp Roman nose, large rough eyebrows, mounted on a well-hung ass. In his fist he held a staff to lean upon, and also bravely to fight whenever he had occasion to alight; and he was dressed in a woman's yellow gown. His followers were all young, wild, clownish people, as hornified as so many kids and as fell as so many tigers, naked, and perpetually singing and dancing country-dances. They were called tityri and satyrs, and were in all eighty-five thousand one hundred and thirty-three.

Pan, who brought up the rear, was a monstrous sort of a thing; for his lower parts were like a goat's, his thighs hairy, and his horns bolt upright; a crimson fiery phiz, and a beard that was none of the shortest. He was a bold, stout, daring, desperate fellow, very apt to take pepper in the nose for yea and nay.

In his left hand he held a pipe, and a crooked stick in his

right. His forces consisted also wholly of satyrs, ægipanes, agripanes, sylvans, fauns, lemures, lares, eleves, and hob goblins, and their number was seventy-eight thousand one hundred and fourteen. The signal or word common to all the army was Evohe.

CHAPTER 29

HOW THE BATTLE IN WHICH THE GOOD BACCHUS OVERTHREW THE INDIANS WAS REPRESENTED IN MOSAIC WORK

IN the next place we saw the representation of the good Bacchus's engagement with the Indians. Silenus, who led the van, was sweating, puffing and blowing, belabouring his ass most grievously. The ass dreadfully opened its wide jaws, drove away the flies that plagued it, winced, flounced, went back, and bestirred itself in a most terrible manner, as if some damn gad-bee had stung it at the breech.

The satyrs, captains, sergeants, and corporals of com panies, sounding the orgies with cornets, in a furious manner went round the army, skipping, capering, bounding, jerking, farting, flying out at heels, kicking and prancing like mad, encouraging their companies to fight bravely; and all the delineated army cried out Evohe!

First, the Mænades charged the Indians with dreadful shouts, and a horrid din of their brazen drums and bucklers, the air rung again all around, as the mosaic work well ex pressed it. And pray for the future don't so much admire Apelles, Aristides the Theban, and others who drew claps of thunder, lightnings, winds, words, manners, and spirits.

We then saw the Indian army, who had at last taken the field to prevent the devastation of the rest of their country. In the front were the elephants, with castles well garrisoned on their backs. But the army and themselves were put into disorder; the dreadful cries of the Bacchæ having filled them with consternation, and those huge animals turned tail and trampled on the men of their party.

There you might have seen gaffer Silenus on his ass, putting on as hard as he could, striking athwart and alongst, and laying about him lustily with his staff after the old fashion of fencing. His ass was prancing and making after the elephants, gaping and martially braying, as it were to sound a charge, as he did when formerly in the Bacchanalian feasts he waked the nymph Lottis, when Priapus, full of priapism, had a mind to priapize while the pretty creature was taking a nap.

There you might have seen Pan frisk it with his goatish shanks about the Mænades, and with his rustic pipe excite them to behave themselves like Mænades.

A little further you might have blessed your eyes with the sight of a young satyr who led seventeen kings his prisoners; and a Bacchis, who with her snakes hauled along no less than two and forty captains; a little faun, who carried a whole dozen of standards taken from the enemy; and goodman Bacchus on his chariot, riding to and fro fearless of danger, making much of his dear carcass, and cheerfully toping to all his merry friends.

Finally, we saw the representation of his triumph, which was thus: first, his chariot was wholly lined with ivy gathered on the mountain Meros; this for its scarcity, which you know raises the price of everything, and principally of those leaves in India. In this Alexander the Great followed his example at his Indian triumph. The chariot was drawn by elephants joined together, wherein he was imitated by Pompey the Great at Rome in his African triumph. The good Bacchus was seen drinking out of a mighty urn, which action Marius aped after his victory over the Cimbri near Aix in Provence.

All his army were crowned with ivy; their javelins, bucklers, and drums were also wholly covered with it; there was not so much as Silenus's ass but was betrapped with it.

The Indian kings were fastened with chains of gold close by the wheels of the chariot. All the company marched in pomp with unspeakable joy, loaded with an infinite number of trophies, pageants, and spoils, playing and singing merry epiniciums, songs of triumph, and also rural lays and dithyrambs.

At the farthest end was a prospect of the land of Egypt; the Nile with its crocodiles, marmosets, ibides, monkeys, trochiloses, or wrens, ichneumons, or Pharaoh's mice, hippopotami, or sea-horses, and other creatures, its guests and neighbours. Bacchus was moving towards that country under the conduct of a couple of horned beasts, on one of which was written in gold, Apis, and Osiris on the other; because no ox or cow had been seen in Egypt till Bacchus came thither.

CHAPTER 30

HOW THE TEMPLE WAS ILLUMINATED WITH A WONDERFUL LAMP

BEFORE I proceed to the description of the Bottle, I'll give you that of an admirable lamp that dispensed so large a light over all the temple that, though it lay underground, we could distinguish every object as clearly as above it at noonday.

In the middle of the roof was fixed a ring of massive gold, as thick as my clenched fist. Three chains somewhat less, most curiously wrought, hung about two feet and a half below it, and in a triangle supported a round plate of fine gold whose diameter or breadth did not exceed two cubits and half a span. There were four holes in it, in each of which an

empty ball was fastened, hollow within, and open o' top, like
a little lamp; its circumference about two hands' breadth.
Each ball was of precious stone; one an amethyst, another an
African carbuncle, the third an opal, and the fourth an
anthracites. They were full of burning water five times distilled in a serpentine limbec, and inconsumptible, like the
oil formerly put into Pallas's golden lamp at Acropolis of
Athens by Callimachus. In each of them was a flaming wick,
partly of asbestine flax, as of old in the temple of Jupiter
Ammon, such as those which Cleombrotus, a most studious
philosopher, saw, and partly of Carpasian flax,* which were
rather renewed than consumed by the fire.

About two foot and a half below that gold plate, the three
chains were fastened to three handles that were fixed to a
large round lamp of most pure crystal, whose diameter was
a cubit and a half, and opened about two hands' breadth o'
top; by which open place a vessel of the same crystal, shaped
somewhat like the lower part of a gourd-like limbec, or an
urinal, was put at the bottom of the great lamp, with such
a quantity of the afore-mentioned burning water, that the
flame of the asbestine wick reached the centre of the great
lamp. This made all its spherical body seem to burn and be
in a flame, because the fire was just at the centre and middle
point, so that it was not more easy to fix the eye on it than
on the disc of the sun, the matter being wonderfully bright
and shining, and the work most transparent and dazzling
by the reflection of the various colours of the precious stones
whereof the four small lamps above the main lamp were
made, and their lustre was still variously glittering all over
the temple. Then this wandering light being darted on the

* Ozell's correction. Motteux reads, "which Cleombrotus a most
studious philosopher, and Pandelinus of Carpasium had, which
were," &c.

polished marble and agate with which all the inside of the temple was pargetted, our eyes were entertained with a sight of all the admirable colours which the rainbow can boast when the sun darts his fiery rays on some dropping clouds.

The design of the lamp was admirable in itself, but, in my opinion, what added much to the beauty of the whole, was that round the body of the crystal lamp there was carved in cataglyphic work a lively and pleasant battle of naked boys, mounted on little hobby-horses, with little whirligig lances and shields that seemed made of vine-branches with grapes on them; their postures generally were very different, and their childish strife and motions were so ingeniously expressed that art equalled nature in every proportion and action. Neither did this seem engraved, but rather hewed out and embossed in relief, or at least like grotesque, which, by the artist's skill, has the appearance of the roundness of the object it represents. This was partly the effect of the various and most charming light, which, flowing, out of the lamp, filled the carved places with its glorious rays.

CHAPTER 31*

HOW THE PRIESTESS BACBUC SHOWED US A FANTASTIC FOUNTAIN IN THE TEMPLE, AND HOW THE FOUNTAIN-WATER HAD THE TASTE OF WINE, ACCORDING TO THE IMAGINATION OF THOSE WHO DRANK OF IT

WHILE we were admiring this incomparable lamp and the stupendous structure of the temple, the venerable priestess Bacbuc and her attendants came to us with jolly smiling looks, and seeing us duly accoutred, without the least diffi-

* "This and the next chapter make really but one, tho' Mr. Motteux has made two of them; the first of which contains but eight lines, according to him, and ends at the words *fantastic fountain*."
—OZELL.

culty took us into the middle of the temple, where, just under
the aforesaid lamp, was the fine fantastic fountain. She then
ordered some cups, goblets, and talboys of gold, silver, and
crystal to be brought, and kindly invited us to drink of the
liquor that sprung there, which we readily did; for, to say
the truth, this fantastic fountain was very inviting, and its
materials and workmanship more precious, rare, and admirable than anything Plato ever dreamt of in limbo.

Its basis or groundword was of most pure and limpid
alabaster, and its height somewhat more than three spans,
being a regular heptagon on the outside, with its stylobates
or footsteps, arulets, cymasults or bunt tops, and Doric un-
dulations about it. It was exactly round within. On the middle point of each angle brink stood a pillar orbiculated in
form of ivory or alabaster solid rings. These were seven in
number, according to the number of the angles.*

Each pillar's length from the basis to the architraves was
near seven hands, taking an exact dimension of its diameter
through the centre of its circumference and inward roundness; and it was so disposed that, casting our eyes behind one
of them, whatever its cube might be, to view its opposite, we
found that the pyramidal cone of our visual line ended at the
said centre, and there, by the two opposites formed an
equilateral triangle whose two lines divided the pillar into
two equal parts.

That which we had a mind to measure, going from one
side to another, two pillars over, at the first third part of
the distance between them, was met by their lowermost and
fundamental line, which, in a consult line drawn as far as
the universal centre equally divided, gave, in a just partition,
the distance of the seven opposite pillars in a right line,
beginning at the obtuse angle on the brink, as you know that

* This sentence, restored by Ozell, is omitted by Motteux.

an angle is always found placed between two others in all angular figures odd in number.

This tacitly gave us to understand that seven semi-diameters are in geometrical proportion, compass, and distance somewhat less than the circumference of a circle, from the figure of which they are extracted; that is to say, three whole parts, with an eighth and a half, a little more, or a seventh and a half, a little less, according to the instructions given us of old by Euclid, Aristotle, Archimedes, and others.

The first pillar, I mean that which faced the temple gate, was of azure, sky-coloured sapphire.

The second, of hyacinth, a precious stone exactly of the colour of the flower into which Ajax's choleric blood was transformed; the Greek letters A I being seen on it in many places.

The third, an anachite diamond, as bright and glittering as lightning.

The fourth, a masculine ruby balas (peach-coloured) amethystizing, its flame and lustre ending in violet or purple like an amethyst.

The fifth, an emerald, above five hundred and fifty times more precious than that of Serapis in the labyrinth of the Egyptians, and more verdant and shining than those that were fixed, instead of eyes. in the marble lion's head near King Hermias's tomb.

The sixth, of agate, more admirable and various in the distinctions of its veins, clouds, and colours than that which Pyrrhus, King of Epirus, so mightily esteemed.

The seventh, of syenites, transparent, of the colour of a beryl and the clear hue of Hymetian honey; and within it the moon was seen such as we see it in the sky, silent, full, new, and in the wane.

These stones were assigned to the seven heavenly planets

by the ancient Chaldæans; and that the meanest capacities might be informed of this, just at the central perpendicular line, on the chapter of the first pillar, which was of sapphire, stood the image of Saturn in elutian* lead, with his scythe in his hand, and at his feet a crane of gold, very artfully enamelled, according to the native hue of the saturnine bird.

On the second, which was of hyacinth, towards the left, Jupiter was seen in jovetian brass, and on his breast an eagle of gold enamelled to the life.

On the third was Phœbus of the purest gold, and a white cock in his right hand.

On the fourth was Mars in Corinthian brass, and a lion at his feet.

On the fifth was Venus in copper, the metal of which Aristonides made Athamas's statue, that expressed in a blushing whiteness his confusion at the sight of his son Learchus, who died at his feet of a fall.

On the sixth was Mercury in hydrargyre. I would have said quicksilver, had it not been fixed, malleable, and unmovable. That nimble deity had a stork at his feet.

On the seventh was the Moon in silver, with a greyhound at her feet.

The size of these statues was somewhat more than a third part of the pillars on which they stood, and they were so admirably wrought according to mathematical proportion that Polycletus's canon could hardly have stood in competition with them.

The bases of the pillars, the chapters, the architraves, zoophores, and cornices were Phrygian work of massive gold, purer and finer than any that is found in the rivers Leede near Montpellier, Ganges in India, Po in Italy, Hebrus in Thrace, Tagus in Spain, and Pactolus in Lydia.

The small arches between the pillars were of the same precious stone of which the pillars next to them were. Thus, that arch was of sapphire which ended at the hyacinth pillar, and that was of hyacinth which went towards the diamond, and so on.

Above the arches and chapters of the pillars, on the inward front, a cupola was raised to cover the fountain. It was surrounded by the planetary statues, heptagonal at the bottom, and spherical o' top, and of crystal so pure, transparent, well-polished, whole and uniform in all its parts, without veins, clouds, flaws, or streaks, that Xenocrates never saw such a one in his life.

Within it were seen the twelve signs of the zodiac, the twelve months of the year, with their properties, the two equinoxes, the ecliptic line, with some of the most remarkable fixed stars about the antarctic pole and elsewhere, so curiously engraven that I fancied them to be the workmanship of King Necepsus, or Petosiris, the ancient mathematician.

On the top of the cupola, just over the centre of the fountain, were three noble long pearls, all of one size, pear fashion, perfectly imitating a tear, and so joined together as to represent a flower-de-luce or lily, each of the flowers seeming above a hand's breadth. A carbuncle jetted out of its calyx or cup as big as an ostrich's egg, cut seven square (that number so beloved of nature), and so prodigiously glorious that the sight of it had like to have made us blind, for the fiery sun or the pointed lightning are not more dazzling and unsufferably bright.

Now, were some judicious appraisers to judge of the value of this incomparable fountain, and the lamp of which we have spoke, they would undoubtedly affirm it exceeds that of all the treasures and curiosities in Europe, Asia, and

Africa put together. For that carbuncle alone would have darkened the pantarbe of Iarchas* the Indian magician, with as much ease as the sun outshines and dims the stars with his meridian rays.

Nor let Cleopatra, that Egyptian queen, boast of her pair of pendants, those two pearls, one of which she caused to be dissolved in vinegar, in the presence of Antony the Triumvir, her gallant.

Or let Pompeia Plautina be proud of her dress covered all over with emeralds and pearls curiously intermixed, she who attracted the eyes of all Rome, and was said to be the pit and magazine of the conquering robbers of the universe.

The fountain had three tubes or channels of right pearl, seated in three equilateral angles already mentioned, extended on the margin, and those channels proceeded in a snail-like line, winding equally on both sides.

We looked on them a while and had cast our eyes on another side, when Bacbuc directed us to watch the water. We then heard a most harmonious sound, yet somewhat stopped by starts, far distant, and subterranean, by which means it was still more pleasing than if it had been free, uninterrupted, and near us, so that our minds were as agreeably entertained through our ears with that charming melody as they were through the windows of our eyes with those delightful objects.

Bacbuc then said, Your philosophers will not allow that motion is begot by the power of figures; look here, and see the contrary. By that single snail-like motion equally divided as you see, and a fivefold infoliature, movable at every inward meeting, such as is the vena cava where it enters into the right ventricle of the heart; just so is the flowing of this

* Motteux reads "Joachas."

fountain, and by it a harmony ascends as high as your world's ocean.

She then ordered her attendants to make us drink; and, to tell you the truth of the matter as near as possible, we are not, heaven be praised! of the nature of a drove of calf-lollies, who (as your sparrows can't feed unless you bob them on the tail) must be rib-roasted with tough crabtree and firked into a stomach, or at least into an humour to eat or drink. No, we know better things, and scorn to scorn any man's civility who civilly invites us to a drinking bout. Bacbuc asked us then how we liked our tiff. We answered that it seemed to us good harmless sober Adam's liquor, fit to keep a man in the right way, and, in a word, mere element; more cool and clear than Argyrontes in Ætolia, Peneus in Thessaly, Axius in Mygdonia, or Cydnus in Cilicia, a tempting sight of whose cool silver stream caused Alexander to prefer the short-lived pleasure of bathing himself in it to the inconveniences which he could not but foresee would attend so ill-timed an action.

This, said Bacbac, comes of not considering with ourselves, or understanding the motions of the musculous tongue when the drink glides on it in its way to the stomach. Tell me, noble strangers, are your throats lined, paved or enamelled, as formerly was that of Pithyllus, nicknamed Theutes, that you can have missed the taste, relish, and flavour of this divine liquor? Here, said she, turning towards her gentlewoman, bring my scrubbing-brushes, you know which, to scrape, rake, and clear their palates.

They brought immediately some stately, swingeing, jolly hams, fine substantial neat's tongues, good hung-beef, pure and delicate botargos, venison, sausages, and such other gullet-sweepers. And, to comply with her invitation, we

crammed and twisted till we owned ourselves thoroughly
cured of thirst, which before did damnably plague us.

We are told, continued she, that formerly a learned and
valiant Hebrew chief, leading his people through the deserts,
where they were in danger of being famished, obtained of
God some manna, whose taste was to them, by imagination,
such as that of meat was to them before in reality; thus,
drinking of this miraculous liquor, you'll find it taste like
any wine that you shall fancy you drink. Come, then, fancy
and drink. We did so, and Panurge had no sooner whipped
off his brimmer but he cried, By Noah's open shop, 'tis vin
de Beaune, better than ever was yet tipped over tongue, or
may ninety-six devils swallow me. Oh! that to keep its taste
the longer, we gentlemen topers had but necks some three
cubits long or so, as Philoxenus desired to have, or, at least,
like a crane's, as Melanthius wished his.

On the faith of true lanterners, quoth Friar John, 'tis gallant, sparkling Greek wine. Now, for God's sake, sweetheart,
do but teach me how the devil you make it. It seems to me
Mirevaux wine, said Pantagruel; for before I drank I sup-
posed it to be such. Nothing can be misliked in it, but that
'tis cold; colder, I say, than the very ice; colder than the
Nonacrian and Dercean* water, or the Conthoporian† spring
at Corinth, that froze up the stomach and nutritive parts of
those that drank of it.

Drink once, twice, or thrice more, said Bacbuc, still changing your imagination, and you shall find its taste and flavour
to be exactly that on which you shall have pitched. Then
never presume to say that anything is impossible to God.
We never offered to say such a thing, said I; far from it; we
maintain he is omnipotent.

* Motteux reads "Deraen."
† Motteux, "Conthopian."

CHAPTER 32

HOW THE PRIESTESS BACBUC EQUIPPED PANURGE IN ORDER
TO HAVE THE WORD OF THE BOTTLE

WHEN we had thus chatted and tippled, Bacbuc asked
Who of you here would have the word of the Bottle? I, your
most humble little funnel, an't please you, quoth Panurge.
Friend, saith she, I have but one thing to tell you, which is,
that when you come to the Oracle, you take care to hearken
and hear the word only with one ear. This, cried Friar John,
is wine of one ear, as Frenchmen call it.

She then wrapped him up in a gaberdine, bound his noddle
with a goodly clean biggin, clapped over it a felt such as
those through which hippocras is distilled, at the bottom of
which, instead of a cowl, she put three obelisks, made him
draw on a pair of old-fashioned codpieces instead of mittens,
girded him about with three bagpipes bound together, bathed
his jobbernowl thrice in a fountain; then threw a handful of
meal on his phiz, fixed three cock's feathers on the right side
of the hippocratical felt, made him take a jaunt nine times
round the fountain, caused him to take three little leaps and
to bump his a— seven times against the ground, repeating I
don't know what kind of conjurations all the while in the
Tuscan tongue, and ever and anon reading in a ritual or
book of ceremonies, carried after her by one of her mystagogues.

For my part, may I never stir if I don't really believe that
neither Numa Pompilius, the second King of the Romans, nor
the Cerites of Tuscia, and the old Hebrew captain ever instituted so many ceremonies as I then saw performed; nor
were ever half so many religious forms used by the soothsayers of Memphis in Egypt to Apis, or by the Eubœans, at

Rhamnus,* to Rhamnusia, or to Jupiter Ammon, or to Feronia.

When she had thus accoutred my gentleman, she took him out of our company, and led him out of the temple, through a golden gate on the right, into a round chapel made of transparent speculary stones, by whose solid clearness the sun's light shined there through the precipice of the rock without any windows or other entrance, and so easily and fully dispersed itself through the greater temple that the light seemed rather to spring out of it than to flow into it.

The workmanship was not less rare than that of the sacred temple at Ravenna, or that in the island of Chemnis in Egypt. Nor must I forget to tell you that the work of that round chapel was contrived with such a symmetry that its diameter was just the height of the vault.

In the middle of it was an heptagonal fountain of fine alabaster most artfully wrought, full of water, which was so clear that it might have passed for element in its purity and singleness. The sacred Bottle was in it to the middle, clad in pure fine crystal of an oval shape, except its muzzle, which was somewhat wider than was consistent with that figure.

CHAPTER 33

HOW BACBUC, THE HIGH-PRIESTESS, BROUGHT PANURGE
BEFORE THE HOLY BOTTLE

THERE the noble priestess Bacbuc made Panurge stoop and kiss the brink of the fountain; then bade him rise and dance three ithymbi.† Which done, she ordered him to sit down between two stools placed there for that purpose, his arse upon the ground. Then she opened her ceremonial book,

* Motteux gives "or by the Embrians, or at Rhamnus."
† "Dances in the honour of Bacchus."—MOTTEUX.

and, whispering in his left ear, made him sing an eplieny, inserted here in the figure of the bottle.

When Panurge had sung, Bacbuc threw I don't know what into the fountain, and straight its water began to boil in good earnest, just for the world as doth the great monastical pot at Bourgueil when 'tis high holiday there. Friend Panurge was listening with one ear, and Bacbuc kneeled by him, when such a kind of humming was heard out of the Bottle as is made by a swarm of bees red in the flesh of a young bull killed and dressed according to Aristæus's art, or such as is made when a bolt flies out of a crossbow, or when a shower falls on a sudden in summer. Immediately after this was heard the word TRINC. By cob's body, cried Panurge, 'tis broken, or cracked at least, not to tell a lie for the matter for even so do crystal bottles speak in our country when they burst near the fire.

Bacbuc arose, and gently taking Panurge under the arms, said, Friend, offer your thanks to indulgent heaven, as reason requires. You have soon had the word of the Goddess-Bottle; and the kindest, most favourable, and certain word of answer that I ever yet heard her give since I officiated here at her most sacred oracle. Rise, let us go to the chapter, in whose gloss that fine word is explained. With all my heart, quoth Panurge; by jingo, I am just as wise as I was last year. Light, where's the book? Turn it over, where's the chapter? Let's see this merry gloss.

CHAPTER 34

HOW BACBUC EXPLAINED THE WORD OF THE GODDESS-BOTTLE

BACBUC having thrown I don't know what into the fountain, straight the water ceased to boil; and then she took

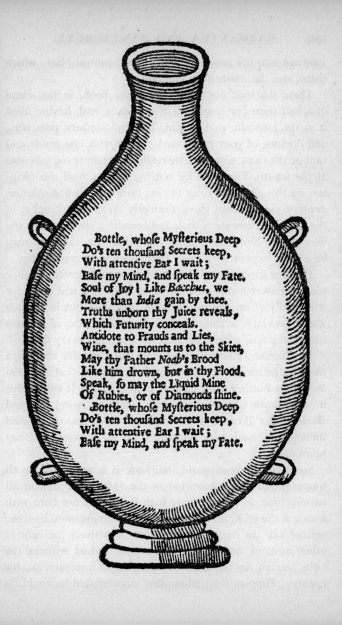

Bottle, whose Mysterious Deep
Do's ten thousand Secrets keep,
With attentive Ear I wait;
Ease my Mind, and speak my Fate.
Soul of Joy! Like *Bacchus*, we
More than *India* gain by thee.
Truths unborn thy Juice reveals,
Which Futurity conceals.
Antidote to Frauds and Lies,
Wine, that mounts us to the Skies,
May thy Father *Noah's* Brood
Like him drown, but in thy Flood.
Speak, so may the Liquid Mine
Of Rubies, or of Diamonds shine.
Bottle, whose Mysterious Deep
Do's ten thousand Secrets keep,
With attentive Ear I wait;
Ease my Mind, and speak my Fate.

Panurge into the greater temple, in the central place. where there was the enlivening fountain.

There she took out a hugeous silver book, in the shape of a half-tierce, or hogshead, of sentences, and, having filled it at the fountain, said to him, The philosophers, preachers, and doctors, of your world feed you up with fine words and cant at the ears; now, here we really incorporate our precepts at the mouth. Therefore I'll not say to you, read this chapter, see this gloss, no, I say to you, taste me this fine chapter, swallow me this rare gloss. Formerly an ancient prophet of the Jewish nation ate a book and became a clerk even to the very teeth! Now will I have you drink one, that you may be a clerk to your very liver. Here, open your mandibules.

Panurge gaping as wide as his jaws would stretch, Bacbuc took the silver book—at least we took it for a real book, for it looked just for the world like a breviary—but in truth it was a breviary, a flask of right Falernian wine as it came from the grape, which she made him swallow every drop.

By Bacchus, quoth Panurge, this was a notable chapter, a most authentic gloss, o' my word. Is this all that the trismegistian Bottle's word means? I' troth, I like it extremely; it went down like mother's milk. Nothing more, returned Bacbuc; for *Trinc* is a panomphean word, that is, a word understood, used, and celebrated by all nations, and signifies drink.

Some say in your world that sack is a word used in all tongues, and justly admitted in the same sense among all nations; for, as Æsop's fable hath it, all men are born with a sack at the neck, naturally needy and begging of each other; neither can the most powerful king be without the help of other men, or can anyone that's poor subsist without the rich, though he be never so proud and insolent; as, for example, Hippias the philosopher, who boasted he could do everything. Much less can anyone make shift without drink than without a sack. Therefore here we hold not that laughing, but that drinking is the distinguishing character of man. I don't say drinking, taking that word singly and absolutely in the strictest sense; no, beasts then might put in for a share; I mean drinking cool delicious wine. For you must know, my beloved, that by wine we become divine; neither can there be a surer argument or a less deceitful divination. Your* academics assert the same when they make the etymology of wine, which the Greeks call OINOE, to be from *vis*, strength, virtue, and power; for 'tis in its power to fill the soul with all truth, learning, and philosophy.

If you observe what is written in Ionic letters on the temple gate, you may have understood that truth is in wine. The Goddess-Bottle therefore directs you to that divine liquor; be yourself the expounder of your understanding.

It is impossible, said Pantagruel to Panurge, to speak more to the purpose than does this true priestess; you may remember I told you as much when you first spoke to me about it.

CHAPTER 35

HOW PANURGE AND THE REST RHYMED WITH POETIC FURY

WHAT a pox ails the fellow? quoth Friar John. Stark staring mad, or bewitched, o' my word! Do but hear the chiming dotterel gabble in rhyme. What o' devil has he swallowed? His eyes roll in his loggerhead just for the world like a dying goat's. Will the addle-pated wight have the grace to sheer off? Will he rid us of his damned company, to go shite out his nasty rhyming balderdash in some boghouse? Will nobody be so kind as to cram some dog's-bur down the poor cur's gullet? or will he, monk-like, run his

* "Varro."—MOTTEUX.

fist up to the elbow into his throat to his very maw, to scour
and clear his flanks? Will he take a hair of the same dog?

Pantagruel chid Friar John, and said:

> Bold monk, forbear! this, I'll assure ye,
> Proceeds all from poetic fury;
> Warmed by the god, inspired with wine,
> His human soul is made divine.
>> For without jest,
>> His hallowed breast,
>> With wine possessed,
>> Could have no rest
>> Till he'd expressed
>> Some thoughts at least
>> Of his great guest.
>> Then straight he flies
>> Above the skies,
>> And mortifies,
>> With prophecies,
>> Our miseries:
> And since divinely he's inspired,
> Adore the soul by wine acquired,
> And let the tosspot be admired.

How, quoth the friar, the fit rhyming is upon you too?
Is't come to that? Then we are all peppered, or the devil
pepper me. What would I not give to have Gargantua see
us while we are in this maggotty crambo-vein! Now may I
be cursed with living on that damned empty food, if I can
tell whether I shall scape the catching distemper. The devil
a bit do I understand which way to go about it; however,
the spirit of fustian possesses us all, I find. Well, by St. John,
I'll poetize, since everybody does; I find it coming. Stay, and

pray pardon me if I don't rhyme in crimson; 'tis my first
essay.

> Thou, who canst water turn to wine,
> Transform my bum, by power divine,
> Into a lantern, that may light
> My neighbour in the darkest night.

Panurge then proceeds in his rapture, and says:

> From Pythian Tripos ne'er were heard
> More truths, nor more to be revered.
> I think from Delphos to this spring
> Some wizard brought that conjuring thing.
> Had honest Plutarch here been toping,
> He then so long had ne'er been groping
> To find, according to his wishes,
> Why oracles are mute as fishes
> At Delphos. Now the reason's clear;
> No more at Delphos they're, but here.
> Here is the tripos, out of which
> Is spoke the doom of poor and rich.
> For Athenæus does relate
> This Bottle is the womb of Fate;
> Prolific of mysterious wine,
> And big with prescience divine,
> It brings the truth with pleasure forth;
> Besides you ha't a pennyworth.
> So, Friar John, I must exhort you
> To wait a word that may import you,
> And to inquire, while here we tarry,
> If it shall be your luck to marry.

Friar John answers him in a rage, and says:

> How, marry! By St. Bennet's boot,
> And his gambadoes, I'll ne'er do't.
> No man that knows me e'er shall judge
> I mean to make myself a drudge;
> Or that pilgarlic e'er will dote
> Upon a paltry petticoat.
> I'll ne'er my liberty betray
> All for a little leapfrog play;
> And ever after wear a clog
> Like monkey or like mastiff-dog.
> No, I'd not have, upon my life,
> Great Alexander for my wife,
> Nor Pompey, nor his dad-in-law,
> Who did each other clapperclaw.
> Not the best he that wears a head
> Shall win me to his truckle-bed.

Panurge, pulling off his gaberdine and mystical accoutrements, replied:

> Wherefore thou shalt, thou filthy beast,
> Be damned twelve fathoms deep at least;
> While I shall reign in Paradise,
> Whence on thy loggerhead I'll piss.
> Now when that dreadful hour is come,
> That thou in hell receiv'st thy doom,
> E'en there, I know, thou'lt play some trick,
> And Proserpine shan't scape a prick
> Of the long pin within thy breeches.
> But when thou'rt using these capriches,
> And caterwauling in her cavern,
> Send Pluto to the farthest tavern

For the best wine that's to be had,
Lest he should see, and run horn-mad.
She's kind, and ever did admire
A well-fed monk or well-hung friar.

Go to, quoth Friar John, thou old noddy, thou doddipolled
ninny, go to the devil thou'rt prating of. I've done with
rhyming; the rheum gripes me at the gullet. Let's talk of
paying and going; come.

CHAPTER 36

HOW WE TOOK OUR LEAVE OF BACBUC, AND LEFT THE ORACLE OF THE HOLY BOTTLE

Do not trouble yourself about anything, here, said the
priestess to the friar; if you be but satisfied, we are. Here
below, in these circumcentral regions, we place the sovereign
good, not in taking and receiving, but in bestowing and giving; so that we esteem ourselves happy, not if we take and
receive much of others, as perhaps the sects of teachers do
in your world, but rather if we impart and give much. All
I have to beg of you is that you leave us here your names
in writing, in this ritual. She then opened a fine large book,
and as we gave our names one of her mystagogues with a
gold pin drew some lines on it, as if she had been writing;
but we could not see any characters.

This done, she filled three glasses with fantastic water,
and giving them into our hands, said, Now, my friends, you
may depart, and may that intellectual sphere whose centre
is everywhere and circumference nowhere, whom we call
GOD, keep you in his almighty protection. When you come
into your world, do not fail to affirm and witness that the

greatest treasures and most admirable things are hidden underground, and not without reason.

Ceres was worshipped because she taught mankind the art of husbandry, and by the use of corn, which she invented, abolished that beastly way of feeding on acorns; and she grievously lamented her daughter's banishment into our subterranean regions, certainly foreseeing that Prosperine would meet with more excellent things, more desirable enjoyments, below, than she her mother could be blessed with above.

What do you think is become of the art of forcing the thunder and celestial fire down, which the wise Prometheus had formerly invented? 'Tis most certain you have lost it; 'tis no more on your hemisphere; but here below we have it. And without a cause you sometimes wonder to see whole towns burned and destroyed by lightning and ethereal fire, and are at a loss about knowing from whom, by whom, and to what end those dreadful mischiefs were sent. Now, they are familiar and useful to us; and your philosophers who complain that the ancients have left them nothing to write of or to invent, are very much mistaken. Those phenomena which you see in the sky, whatever the surface of the earth affords you, and the sea, and every river contain, is not to be compared with what is hid within the bowels of the earth.

For this reason the subterranean ruler has justly gained in almost every language the epithet of rich. Now when your sages shall wholly apply their minds to a diligent and studious search after truth, humbly begging the assistance of the sovereign God, whom formerly the Egyptians in their language called The Hidden and the Concealed, and invoking him by that name, beseech him to reveal and make himself known to them, that Almighty Being will, out of his infinite goodness, not only make his creatures, but even himself known to them.

Thus will they be guided by good lanterns. For all the ancient philosophers and sages have held two things necessary safely and pleasantly to arrive at the knowledge of God and true wisdom; first, God's gracious guidance, then man's assistance.

So, among the philosophers, Zoroaster took Arimaspes for the companion of his travels; Æsculapius, Mercury; Orpheus, Musæus; Pythagoras, Aglaophemus; and, among princes and warriors, Hercules in his most difficult achievements had his singular friend Theseus; Ulysses, Diomedes; Æneas, Achates. You followed their examples, and came under the conduct of an illustrious lantern. Now, in God's name depart, and may he go along with you!

THE END

COMPLETE LIST OF TITLES IN

THE MODERN LIBRARY

For convenience in ordering please use number at right of title

AUTHOR	TITLE AND NUMBER
DREISER, THEODORE	Twelve Men 148
DUMAS, ALEXANDRE	Camille 69
DUMAS, ALEXANDRE	The Three Musketeers 143
DUNSANY, LORD	A Dreamer's Tales 34
DUNSANY, LORD	Book of Wonder 43
ELLIS, HAVELOCK	The New Spirit 95
FABRE, JEAN HENRI	The Life of the Caterpillar 107
FLAUBERT	Madame Bovary 28
FLAUBERT,	Salammbo 118
FLAUBERT	Temptation of St. Anthony 92
FRANCE, ANATOLE	Crime of Sylvestre Bonnard 22
FRANCE, ANATOLE	The Queen Pédauque 110
FRANCE, ANATOLE	The Red Lily 7
FRANCE, ANATOLE	The Revolt of the Angels 11
FRANCE, ANATOLE	Thais 67
GAUTIER, THEOPHILE	Mlle. De Maupin 53
GEORGE, W. L.	A Bed of Roses 75
GILBERT, W. S.	The Mikado, Iolanthe, etc. 26
GILBERT, W. S.	Pinafore and Other Plays 113
GISSING, GEORGE	New Grub Street 125
GISSING, GEORGE	Private Papers of Henry Ryecroft 46
GONCOURT, E. AND J. DE	Renée Mauperin 76
GORKY, MAXIM	Creatures That Once Were Men and Other Stories 48
DE GOURMONT, REMY	A Night in the Luxembourg 120
DE GOURMONT, REMY	A Virgin Heart 131
HARDY, THOMAS	Jude the Obscure 135
HARDY, THOMAS	The Mayor of Casterbridge 17
HARDY, THOMAS	The Return of the Native 121
HAUPTMANN, G.	The Heretic of Soana 149
HAWTHORNE, NATHANIEL	The Scarlet Letter 93
HEARN, LAFCADIO	Some Chinese Ghosts 130
HECHT, BEN	Erik Dorn 29
HUDSON, W. H.	Green Mansions 89
HUDSON, W. H.	The Purple Land 24
HUXLEY, ALDOUS	A Virgin Heart 131
IBSEN, HENRIK	A Doll's House, Ghosts, etc. 6
IBSEN, HENRIK	Hedda Gabler, Pillars of Society, The Master Builder 36
IBSEN, HENRIK	The Wild Duck, Rosmersholm, The League of Youth 54
JAMES, HENRY	Daisy Miller, etc. 63
JAMES, WILLIAM	The Philosophy of William James 114
JOYCE, JAMES	Dubliners 124